THE TOXICOLOGY OF RADIOACTIVE SUBSTANCES

VOLUME 2

Radioactive Cobalt, Sodium Phosphorus and Gold

THE TOXICOLOGY OF RADIOACTIVE SUBSTANCES

VOLUME 2

Radioactive Cobalt, Sodium Phosphorus and Gold

Edited by
A. A. LETAVET
and
E. B. KURLYANDSKAYA

Translated by
R. E. TRAVERS

Translation edited by
ELIZABETH LLOYD
M.R.C. Group for Research on Bone-seeking Isotopes
Churchill Hospital, Oxford

A Pergamon Press Book

THE MACMILLAN COMPANY
NEW YORK
1963

THE MACMILLAN COMPANY
60 Fifth Avenue
New York 11, N.Y.

This book is distributed by
THE MACMILLAN COMPANY
pursuant to a special arrangement with
PERGAMON PRESS LIMITED
Oxford, England

Copyright © 1963
PERGAMON PRESS LTD.

Library of Congress Catalog Card Number 61–9783

This is a translation of the original Russian *Toksikologiya radioaktivnykh veshchestv*, published in 1960 by Medgiz, Moscow

Set in Times New Roman 10 on 12 pt
PRINTED IN POLAND (PWN—DRP)

CONTENTS

E. B. Kurlyandskaya: Further Research on the Toxicology of Radioactive Substances	1
G. A. Abrunina: ^{60}Co Metabolism in Rats and Rabbits after Single Administration and Calculation of Body Dose	14
G. A. Abrunina: Accumulation and Excretion of ^{60}Co in Animals and Tissue Doses during Daily Oral Administration	30
N. L. Beloborodova: Changes in Hemopoiesis during Prolonged Internal Administration of ^{60}Co	44
N. L. Beloborodova, V. L. Viktorova and E. K. Red'kina: Hemopoiesis in the Offspring of Rats which have undergone Prolonged ^{60}Co Administration	61
Ye. D. Grishchenko: Changes in the Fractional Composition of the Serous Proteins and Residual Nitrogen Content of Rabbits during Chronic Internal Administration of ^{60}Co	74
N. I. Vinogradova: The Effect of ^{60}Co on Carbohydrate Metabolism in Rat Liver	90
N. I. Vinogradova and Ye. D. Grishchenko: Impairment of Some Aspects of Carbohydrate-Phosphorus Metabolism in Rabbits after Prolonged Administration of ^{60}Co	98
A. A. Rubanovskaya: Changes in Capillary Permeability of Eyes and Skin of Rabbits during Chronic Internal Administration of ^{60}Co	108
A. O. Saitanov: Electrocardiographic Investigations of Rabbits during Prolonged Internal Administration of Small Doses of Stable and Radioactive Cobalt	119
I. N. Golovshchikova: The Electrocardiogram of Rabbits during Functional Tests (Aschner's test, ammonia inhalation and adrenalin injection) in conditions of Chronic Administration of Small Doses of ^{60}Co	140
A. S. Kaplanskii: Morphological Changes in Rabbits during Chronic Internal Administration of ^{60}Co	151
A. A. Rubanovskaya: The Effect of Cyclohexandiaminotetra-acetic Acid (CDTA) on Excretion of Radioactive Strontium and Cobalt	164
T. A. Kochetkova and G. A. Abrunina: The Long-term Effects of Intratracheal Injection of Soluble and Insoluble Compounds of Certain Radioisotopes (^{24}NaCl, Cr^{32}PO$_4$ and colloidal ^{198}Au)	174
Index	186

PREFATORY NOTE

THIS collection contains results of investigations on the chronic effects of radioactive cobalt on the body and the effects of intratracheal injection of soluble radioactive sodium chloride and insoluble compounds of radioactive phosphorus and gold.

Data are presented on the metabolism of radioactive cobalt after single and chronic internal administration and the resultant tissue doses.

The papers included in the collection are devoted to the effect of radioactive cobalt on the hemopoietic system, certain aspects of metabolism (protein and carbohydrate), changes in the cardiovascular system, pathomorphological shifts in the organs and the stimulation of excretion of radioactive isotopes from the body. On the basis of the results of the chronic experiment maximum permissible concentrations of radioactive cobalt in water are proposed.

The difference in effect of soluble and insoluble compounds of radioisotopes (sodium, phosphorus and gold), and the occurrence of growths in the lungs after intratracheal njection of insoluble compounds of radioactive phosphorus and gold are established. Tissue doses resulting in blastomogenic growth are calculated.

This collection is intended for those working in the fields of radiobiology and radiohygiene, doctors in medical departments and epidemiological hospitals, physicists and others concerned with the establishment of maximum permissible doses of radioisotopes.

INTRODUCTION

FURTHER RESEARCH ON THE TOXICOLOGY OF RADIOACTIVE SUBSTANCES

E. B. KURLYANDSKAYA

For a number of years workers in the Radiotoxicology Laboratory of the Institute of Hygiene, Work and Occupational Diseases, Academy of Medical Sciences, U.S.S.R. have been studying the toxicology of radioactive substances. The main task of these investigations has been a study of their characteristic behaviour in the body and particularly their long-term effects, since this aspect may be important in the peaceful uses of ionizing radiation.

The experimental results obtained will aid the explanation of the pathogenesis of sickness resulting from the constant intake by the body of small quantities of radioactive matter and its earlier diagnosis. This is especially important since the chemical, physical and biological properties of radioactive substances, in particular those whose stable isotopes are microelements, may join with the radiation emitted to produce a combined effect. Our experimental results confirm that the early symptoms of the effect of different radioisotopes may vary as a result of this.

Problems concerning the long-term consequences of internal administration of soluble and insoluble radioactive compounds, their effect on pregnancy and offspring and the search for means of stimulating excretion of radioisotopes have an important place in our investigations. The results obtained may serve as a basis for a biological evaluation of maximum permissible concentrations of radioisotopes.

Earlier work has been published in the collection *The Toxicology of Radioactive Substances,* Vol. I, which dealt with radioactive strontium, caesium, ruthenium and radon.

The material in the present collection represents a logical development of the Laboratory's work on the chronic effects of radioisotopes and concerns mainly the toxicology of radioactive cobalt (^{60}Co).

This isotope was chosen because of its widespread application. It is not only used as a source of external radiation but is also widely used in scientific investigations and as a control for technological processes in industry both in powder and solution form. It can also be added to metal in the smelting process, appear in the form of an aerosol when turning radioactive metal, and so on. The cheapness and ease of production of ^{60}Co will probably extend its application still further.

However, the physical and chemical properties of this radioisotope, its long life and the properties of its stable isotope as a microelement constrain us to approach its further application with great caution and make still more important the study of its biological effects, especially the chronic effect of small doses.

A brief description of the physical and chemical characteristics of ^{60}Co must be given.

^{60}Co has a half-life of 5.3 years. It emits β-particles (maximum energy 0.3178 MeV) and successively 2 γ quanta with energies of 1.17 and 1.33 MeV.

The stable isotope of cobalt is widely found in nature. According to A. E. Fersman the content by weight of cobalt in the earth's crust is 2×10^{-3} per cent.

The presence of cobalt in plants and animals was discovered in 1922 by Academician V. I. Vernadskii. Subsequently the physiological role of cobalt has been established by numerous investigators. It is contained in the organic complex of vitamin B$_{12}$ and is a microelement which participates in hemopoiesis, stimulating erythropoiesis. This property of stable cobalt makes the study of the biological effects of its radioactive isotope particularly interesting, when considering the effect of ionizing radiation on the hemopoietic processes.

This collection represents the results of 2 years of experimental work by the Radiotoxicology Laboratory of the Institute of Hygiene, Work and Occupational Diseases, Academy of Medical Sciences U.S.S.R. on the chronic effects of ^{60}Co on rats and rabbits.

The main experiment was carried out on rabbits. In total, five groups of animals were included in the chronic experiment (continuing for 2 years). The first group of 10 rabbits received ^{60}CoCl$_2$ in a daily dose of 1.25 μc/kg weight. The second group of 13 rabbits received 12.5 μc/kg of ^{60}CoCl$_2$ daily. The third control group of 5 rabbits received daily 1.9 γ of stable cobalt, corresponding to the quantity of cobalt (calculated for the metal) given to the rabbits of the first group. The fourth group (5 rabbits) was a control for the second group and received 19 γ of stable cobalt daily. The fifth group of 10 rabbits served as a biological control.

A sixth group of rabbits, which received for 2 months a large dose of ^{60}Co, 65 μc/kg (87 γ stable cobalt), was included in the experiment for particular tests (dosimetrical, biochemical, etc.). The pH of the ^{60}CoCl$_2$ solution was brought close to neutral.

The quantity of ^{60}Co—1.25 and 12.5 μc/kg of body weight—exceeded the maximum permissible concentration for water, proposed by Morgan, by 100 and 1000 times.*

Systematic observation was maintained on the animals' general condition and the following factors were studied:

(1) absorption, excretion and distribution of ^{60}Co at different periods during administration and determination of tissue doses;
(2) the state of the hemopoietic system (peripheral blood and bone marrow by intra-vitam puncture) with application of functional stresses (bleeding, parturition);
(3) capillary permeability of eyes and skin;
(4) electrocardiographic changes during the intoxication period of administration and also during application of functional stresses (Aschner's test, olfactory-cardiac reflex with inhalation of ammonia, pharmacological tests);
(5) certain aspects of protein metabolism (total protein, its separate fractions, residual nitrogen);
(6) certain aspects of carbohydrate metabolism (blood sugar, glycogen content and its ease of breakdown by β-amylase, activity of phosphorylase and hepatal amylase);
(7) morphological changes;
(8) methods for stimulating excretion of ^{60}Co from the body;
(9) the long-term effects of both ^{60}Co and intratracheal injection of ^{24}Na, ^{32}P in the form of chromium phosphate and colloidal ^{100}Au.

All the main tests were carried out on all the animals at the same time intervals. Firstly it was interesting to determine the distribution of ^{60}Co in rats and rabbits resulting from a single administration by different routes (oral and subcutaneous) and to evaluate from the data obtained the amount of β- and γ-radiation present in the animals. The results obtained are presented in the paper by G. A. Abrunina, "^{60}Co Metabolism in Rats and Rabbits after Single Administration and Calculation of the Body Dose". The author has established that after both oral and subcutaneous administration of ^{60}CoCl$_2$ the greatest radioactivity is found during the first 1–3 hr, after which ^{60}Co is rapidly excreted from the body. In rats during the first 7 days after subcutaneous injection 77 per cent of ^{60}Co is excreted in the urine and 10 per cent in the feces. The corresponding figures for rabbits are 84 per cent in the urine and 5 per cent in the feces. After oral administration in rats 13 per cent of the administered dose is excreted in the urine and 80 per cent in the feces. In rabbits the correspond-

* Recommendations of the International Commission on Radiological Protection, *Brit. J. Radiol.* No. 6, 1955.

ing figures are 11 and 54 per cent. In rats from 17 to 33 per cent of administered ^{60}Co is absorbed from the gastro-intestinal tract; in rabbits—from 13 to 30 per cent.

The highest specific activity by both means of administration is found in the liver, kidneys, suprarenals and pancreas. The skeletal muscles, nervous system and bones exhibit low specific activity. The results obtained somewhat contradict those of foreign writers who have considered the spleen to be the second critical organ, whereas according to G. A. Abrunina's results the kidneys exhibit the second highest specific activity. A relationship was found between the quantity administered and the average amount of radioactivity in the body of animals which can be expressed by the equation:

$$A = ad^b$$

where A is activity found in the body, d—daily amount administered and a and b are constants, $b < 1$.

Study of the accumulation and excretion of ^{60}Co in rabbits and rats during daily oral administration over 2 years (G. A. Abrunina—*Accumulation and Excretion of ^{60}Co in Animals and Tissue Doses during Daily Oral Administration*) disclosed characteristics similar to those earlier established by E. B. Kurlyandskaya and A. A. Rubanovskaya for ^{89}Sr and ^{134}Cs. It was found that during chronic administration of ^{60}CoCl$_2$ an equilibrium is rapidly established (from 2 weeks to 1–2 months) between the administered and excreted quantities of ^{60}Co. Consequently, the radioactivity of all animals which died at intervals between 2 and 22 months was very similar. A level of radiation dose has also been established.* Thus the daily β-radiation dose for a daily oral administration of 1.25 μc/kg of ^{60}Co is 0.10 rep to the liver and 0.084 rep to the kidneys. With administration of 12.5 μc/kg of ^{60}Co to rabbits, the daily dose is 0.61 rep to the liver and 0.29 rep to the kidneys. The corresponding average doses of γ-radiation to the body for the same administered dose were 0.24–1.16 r per day and for the abdominal cavity—0.57–3.30 r per day. The data obtained show that the radiation dose in the body cannot be calculated from the activity administered. Administration of the same activity can lead to different ionizing doses depending on the character and course of distribution of the isotope. The behaviour of the isotope in the body depends on its chemical properties, the form in which it is administered, the ratio of stable to radioactive isotope in the preparation and on other biological, physical

* The present collection of papers was at the printers when the publication GOST 8848-58, 1st Jan. 1959, expressing absorbed radiation dose in rads was issued. The units used here are the roentgen for X-and γ-radiation and the rep for β-radiation. Expressed in rads, these values would be 10–15 per cent higher.

and chemical factors. This is illustrated by the papers of G. A. Abrunina and T. A. Kochetkova and G. A. Abrunina. Thus, for example, if the ^{60}Co daily dose administered to rabbits in the chronic experiment is calculated in microcuries then these doses exceed the maximum permissible concentrations for water as proposed by Morgan by 100 and 1000 times. According to the calculation the doses of internal radiation would also exceed the maximum permissible by 100 and 1000 times. In fact it appears that the average radiation dose in the body after administration of 1.25 μc/kg ^{60}Co exceeds the generally accepted maximum permissible (0.05 r) by only 5 times, and in the "critical" organ—the liver*—by 14 times. With administration of 10 times the amount of ^{60}Co (12.5 μc/kg) the average radiation dose in the body is raised by 25, and in the "critical" organ— by 80 times. Consequently, to establish the true radiation dose in the body study of the isotope's behaviour is needed, as the radiation dose in a tissue is proportional to the radioactivity of that tissue and only in relationship to this dose can its biological effectiveness be evaluated.

Similarly chronic radiation sickness develops in rabbits which have received daily a quantity of ^{60}Co sufficient to create an average γ-radiation dose for the whole body of 0.24 and 1.16 r per day (in total during 18–24 months the animals of the first group received 135–185 r and the second group during 7½–24 months—250–825 r).

During the first 4 months of observation the increase in weight of the animals of the first (1.25 μc/kg) and second (12.5 μc/kg) groups was somewhat higher than that of the control animals. Subsequently the weight of the experimental animals did not differ from that of the controls. A significant loss of weight before death was observed in the experimental animals.

Two weeks after commencement of ^{60}Co administration to rabbits in a dose of 12.5 μc/kg changes in erythrocyte count occurred in the form of an increase of 1.5–2 millions (N. L. Beloborodova—*Changes in Hemopoiesis during Prolonged Internal Administration of* ^{60}Co). This increase took place without the reticulocytosis which was observed by N. L. Beloborodova during chronic administration of ^{134}Cs, ^{89}Sr and ^{106}Ru. Hemoglobin and colour index were also increased by 30–40 per cent. After 15 months a decrease of 25–28 per cent occurred in the erythrocyte number, which was scarcely reflected in the reticulocyte number. It should be noted that with the smaller doses of ^{60}Co (1.25 μc/kg) the decrease in the erythrocyte number was accompanied by an increase in the number of reticulo-

---

* For the "critical" organ—the liver—Abrunina took the dose of γ-radiation as calculated for the abdominal cavity, which is higher than the average for the whole body. The β-radiation dose in the organ was also calculated.

cytes up to the upper limits of normal (up to $45°/_{00}$), but that with a dose of 12.5 μc/kg the number remained at $20-25°/_{00}$.

Thus changes in erythropoiesis differed from those observed by us with administration of other isotopes. We connect this with the specific effect of cobalt as a microelement participating in the hemopoietic processes. It must be noted that an equal weight of stable cobalt did not produce similar effects. It is possible that these effects were the result of the combined action of cobalt as a microelement and its radioactivity on the functioning of the hemopoietic organs.

The impairment of leukopoiesis was slight in rabbits which received 1.25 μc/kg ^{60}Co but much more pronounced with a dose of 12.5 μc/kg. In rabbits receiving the larger dose a gradual decline in the general leukocyte number to 4900 (as against 9000 in the control animals) was observed after the ninth month.

Changes in lymphopoiesis in the animals of the first group (1.25 μc/kg) took the form of lymphocytosis. This was also observed by us after administration of other isotopes. In the rabbits of the second group (12.5 μc/kg) a gradual but constant decline of the relative and absolute lymphocyte numbers began in the first month of administration. This may be explained either by a decline in the formative capacities of the spleen as a result of the destruction of lymphoid tissue which occurred in a series of rabbits, or by a retardation of lymphocyte maturation. The possibility of a shortening of the life-span of lymphocytes in the peripheral blood as a consequence of constant prolonged irradiation is not excluded.

The defectiveness of the hemopoietic system was especially evident in parturition and blood loss. On the first and following 3–4 days after parturition acute reticulopenia was observed in all females. In the majority prolonged post-partum anemia developed. These changes were noticed at later periods during ^{134}Cs and ^{89}Sr administration. We were unable to study post-partum blood changes at a later stage of administration (16–20 months) because pregnancy either failed to occur or terminated.

After loss of blood (1 per cent by body weight of blood was removed) reticulocytosis of up to $70°/_{00}$ occurred in the control rabbits after the first day but only towards the 8th day in those receiving ^{60}Co.

Leukocytosis was observed in the control animals in the first days after blood loss, but in the experimental animals only on the 8–9th day, chiefly because of an increase in the number of neutrophils.

Progressive observation of the morphological composition of the bone marrow disclosed an abnormality in the red branch. In the 14th month of administration an enlargement of the red branch was detected in 50 per cent of rabbits receiving 12.5 μc/kg ^{60}Co (1.16 r per day), preceding and then accompanied by developing hyporegenerative anemia.

After 20–22 months this enlargement of the red branch was observed in all the animals of this group.

Attention is drawn to the acute decrease of the number of monocytes and lymphocytes in the bone marrow, indicating profound changes in the reticulo-endothelial and lymphoid tissues. These observations are confirmed by the picture of changes in the spleen. In contact preparations of the spleen of these rabbits an average 20 per cent fall in the general lymphocyte number was observed and a relative increase of prolymphocytes and large lymphocytes giving evidence of a retardation of lymphocyte maturation. Possibly this factor is the cause of the developing lymphopenia. These same preparations disclosed foci of ectopic myeloid hemopoiesis (up to 21 per cent neutrophils) not normally found.

Observation of the morphological composition of the bone marrow after bleeding showed a sharp shift in the red branch. Thus, in the control animals after bleeding, an increase of more than 50 per cent occurred, chiefly in the form of polychromatophilic erythroblasts and young cells and by the 9th day the red branch had become entirely normal. In the experimental animals activation of the red branch of the bone marrow was absent on the 4th day and began on the 9th solely on account of polychromatophilic normoblasts. The number of young cells fell. This retardation of the reaction of the bone marrow in the experimental animals was accompanied by impairment of the maturation processes, which was reflected in the peripheral blood by the extremely slow growth of the reticulocyte number after bleeding.

The changes in lymphopoiesis after bleeding are of interest. Whereas in the control animals in the first days after bleeding lymphocytosis was observed, in the experimental animals the number of lymphocytes fell to 1500–2000 per mm^3.

The absence of gross pathomorphological changes in the bone marrow (T. A. Kochetkova, A. S. Kaplanskii), and the slow restoration of the erythrocyte and leukocyte numbers after bleeding are evidence of functional changes in hemopoiesis and the preservation of compensatory mechanisms after chronic (up to 16 months) administration of ^{60}Co.

Changes in the hemopoietic system were also found in the offspring of rats to which ^{60}Co had been administered orally in a daily dose of 150 μc/kg weight before and during pregnancy and after parturition. Here the γ-radiation dose in the body was established at a level of about 1 rep per day, i.e. it was close to that found in rabbits by daily administration of a much smaller quantity of ^{60}Co (12.5 μc/kg). This supports what has been said above concerning the part played by biological factors in the evaluation of ionizing doses, in this case the specific species characteristics of the animals.

N. L. Beloborodova, E. K. Red'kina and V. L. Viktorova have shown that in the offspring of rats which have received ^{60}Co impairment of erythropoiesis occurs, particularly pronounced in the spleen where progressive "active" hyperplasia of the erythroblastic tissue arose. There were no important changes in white blood formation.

In rabbits receiving 12.5 µc/kg ^{60}Co changes appeared after 2 months in the albumin–globulin ratio in the blood serum, namely a lowering of the albumin–globulin coefficient chiefly due to an increase of the globulin fraction (E. D. Grishchenko). This latter was accompanied sometimes by a lowering of the absolute albumin level, but more often by an increase of the general protein content. This disproportion in the protein composition of the serum lasted 7–9 months, after which the normal ratio of the above mentioned protein fractions and the protein content were re-established. Subsequently the normal albumin–globulin coefficient was maintained but protein content again increased. A similar picture was obtained with rabbits receiving the smaller dose (1.25 µc/kg) with this difference only, that disruption of the albumin–globulin balance extended over a somewhat longer period (up to 10 months). Irreversible changes in the protein complement of the blood serum in the animals under test usually occurred before death. After 15–20 months electrophoretic examination of proteins showed an increase of globulins, chiefly of γ-globulin.

It is interesting to note that changes in the A/G ratio occur after bleeding, which is evidence of a weakening of the systems which synthesize albumins.

Thus, changes in the protein fractions arose at an early phase of chronic radiation damage. Then, at 8–9 months, the ratio of the protein fractions returned to normal, being again disrupted after 14–17 months. The final period (21–23 months after commencement of administration of ^{60}Co) is characterized by pronounced changes of the protein fractions, chiefly of γ-globulins, and the immunobiological resistance of the animals declines. This is corroborated morphologically by tissue microbism of organs and also by the death of the majority of the animals from secondary infections.

In rabbits receiving a daily dose of 1.25 and 12.5 µc/kg of ^{60}Co a steady tendency to lowering of the blood sugar level was detected. At this period the sugar curves, taken after loading with glucose, display a clearly hypoglycemic character. By the 18th month of administration the sugar level before and after loading with glucose is normal. By the 21st–23rd month, significant hyperglycemia develops. This, as determination of the glycogenolytic activity of water-soluble liver extracts showed, develops as a result of direct damage to the enzyme systems of this organ. The phosphorylase is the first to suffer.

Glycogen structure is significantly changed. Whereas with a liver dose of β- and γ-radiation of approximately 0.7 rep per day for 21–23 months the breakdown of glycogen by β-amylase remains normal over this period, with a dose of 3.3 rep per day (12.5 μc/kg) it is 25 per cent, and with a dose of 11.4 rep 6 per cent, as against 42–47 per cent in the control. Glycogen content of the liver is unchanged. Thus the synthesizing capacity of the liver in relation to glycogen begins to be impaired only at a liver dose of 3.3 rep (in the conditions of our experiment with a general body dose of 1.16 r per day). This is demonstrated by the fact that the liver begins to form glycogen with shortened side chains, and also by the changes of the sugar curves after loading with glucose, as shown in the work of N. I. Vinogradova and Ye. D. Grishchenko (*Impairment of Some Aspects of Carbohydrate-Phosphorus Metabolism in Rabbits after Prolonged Administration of* ^{60}Co), and also of N. I. Vinogradova (*The Effect of* ^{60}Co *on Carbohydrate Metabolism in Rat Liver*).

Changes in capillary permeability of the eye, determined by penetration of fluorescein in the aqueous humour of the anterior chamber and by its protein content were detected in the 7th–9th months of ^{60}Co administration of 12.5 μc/kg. After 9–11 months capillary permeability for fluorescein in the eye increased in the majority of the experimental animals. Protein content of the aqueous humour also increases at this period. Subsequently, some decrease of capillary permeability occurs, but is does not return to normal throughout $19\frac{1}{2}$ months of observation. A tendency towards a change of cutaneous permeability was detected only at the 9th–11th months and took the form of an increase in the number of cases with a large area of stain diffusion in the ^{60}Co group of rabbits compared with the control (A. A. Rubanovskaya—*Changes in Capillary Permeability of Eyes and Skin of Rabbits during Chronic Internal Administration of* ^{60}Co).

Thus, changes in capillary permeability occur with large dosage and at a later period than do changes in the morphological composition of the blood and in protein metabolism. This indicates, presumably, the secondary character of these changes, developing against a background of pronounced trophic impairments.

At the 7th month of administration in rabbits fluctuations of all waves of the electrocardiogram were found, largely in the form of an increase mainly of the *QRS* complex in the thoracic, but also frequently in standard leads. Changes in voltage height of the electrocardiogram bore a phasic character: at 7–8 months the *P* and *T* waves increased more than twice, at 12–13 months voltage was normal and at 18–20 months decreased.

Pronounced changes were noticed in the terminal part of the ventricular complex, mainly of the *T* wave. In the last period of administration gradual lowering takes place, and subsequently in some rabbits inversion of the T wave. In some rabbits receiving the low ^{60}Co dose (1.25 μc/kg per day) the electrocardiogram returned to normal, in others not. The normalization of the terminal part of the ventricular complex in certain rabbits is evidence that the changes of the myocardium in our experimental conditions are functional rather than organic (*Electrocardiographic Investigations of Rabbits during Prolonged Internal Administration of Small Doses of Stable and Radioactive Cobalt*—A. O. Saitanov). This is confirmed by the histological investigation of the cardiac muscles carried out by A. S. Kaplanskii. No large-scale structural lesions of the cardiac muscle were discovered in the majority of rabbits. Only lesions connected with general changes of blood vessels were noticed.

The use of functional tests (Aschner's test, the olfactory-cardiac reflex during ammonia inhalation, adrenaline injection) disclosed certain changes in the heart's electrical activity apparently connected with the impairment of nervous regulation. Thus, an increase of excitability of the vagus nerve and a raising of the threshold of sensitivity to adrenaline were detected in the experimental animals by contrast with the controls (*The Electrocardiogram of Rabbits during Functional Tests (Aschner's test, ammonia inhalation and adrenaline injection) in conditions of Chronic Administration of Small Doses of* ^{60}Co—I. N. Golovshchikova). The importance of the so-called functional stresses, enabling the detection of changes in the nervous regulation of the heart and other systems, must be emphasized.

Pathomorphological analysis (*Morphological Changes in Rabbits during Chronic Internal Administration of* ^{60}Co—A. S. Kaplanskii) of the organs of experimental animals disclosed significant pathological changes in animals dying at various intervals after administration. The following were detected: pronounced changes of the hemopoietic organs; proliferation of cells of the reticulo-endothelial system in different organs; so-called specific pneumonias; atrophic and sclerotic lesions of the mucous membrane of the gastro-intestinal tract; dystrophic and sometimes also necrobiotic lesions of the liver, diffuse interstitial focal sclerosis of the liver; lesions of the urinary bladder epithelium, dystrophic and atrophic lesions of the gonads and hemosiderosis of internal organs. These lesions were very pronounced in rabbits which received 12.5 μc/kg of ^{60}Co and to a lesser degree at the dose of 1.25 μc/kg.

In certain females, intrauterine fetal death and development of tumours at different foci were observed. The extent of these occurrences was dependent upon dose and individual sensitivity of the animal.

Thus, these investigations have demonstrated the particular characteristics of the radiotoxic effects of ^{60}Co by comparison with other isotopes. The order of development of each pathological process was established.

Thus, it has been shown that changes in the hemopoietic system and in the ratio of the serous protein fractions in rabbits undergoing chronic ^{60}Co administration arise considerably earlier and with smaller doses than changes in carbohydrate metabolism, the bioelectrical properties of the heart and the capillary permeability of the eyes and skin. Obvious changes in nervous regulation of the heart also occur against the background of already pronounced biochemical changes.

The investigations also disclosed effects of ^{60}Co on the body similar to those of other isotopes studied earlier. Thus, in published material on the biological effects of ^{134}Cs, ^{106}Ru and ^{89}Sr we indicated the existence of stages in the development of the pathological process during chronic administration of these isotopes to rabbits (cf. the collection: *The Toxicology of Radioactive Substances*, Vol. 1, 1957). We had grounds for speaking of three stages of which the first stage was characterized by a state of stimulation and lability of the hemopoietic system. During this period more or less sharp fluctuations of the numbers of reticulocytes and thrombocytes, the total number of leukocytes and their separate forms, etc. were observed. In the second stage some stabilization of the majority of blood factors at the initial level occurred (11–20 months after commencement of administration). In the third stage a distinct weakening of the hemopoietic function was observed. M. S. Lapteva-Popova, studying the effect of small doses of external γ-radiation on the hemopoietic system in the chronic experiment, has detected four successive stages in the development of chronic radiation sickness: the first stage—primary reaction, second stage—depression, third stage—compensation, and fourth stage—terminal. In our experimental conditions we were unable to distinguish the second stage—depression, which occurs in M. S. Lapteva-Popova's investigations before the compensation stage.

Study of the course of development of chronic radiation sickness during daily oral administration of ^{60}CoCl$_2$ for 2 years again disclosed the same three stages of development, more clearly marked with a low ^{60}Co dose and effaced with larger doses (12.5 μc/kg).

These stages may not coincide in the different systems. Thus, the compensatory stage for the blood and serous protein systems occurs considerably earlier than for the bioelectrical activity of the heart, carbohydrate metabolism, etc.

The analysis of extensive experimental results has shown that during oral administration of ^{60}Co in doses exceeding the maximum permissible for water (according to Morgan) by 100 and 1000 times pathological changes develop in the body. When it is realized that with a quantity of ^{60}Co 100 times in excess of Morgan's maximum permissible, the average dose of general γ-radiation to the rabbit's body exceeds the generally accepted body dose of 0.05 r by only a factor of 5 it must be concluded that these maximum permissible concentrations are much too high. At this dose since reaction occurs in the first months of administration of ^{60}Co, the safety factor, taking into account the possibility of delayed effects, must in our opinion be not less than 1000. Thus, Morgan's maximum permissible concentrations are no less than two orders too high, which leads us to recommend, as biologically proven, the maximum permissible concentration of ^{60}Co for water accepted in the Soviet Union, namely 5×10^{-9}c/l. The investigations undertaken sharply emphasize the necessity for experimental verification of existing maximum permissible concentrations of radioactive isotopes in water and air.

One of the urgent problems of radiotoxicology is the search for methods of shortening the period of retention of radioisotopes in the body. Therefore this Laboratory has been seeking means of stimulating excretion of ^{60}Co from the body (*The Effect of Cyclohexandiaminotetra-acetic Acid (CDTA) on Excretion of Radioactive Strontium and Cobalt*—A. A. Rubanovskaya). The great effectiveness of the calcium disodium salt of cyclohexandiaminotetra-acetic acid was demonstrated. With administration of this preparation in an amount of 15–20 mg per 100 g weight excretion of ^{60}Co in the urine and feces increased by 67 per cent by comparison with the control. Radioactivity of the liver of rats after this treatment was 14–22 times less than in the control animals. It must be noticed that this complex, like others, is only effective when administered at an early stage after intake of ^{60}Co. In regard to strontium the complex had little effect, as also did other methods.

Much attention has been paid in the Radiotoxicological Laboratory to the long-term effects of administration of soluble and insoluble compounds of radioisotopes. These problems, apart from the theoretical interest of the role of whole body dose and doses, to particular tissues single and repeated doses, the time factor and other factors in the occurrence of tumours have also great practical importance for an approach to the establishment of maximum permissible radioisotope concentrations in water and air.

T. A. Kochetkova and G. A. Abrunina have studied the effect of intratracheal injection of soluble and insoluble compounds of radioisotopes. Different amounts of ^{24}NaCl (from 0.17 to 2.14 mc per rat for single injection and from 0.1 to 1.9 mc for repeated injections, 5–6 times) were used as a soluble compound which is diffusely disseminated and rapidly removed from the site of injection. During the first 3 days the lungs received a dose of from 35 to 460 rep after a single injection and 185–1050 rep after repeated injection. In these conditions the animals died at different intervals—from a few days to 12 months. Histological examination of the lungs disclosed a chronic interstitial process, enlargement of the alveolar septa resulting from proliferation of histiocytic elements and peribronchial and perivascular sclerosis. At a later stage in 2 rats metaplasia of the epithelium of the mucous membrane of the bronchi from cylindrical to stratified, squamous, was detected. In some animals (16 of 77) bone tissue growths were found in the blood vessels of the soft meninges, in the ovarian and spermatic artery walls, in the cartilage of the trachea and elsewhere. Thus, even with relatively large doses (460–1050 rep) no malignant tumours were found in the lungs.

Intratracheal injection of insoluble radioactive chromium phosphate in an amount of from 0.04 to 0.270 mc per rat produced different effects. In these conditions in 10 rats which died at from 193–395 days, and in one rat, which died on the 510th day, keratinous squamous cell carcinoma was found in the lungs with metastases in the pleura and regional nodes. The total lung dose received during life was 4500–18,000 rep. The same results were obtained when the lungs were injected with 0.32 mc of insoluble colloidal gold (half-life—2.63 days). In 4 of 13 white rats pronounced focal metaplasia of the epithelium of the mucous membrane of the bronchi was found, after 4–69 days developing into stratified squamous. In 2 of these cases it had a blastomatous character and in 4 animals (dying at 36–70 days) foci of keratinous squamous cell carcinoma were observed. The dose of β-radiation in the lungs when colloidal gold was present reached 12,000–13,000 rep, (3200–3400 rep daily). Foci of squamous cell carcinoma were also found after 9, 15 and 19 months in 3 of 30 animals which had received ^{198}Au in an amount of 0.1–0.15 mc. It must be emphasized that with large local doses the total body dose was small. Thus, for ^{24}Na the body dose of γ-radiation during the first 3 hours did not exceed 10 r. For gold the γ-radiation dose in the surrounding tissues during the first days was not more than 0.6 per cent of the β-radiation dose received by the lungs. With injection of ^{32}P, a β-ray emitter, a significant dose may be received only by tissue in the immediate vicinity of the lungs, to a depth of a few millimetres. No pronounced symptoms of acute or chronic radiation sickness were observed in the majority of animals at these doses.

Although the results obtained do not enable us to postulate threshold tissue doses of radioisotopes sufficient to produce tumours, it is obvious that with entry into the lungs even of small amounts of insoluble radioactive compounds, fine foci are formed where huge tissue doses are created which are possibly sources of blastomogenic growth. From this the practical problem arises as to the necessity for strict regulation of the atmospheric content of insoluble compounds.

The experimental results presented in the present collection are a continuation of the work of the Laboratory of Radiotoxicology in the study of the toxicology of radioactive substances.

{}^{60}Co METABOLISM IN RATS AND RABBITS AFTER SINGLE ADMINISTRATION AND CALCULATION OF BODY DOSE

G. A. Abrunina

In studying the biological effects of radiation from radioactive isotopes administered internally it is essential to compare changes in the body with the magnitude of dose received by the separate tissues and by the body as a whole. This is particularly important in working out and establishing maximum permissible concentrations of radioisotopes in different media (water, air, the body, etc.).

The evaluation of the radiation dose resultant upon intake of radioactive substances is an extremely difficult task, since at the present time there are no means of direct measurement. The only way of determining tissue doses is to study the course of distribution of the isotope and make approximate calculations of the radiation doses corresponding to this distribution.

Thus, tissue dosimetry is closely connected with the metabolism of isotopes in the body.

^{60}Co metabolism in rats has been studied by M. G. Petrovnin, Ulrich and their colleagues.

Lee and Wolterink have made a detailed investigation of the excretion of ^{60}Co in dogs. Data has been published on the excretion of ^{60}Co in rats after a single oral administration by P. G. Kryukov.

All these results indicate that ^{60}Co belongs to the group of isotopes with "hepatal", or even perhaps, a diffuse type of distribution. It is also indicated that cobalt is rather poorly absorbed from the gastro-intestinal tract and is very rapidly excreted, after oral administration—mainly in the feces and after parenteral administration—chiefly in the urine.

No attempts to calculate the radiation dose received by the body after internal administration of ^{60}Co have been found.

We have studied the course of distribution of ^{60}Co in rats after single subcutaneous and oral doses of ^{60}Co chloride.

The similarity of ^{60}Co distribution in rats and rabbits was verified wtih a number of rabbits and the speed of its uptake by the blood and excretion from the body demonstrated.

On the basis of distribution data an evaluation was attempted of the mean doses of β-radiation received by individual tissues and of the order of magnitude of the γ-radiation dose.

EXPERIMENTAL PROCEDURE AND DOSE CALCULATION

Forty-eight white rats, weighing 170–280 g and maintained on a normal diet were used in the tests. Twenty-two rats were given a subcutaneous injection of a 1 ml. solution of $^{60}CoCl_2$ with an activity of 3.3–93 μc in the dorsal region. Twenty-six rats were given 1 ml. of the same solution with an activity of 15–113.5 μc orally by tube. The quantity of stable cobalt did not exceed 50 μg.

Tests were also made on 9 rabbits weighing 3–4 kg. In one rabbit ^{60}Co distribution was studied after 3 hr, in another—after 24 hr and in a third—after one week following a single subcutaneous injection of the isotope in an amount of 15–25 μc/kg. Distribution of the isotope was studied in 2 rabbits after a single oral administration of a dose of about 50 μc/kg. The stable cobalt content reached 85 μg. In the remaining 4 rabbits, housed in special cells, excretion of ^{60}Co was measured.

All the rats after administration of the solution were housed in individual interchangeable cells and killed after 1, 3, 6, 12, and 24 hr and after 5–10 days. Urine and feces were collected separately from all the animals and the activity excreted during the above intervals measured.

For animals which lived for the longer periods the excreted activity was measured at 1–2-day intervals and aggregated.

Rats were killed by decapitation and rabbits by aeroembolism. Blood for measurement of activity was collected in citrate solution. The liver, kidneys, spleen, lungs, femoral muscles, pancreas and adrenals were always removed for examination. Also the radioactivity of the heart, lymph nodes, sex organs, brain, bone marrow, femoral bones and skull was measured. After subcutaneous injection the radioactivity of the stomach wall and the large and small intestine was measured. After oral administration the activity of the whole gastro-intestinal tract, together with its contents, was measured.

Samples for measurement were prepared on aluminium trays 9.5 cm^2 in area from weighed amounts of moist tissue of up to 1 g, triturated and dispersed in an even layer. Blood and urine were transferred to a tray in a layer of 0.5–1 ml. and allowed to dry. Feces and organs of the gastro-intestinal tract after dry incineration were dissolved in a 2N solution of HCl and transferred to a tray in an amount of 0.5–1 ml.

Measurement of γ-radiation was carried out with a counter AMM-4 on a counting apparatus. The count had an accuracy of $\pm$ 5 per cent. Absolute activity was determined by comparing it with a ^{60}Co standard the activity of which was measured with an end-window counter making the appropriate corrections (N. G. Gusev, V. V. Bochkarev et al.). Where the measured activity was very low the material had to be measured again in much larger quantities. For this a γ-probe was used, immersed in a vessel containing 150 ml. of the liquid to be measured. This liquid might be urine, blood, a solution of ashes from dry incineration dissolved in HCl or a mixture obtained from wet incineration of the necessary amount of material. Graduation of the probe was carried out with a standard solution of $^{60}CoCl_2$, measured with an end-window β-counter or a γ-counter. Thus comparability of results was guaranteed regardless of the method of measurement. In view of the long half-life of ^{60}Co no correction was made for decay. The measurements obtained were expressed as a ratio of specific tissue activity to the average activity administered per 1 g animal weight, i.e. normalized to the figure for an animal receiving 1 $\mu c/g$ of the isotope. This enables a comparison to be made of data obtained from animals of differing weights receiving different amounts of activity. Also it clearly reflects the capacity of tissues for selective deposition of the isotope. For this reason the ratio is called the Joyet coefficient of tissue selectivity and designated by the letter "S" (from the French "selectivité"). This method is only suitable in conditions where change in amount of activity administered does not affect distribution of the isotope. Within the limits of the amounts administered by us no such variations were detected.

In order to calculate S for an isotope with a short half-life it is necessary that all activity measurements must be corrected to the same time. S varies with time, consequent on the excretion and redistribution of the isotope in the body. Therefore it is convenient to use curves of S with time for different organs for the calculation of the β-radiation dose in these organs. Curves were obtained at intervals useful for consideration of the course of distribution of the isotope.

The dose of β-radiation received by a certain volume of tissue in which the isotope is evenly distributed and has constant concentration right up to complete decay is expressed as:

$$D_{\beta\infty} = 88 \, c\bar{E}T_{\frac{1}{2}} \tag{1}$$

where c is concentration of the isotope in $\mu c/g$; $\bar{E}$—mean energy of β-particles in MeV; $T_{\frac{1}{2}}$—physical half-life in days.

The dose during a finite time t being:

$$D_{\beta t} = 88 \, c\bar{E}T_{\frac{1}{2}}\left[1-\exp\left(-\frac{0.693t}{T_{\frac{1}{2}}}\right)\right] \tag{1a}$$

The coefficient in formulae (1) and (1a) is deduced from the fact that a dose of 1r liberates in 1 cm³ of tissue an energy of 85 ergs. Doses in "rads" are expressed by the same formulae but the coefficient is 75. Using these formulae Marinelli *et al.* have calculated doses and compiled a table of radiation doses for a series of radioactive isotopes.

If isotope concentrations, or specific tissue activity, change exponentially with time, i.e. if there is biological half-life T_b for a given tissue or organ, then the dose can be determined by the same formulae but instead of $T_{\frac{1}{2}}$ the effective half-life is included:

$$Te_{\frac{1}{2}} = \frac{T_{\frac{1}{2}} \times T_b}{T_{\frac{1}{2}} + T_b} \qquad (2)$$

and in place of c, the initial isotope concentration—c_0. Where the specific tissue activity does not change exponentially, which is more often the case, the β-radiation dose can be determined with experimental curves, characterizing change of specific tissue activity, for example curves of S with time. If $T_{\frac{1}{2}}$ is very long, as in the case of ^{60}Co ($T_{\frac{1}{2}} = 5.3$ years), the expression (1a) is simplified and

$$D_{\beta t} = 61\, c\overline{E} t \qquad (3)$$

in the case of constant specific activity.

In the general case where change of specific tissue activity is characterized by a curve of S with t (Fig. 1), the β-radiation dose is determined by the equation:

$$D_{\beta t} = 61 c_0 \overline{E} \times \square AOtB \qquad (4)$$

where $\square AOtB$ is the area bounded by the segment of the curve $S(t)$ corresponding to the time interval t, where c_0—the mean activity administered per 1 g weight. For cobalt $E = 0.1$ MeV and

$$D_{\beta t} = 6.1 c_0 \square AOtB \qquad (5)$$

This method of dose calculation was proposed by Joyet.

The area $AOtB$ can be found by weighing on a balance the figure $AOtB$ cut out from the paper and dividing its weight into the weight of the "unit area" $A'OCB'$.

The calculation of γ-radiation doses presents still greater difficulties because, besides the distribution of the isotope, this dose depends on the form and dimensions of the examined mass.

It is comparatively simple to calculate the γ-radiation dose inside a sphere containing a uniform distribution of the isotope, but even in this case the dose is higher in the centre than at the periphery. The mean magnitude of the dose in this case is:

$$D_\gamma = I_\gamma c \times 3_\pi R \; r/\text{hour} \qquad (6)$$

where I is the ionization constant of the given isotope in $r \times cm^2/mc \times hours$, c—concentration, or specific activity in mc/cm^3; R—radius of the sphere in cm. In formula (6) the absorption and scattering of γ-radiation is not taken into account.

Doses are calculated with consideration of these processes by the formula:

$$D_\gamma = 88 \Sigma n_i h v_i (1 - c^{-\gamma x})$$

(hv_i—energy of γ-quantum; n_i—the number of γ-quanta per disintegration; γ—the coefficient for absorption and repeated scattering of γ-quanta; x—linear dimensions of the object), and prove somewhat higher but have the same order of magnitude.

The dose for time t with constant specific activity is obtained by simple multiplication of expression (6) by time t. In the case of changing activity the dose is determined by the curve $S(t)$ (Fig. 1) in exactly the same way as the β-radiation dose for separate tissues.

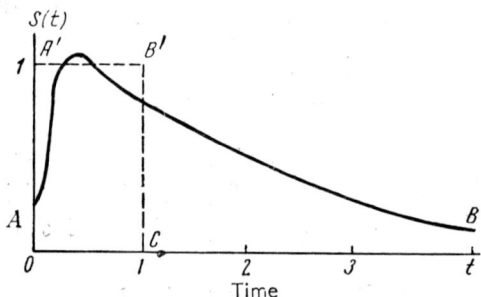

FIG. 1. The pattern of the curve S with t for calculation of the radiation dose in an organ.

According to Bush, the γ-radiation dose in any geometric form differs from the dose in a sphere by not more than 25 per cent. In view of this it was thought possible to evaluate the γ-dose by calculation of the dose

TABLE 1

The γ-radiation doses of ^{60}Co in the body of animals of different weights, equated to a sphere with a specific activity of 1 µc/g

Weight of animal (g)	R of equivalent sphere (cm)	Magnitude of dose (r/hr)	Dose per day (r)
150	3.30	0.40	9.6
200	3.63	0.43	10.3
250	3.91	0.46	11.0
300	4.16	0.49	11.7
350	4.38	0.51	12.3
400	4.57	0.55	13.2
500	4.92	0.58	13.9
600	5.23	0.61	16.6
1500	7.12	0.87	20.9
2000	7.80	0.94	22.6
2500	8.40	1.01	24.2
3000	9.00	1.07	25.7
3500	9.42	1.10	26.2

for a sphere of the same weight as that of the animal, with assumed uniform distribution of the isotope in the sphere and concentration equal to mean specific activity in the body of the animal. The mean density of the animal's body was taken as 1, by which body weight equalled volume.

Clearly, γ-radiation doses calculated with all these simplifying admissions are only estimates and permit at best an estimation of the order of magnitude of the doses.

In Table 1 are presented γ-radiation doses calculated in this way for ^{60}Co during a day, for animals of different weights with mean specific body activity of 1 μc/g. For deviations of the geometry of the body from the spherical, Bush's corrections have been incorporated.

DISCUSSION OF EXPERIMENTAL DATA

Figures 2 and 3 show curves of excretion of ^{60}Co in urine and feces after single oral or subcutaneous administration. Each point on the curves represents mean values for 4–8 rats. It can be seen, with both methods of administration, that most of the isotope (up to 67 per cent) has been

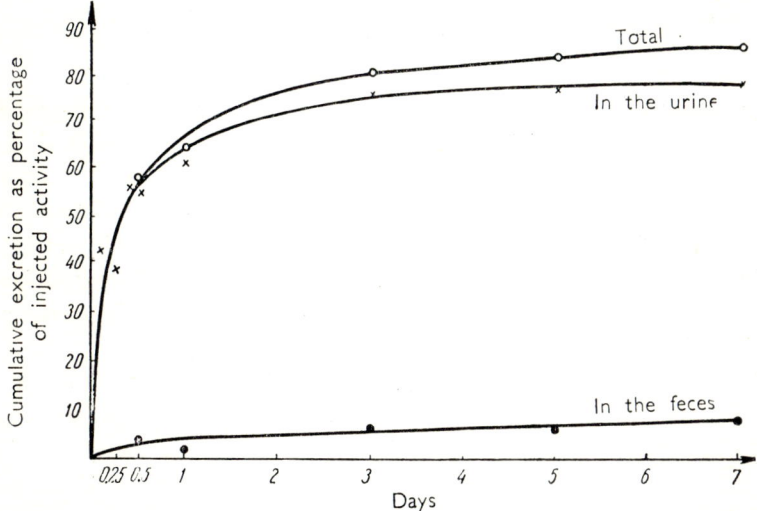

FIG. 2. Excretion of ^{60}Co in rats after a single subcutaneous injection of ^{60}CoCl$_2$.

excreted by the end of the first day. After 3 days excretion has fallen to a very low level. By the 5–7th days after subcutaneous injection, up to 87 per cent of the isotope has been excreted and after oral administration up to 93 per cent.

With subcutaneous injection most of the isotope (77 per cent) is excreted by the kidneys and only 10 per cent via the intestine. After oral administration 80 per cent is excreted in the feces and 13 per cent in the urine. If it is realized that cobalt absorbed into the blood stream will behave as after parenteral injection, then according to the amount of ^{60}Co excreted in the urine, the proportion absorbed from the gastro-intestinal tract can be estimated.

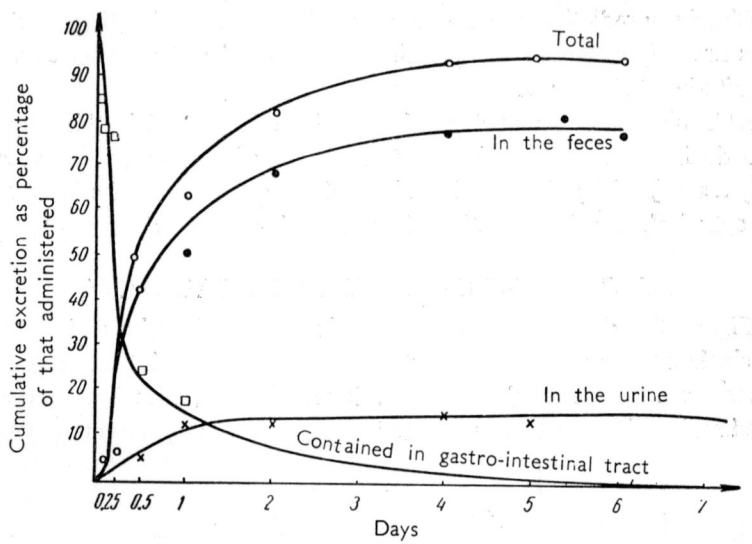

FIG. 3. Excretion of ^{60}Co in the urine and feces of rats after a single oral administration of ^{60}CoCl$_2$. ^{60}Co content of the gastro-intestinal tract.

In Fig. 3, as well as excretion, retention of orally administered ^{60}Co in the gastro-intestinal tract is shown. Virtually all the activity which, at a given time, has not been absorbed or excreted in the feces remains in the gastro-intestinal tract because the amount of ^{60}Co, which returns to the intestine from the blood stream, is relatively small.

The amount of absorbed ^{60}Co may be considered equal to the difference between the administered quantity, and the sum of the amounts found in the intestine and excreted in the feces. From the graph shown in Fig. 3 it can be seen that this difference reaches its highest value of 33 per cent, approximately 6 hr after administration. From this it can be concluded that absorption also terminates at this time attaining 33 per cent of the dose. Although this method gives an estimate of the absorption the figure obtained—33 per cent, and also the time—6 hr, are too high, because in collection of excreta unavoidable losses of up to 10–15 per cent are incurred. Therefore the values of ^{60}Co excreted in the urine after oral and parenteral administration seem to us more certain as no losses are sustained in measurement.

Figure 4 shows curves of excretion of ^{60}Co in rabbits after subcutaneous and oral administration. It can be seen that with subcutaneous injection the isotope was excreted as in rats: up to 67 per cent during the first day, of which 2 per cent was excreted in the feces and 65 per cent in the urine. By the end of a week excretion had reached 89 per cent, of which 84 per cent was excreted in the urine.

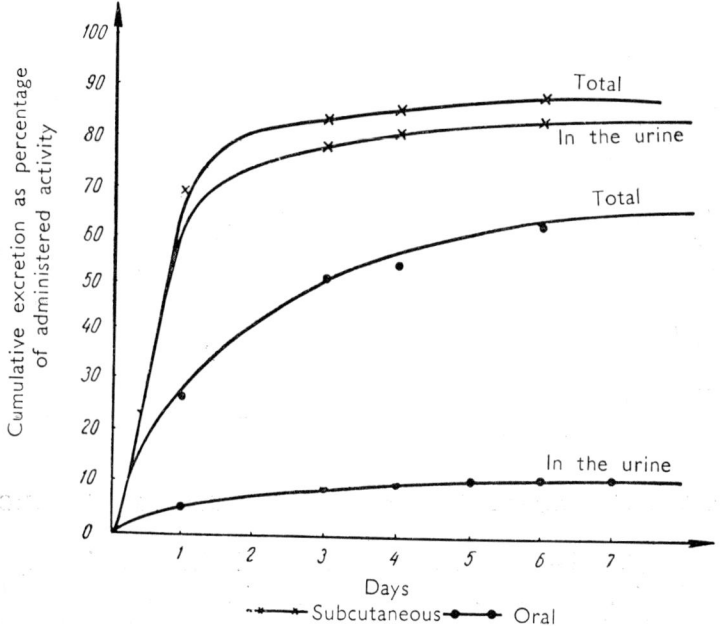

FIG. 4. Excretion of ^{60}Co in the urine and total (urine + feces) in rabbits after a single administration of ^{60}Co, subcutaneous or oral.

After oral administration excretion proceeded more slowly. The total excreted in one week reached 65 per cent of which 11 per cent was in the urine. From 5 to 40 per cent was found in the intestine during this period (Table 4). Half of the administered activity had been excreted after approximately 3 days.

By the ratio of the quantity excreted during this period in the urine (11 per cent after oral and 84 per cent after subcutaneous administration) it could be deduced that 13 per cent of the administered quantity of ^{60}Co is absorbed. However if the calculation is made by the comparison of tissue activity with each method of administration (Table 4), absorption comprised approximately 30 per cent. Therefore we consider that within given limits absorption also takes place in the gastro-intestinal tract of the rabbit.*

* As will be seen from the following articles, absorption may depend on the content of stable cobalt in the administered solution.

In Fig. 5 is shown the course of activity of rabbit blood after a single administration of ^{60}Co. Peak blood activity is reached after 3 hours. It may be assumed that by about this time most of the absorption has taken place. By the end of a day blood activity has fallen to about 32.5 per cent of its maximum value.

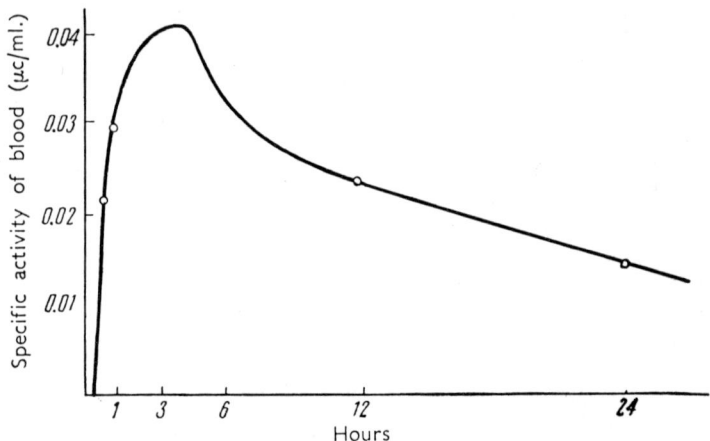

FIG. 5. Blood activity of rabbits after oral administration of 65 μc/kg ^{60}CoCl$_2$.

Tables 2, 3 and 4 show mean values of specific tissue activity, expressed in S units, i.e. normalized to a dose of 1 μc/g.

For evaluation of the γ-radiation dose for each period the mean body activity was also calculated on the basis of the following average weight distribution of tissues and organs (Table 5) found in the experimental animals.

The quantity of ^{60}Co determined in this way including the excreta was approximately 78.3±2.1 per cent of the amount administered. In particular cases whole corpses were incinerated to test the calculations. In this case the mean quantity of detected activity plus that excreted was 80±6.2 per cent of the dose administered, and the difference between the activity as calculated and as found in the corpses was on average 12±6 per cent. This confirms in our opinion the validity of body activity calculations by specific tissue activities using Table 5.

Distribution of body activity is roughly similar in rabbits and rats. After a week, the specific activity of rabbit organs is higher than that of rat organs. The specific activity of all organs after oral administration is 3–4 times less than after subcutaneous injection except in the liver where it is only a factor of 2 less. This clearly is connected with the longer retention of activity in the intestine and consequently more prolonged absorption with oral administration.

TABLE 2

The course of distribution of radioactivity in the body of rats after subcutaneous injection of $^{60}CoCl_2$. Data in units $S \pm \sigma$
(σ—means square error of the mean)

Time Organ or tissue	1 hr S	1 hr σ%	3 hr S	3 hr σ%	6 hr S	6 hr σ%	12 hr S	12 hr σ%	24 hr S	24 hr σ%	6 days S	6 days σ%	10 days S	10 days σ%
Liver	5.45	±34	4.60	±15	2.60	±17	1.60	±17	1.40	±13	0.42	±15	0.32	±50
Kidneys	3.97	±10	3.00	±18	2.30	±13	1.96	±4	1.3	±10	0.31	±10	0.28	±34
Spleen	0.36	±8	0.38	±18	0.29	±9	0.16	±13	0.12	±17	0.45	±16	0.08	±5
Lungs	0.76	±12	0.54	±16	0.34	±12	0.23	±9.5	0.20	±10	0.08	±28	0.04	±0
Heart	0.82	±16	—	—	0.43	±3	0.23	±0.5	—	—	0.15	±6	0.17	±9
Pancreas	1.55	±32	2.2	±20	1.26	±20	0.26	±44	0.4	±28.5	0.22	±58	—	—
Stomach	0.62	±4	0.49	±20	0.38	±15	0.20	±3	0.20	±15	0.05	±19	—	—
Small intestine	0.72	±12	0.60	±24	0.73	±27	0.28	±2.5	0.15	±10	0.05	±27	—	—
Large intestine	0.67	±7	0.50	±15	0.46	±20	0.23	±4	0.21	±11.5	0.04	±22	—	—
Suprarenal	0.55	±34	0.54	±27	0.42	±17	0.29	±39	0.41	±27	—	—	—	—
Blood	0.93	±34	0.60	±13	0.36	±26.5	0.22	±13	0.16	±16	0.03	±18	0.02	±40
Bone marrow	—	—	0.47	±9.5	0.31	±30	0.18	±8	—	—	—	—	—	—
Skeletal muscle	0.13	±6	0.13	±16	0.07	±15	0.04	±28	0.03	±13	0.02	±0	0.01	±27
Brain	—	—	0.10	±4	0.04	±8.5	0.03	±5	0.04	±9	0.02	±21	—	—
Femoral bone	—	—	0.25	±29	0.11	±50	0.16	±18	—	—	—	—	—	—
Mean specific activity of the body	0.42		0.36		0.22		0.13		0.1				0.04	

TABLE 3

The course of distribution of radioactivity in the body of rats after oral administration of ^{60}CoCl$_2$. Data in units $S \pm \sigma$

Organ or tissue	1 hr S	1 hr σ%	3 hr S	3 hr σ%	6 hr S	6 hr σ%	12 hr S	12 hr σ%	24 hr S	24 hr σ%	5 days S	5 days σ%	10 days S	10 days σ%
Liver	1.85	±9	1.3	±30.5	0.01	±19	0.82	±27	0.41	±22	0.15	±19	0.11	±6.5
Kidneys	0.77	±8	0.60	±23	0.48	±12	0.31	±17	0.23	±4	0.09	±8	0.07	±18.5
Spleen	0.07	±15	0.09	±20	0.06	±16	0.03	±18	0.03	±26	0.01	±6.5	0.02	±20
Lungs	0.13	±10	0.11	±29.5	0.07	±20	0.04	±15	0.03	±0	0.01	±30	0.01	±16
Heart	0.10	±6	0.10	±20.5	—	—	0.05	±22	—	—	—	—	0.03	±30
Pancreas	0.33	±5.5	0.25	±20	0.14	±23	0.13	±40	0.15	±20	0.03	±30	0.01	±14
Suprarenal	—	—	—	—	—	—	—	—	0.05	±20	0.04	±25	—	—
Blood	0.16	±9	0.14	±24	0.07	±5	0.03	±15	0.08	±5	0.002	±3.5	0.003	±16.5
Skeletal muscle	0.10		0.08		0.06		0.04		0.02		—	±15.5	0.004	±1
Mean specific activity in the body	0.023	±15.5	0.014	±25.5	0.03	±25	0.006	±23	0.004	±50	0.004	—	—	—

TABLE 4

The distribution of radioactivity in rabbits after a single subcutaneous or oral administration of $^{60}CoCl_2$

Organ	Specific activity (S) subcutaneous 3 hr	24 hr	7 days	oral 7 days
Liver	6.03	0.94	0.55	0.28
Kidneys	3.55	0.68	0.48	0.17
Spleen	1.12	—	0.16	0.06
Lungs	0.98	0.27	0.24	0.10
Heart	1.0	0.21	0.32	0.09
Suprarenal	—	—	0.47	0.13
Blood	1.87	0.54	0.16	0.04
Skeletal muscle	0.10	—	0.036	0.01
Brain	0.07	—	0.034	—
Bone marrow	—	—	0.074	0.03
Mediastinal lymph node	—	0.29	—	—
Stomach wall	0.68	0.16	—	—
Testes	—	—	0.075	0.023
Femoral bone	—	0.07	0.047	0.014
Contents of gastro-intestinal tract (percentage of administered activity)	—	—	—	5–40

TABLE 5

Average weight of tissues and organs as percentage of body weight

Organ or tissue	Percentage of body weight	To the radioactivity of which organ activity is compared
Liver	3.5	Liver
Kidneys	0.6	Kidneys
Lungs	0.4	Lungs
Spleen	0.3	Spleen
Other parenchymatous organs (lymph nodes, bone marrow, gonads, etc.)	3.2	,,
Gastro-intestinal tract without contents (subcutaneous injection)	3	Stomach, small and large intestine (average)
Gastro-intestinal tract with contents (oral administration)	10	
Blood	7.5	Blood
Corpse (muscles, bones, nervous system, skin, fat, hair)	74.5	Muscles

From the tables presented it can be seen that in both rats and rabbits, tissues can be divided according to specific activity into three groups. To the first can be assigned the liver and kidneys for which organs S remains greater than 1 for a significant time. The second group comprises all the other parenchymatous organs and the blood, for which S is initially close to 1, but falls with excretion of ^{60}Co from the body. The skeletal muscles, brain and bones, for which S is always less than 1, belong to the third group. The pancreas and suprarenals occupy a somewhat special position. The activity of these organs varies within significant limits in different animals, killed at the same time, and sometimes reaches values close to those for the liver and kidneys. At later periods the activity of the heart is also higher.

Figure 6 shows curves of S with time for the main organs representing the three groups in rats. The broken line delimits the "unit area" for calculation of the square $AOtB$ for determination of radiation dose.

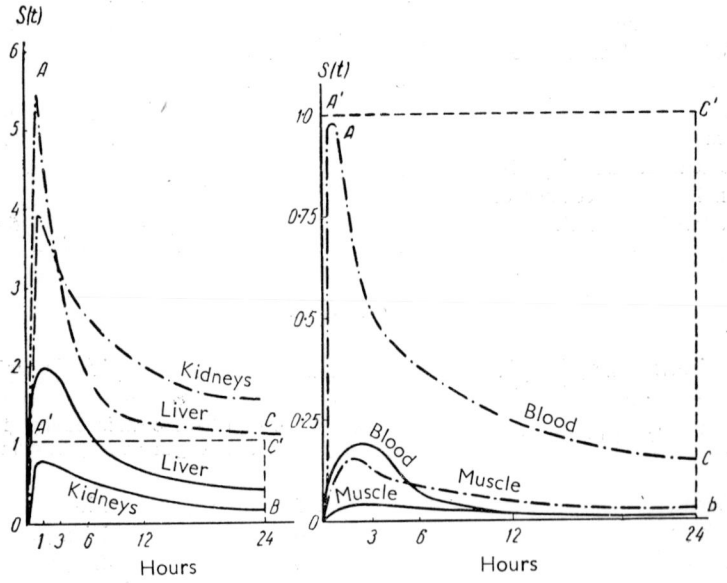

Fig. 6. Activity of the blood and organs of rats during the first days after ^{60}CoCl$_2$ administration, subcutaneous and oral. —·—Subcutaneous, —Oral.

In Table 6 are presented the β-radiation doses received by these tissues during the first day after administration of ^{60}CoCl$_2$, subcutaneously and orally, and the mean γ-radiation dose in the whole body for the same period. For ease of comparison the data are presented for an equal magnitude of administered activity of 1 μc/g. In fact the doses indicated earlier were administered. After the first day the radiation doses received on the following days do not exceed 10–15 per cent of the dose on the first day.

TABLE 6

Radiation doses after administration of ^{60}Co to rats (calculated for administration of 1 µc/g)

Organ or tissue	Subcutaneous β-radiation dose for first days (rep)	Subcutaneous mean γ-radiation dose for first days (r)	Oral β-radiation dose for first days (rep)	Oral mean γ-radiation dose for first days (r)	β-radiation doses for subcutaneous injection expressed as a percentage for administration
Liver	11		4.9		44.5
Kidneys	13.5	2.2	2.3	4.35*	17
Blood	2.14		0.32		15
Muscles	0.36		0.07		19.5

* In the case of oral administration of ^{60}Co the activity contained in the gastrointestinal tract was also taken into account.

In rats, for all organs except the liver the ratio of doses with subcutaneous and oral administration corresponds to the absorption indicated above (17–30 per cent). The exception is the liver, the activity of which, and consequently the radiation dose, is disproportionately high with oral administration. This, it seems to us, is connected with the fact that with oral administration the liver is the first organ on the route of blood flowing from the intestine through the portal vein. With gradual absorption of

TABLE 7

Ratio of specific tissue activity to specific blood activity in rats after administration of $^{60}CoCl_2$

Organ	Method of administration	1 hr	3 hr	6 hr	12 hr	24 hr	6 days	10 days
Liver	Subcutaneous	6.00	6.30	6.50	6.40	8.30	18.80	17.30
	Oral	14.00	10.00	9.00	28.00	50.00	51.00	36.50
Kidney	Subcutaneous	4.30	5.00	5.75	8.00	8.10	16.70	15.50
	Oral	5.80	5.00	7.00	10.00	27.00	—	26.40
Spleen	Subcutaneous	0.40	0.60	0.70	0.56	0.87	2.50	4.40
	Oral	0.50	0.56	0.85	1.00	3.00	5.00	5.20
Lungs	Subcutaneous	0.90	0.90	0.88	0.96	1.20	2.70	2.41
	Oral	0.97	0.82	1.00	1.40	3.50	5.00	3.40
Muscles	Subcutaneous	0.13	0.21	0.18	0.14	0.19	0.74	0.73
	Oral	0.17	0.10	0.18	0.20	0.50	1.60	1.23

^{60}CoCl$_2$ the concentration of the isotope created in this blood is higher than in the circulatory system as a whole.

The higher selectivity of the liver with oral administration of ^{60}Co becomes clearer if we turn to Table 7, where ratios of tissue specific activity to blood specific activity are presented for subcutaneous and oral administration. Whereas for all other organs the ratio of specific activity for tissue to blood specific activity has little connection with the means of administration, for the liver the ratio is several times higher after oral than after subcutaneous administration.

CONCLUSIONS

1. With subcutaneous or oral administration of ^{60}CoCl$_2$ to rats the greatest tissue activity is observed in the first 1–3 hr after administration. Subsequently, activity falls in conformity with the rapid excretion of the isotope.
2. By both means of administration, specific activity is highest in the liver and kidneys, and also in the pancreas and suprarenals. The skeletal muscles, nervous system, bones, skin and fat exhibit low specific activity. The remaining tissues have a specific activity close to the mean specific activity of the body as a whole.
3. The specific activity of tissue after subcutaneous injection is 4–6 times higher than after oral administration. The exception is the liver, where specific activity after oral administration is only 2–3 times lower than after subcutaneous.
4. By comparing specific tissue activity and degree of excretion of ^{60}Co in the urine with both methods of administration it can be concluded that 17–30 per cent of administered ^{60}CoCl$_2$ is absorbed in the intestine.
5. Almost all administered ^{60}Co is excreted within a week. With oral administration the greater part is excreted by the intestine; with subcutaneous mainly by the kidneys.
6. Rabbits exhibit similar characteristics of distribution and excretion of ^{60}Co.
7. The β-radiation doses in particular tissues, and the mean doses of γ-radiation in the body of rats during the first day after administration of 1 μc/g ^{60}Co were calculated. After subcutaneous injection β-radiation doses are: in the liver—11 rep, in the kidneys—13.5 rep, in the blood—2.14 rep and in the muscles—0.36 rep. After oral administration the doses in all organs except the liver are lower in conformity with the coefficient of absorption. The γ-radiation dose in the gastro-intestinal tract after subcutaneous injection is 2.2 r, and after oral administration 4.35 r.

REFERENCES

Bochkarev V., Keirim-Markus I., L'vova M. and Pruslin Ya., *The Measurement of Activity of Beta- and Gamma-radiation.* (Izmereniye aktivnosti beta- i gamma-izlucheniya.) Izd. Akad. Nauk SSSR (1953).

Bush F., *Brit. J. Radiol.* **22**, 254, 96–105 (1949).

Gusev N. G., *Papers on the Application of Radioactive Isotopes in Biology and Medicine.* (Trudy po primeneniyu radioaktivnykh izotopov v biologii i meditsine.) Medgiz (1953).

Joyet G., *J. Radiol. et d'Electol.* **30**, 5–6, 310–315 (1949).

Kryukov P. G., *Vestnik rentgenologii i radiologii* **4**, 58 (1954).

Lee C. C. and Wolterink L. F., *Amer. J. Physiol.* **183**, 1, 167–173 (1955).

Marinnelli L. D., Quimby S. H. and Hine G. J., *Amer. J. Roentgenol.* **59**, 260–281 (1948).

Ulrich F. and Coop D. H., *Arch. Biochem. Biophys.* **31**, 1, 148–153 (1951).

ACCUMULATION AND EXCRETION OF ^{60}Co IN ANIMALS AND TISSUE DOSES DURING DAILY ORAL ADMINISTRATION

G. A. ABRUNINA

INFORMATION concerning the behaviour of isotopes in the body during chronic administration is very scarce. The results of E. B. Kurlyandskaya, L. N. Burykina, N. L. Beloborodova, Bustad, George *et al.*, almost exhaust such information as there is. We have been able to find no data in the literature on the distribution and excretion of ^{60}Co during chronic oral administration.

As E. F. Baranova, N. L. Beloborodova, E. B. Kurlyandskaya, A. A. Rubanovskaya *et al.* have shown with daily oral administration of ^{89}Sr and ^{134}Cs, the activity in the animal's body and also the specific activity of particular organs increases with time to a point where it becomes virtually constant, despite continuing administration of the isotope. Daily excretion also increases until at the same point in time it reaches its peak, being almost equal to the quantity of the isotope daily administered. The level of activity reached is that much greater than the amount daily administered.* This leads us to a consideration of some progressive equilibrium between the administered and excreted amounts of the isotope, rather than that of saturation, which may first suggest itself. With the establishment of a constant level of activity in the body the daily radiation dose is also constant and the total dose received by the body throughout the period following the achievement of equilibrium is found by simple multiplication of the daily dose by the time elapsing from this moment. Where the time to reach equilibrium is long compared with the length of the experiment the increase in the intensity of the radiation at the beginning of the experiment can be disregarded and the daily dose taken as constant throughout. In order to take the initial period of increase into account it is necessary to rearrange the experimental results or carry out an approximate calculation.

---

* Here and later by daily administration is meant the daily administered activity in μc/day, and by daily radiation dose the dose energy in rep/day.

In order to determine radiation doses and certain characteristics of ^{60}Co metabolism in the chronic experiment the excretion, distribution and retention of the isotope in the intestine during daily oral administration of ^{60}Co chloride was investigated on rats and rabbits. The methods employed for the measurement and calculation of radiation doses are described in the preceding article.

Two groups, each comprising 5 rats, received twelve daily doses of 11.5 μc of ^{60}Co. No doses were given on Sundays. After the 12th administration one group of animals were killed 24 hr later and the other group 7 days later, and the distribution of body activity studied. Throughout the entire period excretion of ^{60}Co in the urine and feces was measured. Curves of excretion of ^{60}Co for both groups are presented in Fig. 1. The upper

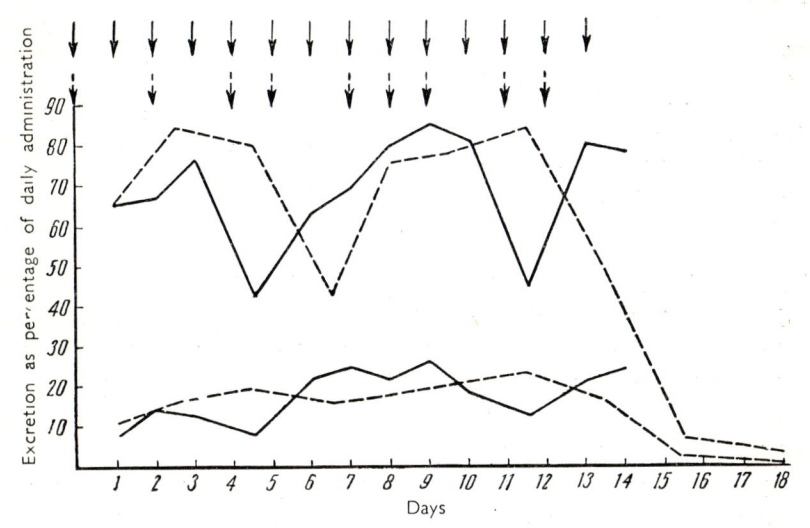

FIG. 1. Daily excretion of ^{60}Co in the urine and feces of rats receiving 11.5 μc ^{60}Co orally per day. The firm and broken lines relate to the two similar experiments. Each administration is marked by an arrow. Each point is the average for 5 rats.

curves describe total excretion, the lower excretion in the urine. It can be seen that total excretion has already become established at its maximum level after 1–2 days, but falls sharply after a Sunday with no administration. Excretion of ^{60}Co in the urine varies much less. This indicates that the level of activity established in the body remains fairly constant and variations in excretion are connected with the excretion of unabsorbed ^{60}Co in the feces. The data presented in Table 1 also point to the same explanation. Although after termination of administration excretion falls within a week almost to nothing, mean activity in the body as a whole falls by half and only in particular tissues does it fall to $\frac{1}{5}$. It should be pointed out here that the amount of ^{60}Co fixed in the body one day after the last administra-

TABLE 1

Specific and total activity of rat organs after oral intake of 11.5 μc ^{60}Co *per day (mean data for 5 rats)*

Organ	After last administration			
	24 hr		7 days	
	specific activity (μc/g)	total activity (μc)	specific activity (μc/g)	total activity (μc)
Liver	0.390	2.240	0.116	0.950
Kidneys	0.152	0.165	0.075	0.100
Lungs	0.030	0.021	0.015	0.009
Spleen and other parenchymatous organs	0.034	0.380	0.025	0.340
Blood	0.003	0.038	0.004	0.070
Muscles and other organs of equivalent activity	0.004	0.570	0.002	0.350
Total body activity	—	3.650	—	1.800
Total body activity as a percentage of daily administration		31.7		15.7

tion comprises 32 per cent of the daily administration. With usual losses and errors of measurement (10–15 per cent), the quantity fixed in the body is often less than the magnitude of this error. Therefore absolute body activity cannot be calculated by the difference between administered and excreted activity; hence direct measurement or calculation by specific activity of organs is unavoidable.

Excretion of ^{60}Co was investigated in 3 rabbits which received daily (excluding Sundays) 195 μc of ^{60}Co (65 μc/kg).*

The rabbits were housed in specially constructed cells which permitted separate collection of urine and feces with minimal losses. The activity of excreta was measured for 42 days (each test was made for 1–2 days). The activity of blood taken from the auricular vein was also measured; on the first day after 30 min, 1, 3, 6, 12, 24 hr, then for the next four days, daily after administration, and finally, at the same time once a week up to the 54th day. On the 57th day two of the rabbits were killed, and the third was not given ^{60}Co for a further 7 days. Figure 2(a) shows daily excretion of ^{60}Co in these rabbits, total (upper curve) and in the urine (lower curve).

It can be seen that the activity excreted daily shows large fluctuation. The fall in the excretion curve after Sundays is less marked with rabbits

---

* A large dose was chosen in order to enable measurement of blood activity.

than with rats. Excretion in the urine fluctuates, as in rats, within narrower limits. By expressing the excretion as the average of the daily excretion for each week (Fig. 2b) it becomes apparent that total excretion in the first two weeks is increasing and reaches its highest level at the end of

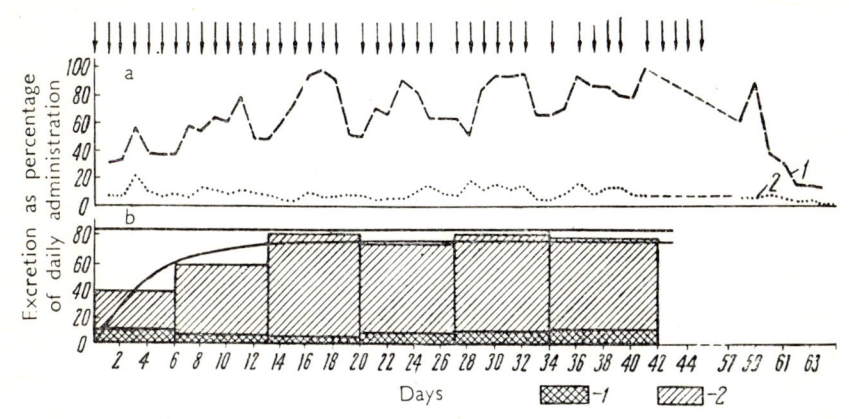

FIG. 2. Excretion of ^{60}Co in the urine and feces of rabbits during daily oral administration of ^{60}CoCl$_2$. a—total daily excretion (1) and excretion in the urine (2); b—average daily excretion per week, 1—in the urine, 2—in the feces. Horizontal line—average daily administration per week, equal to 85% of daily administration.

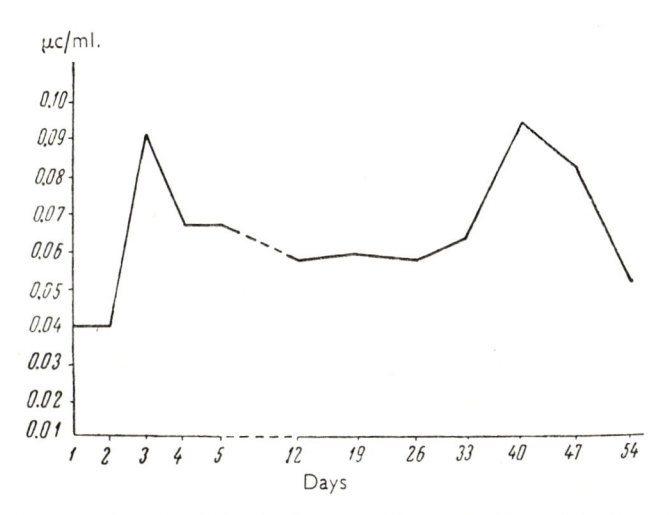

FIG. 3. Specific blood activity of rabbits receiving orally 195 μc ^{60}Co (65 μc/kg) per day.

that period, a level close to the average daily amount of ^{60}Co administered per week (85 per cent of the daily administration). Excretion subsequently remains at this level. Excretion in the urine, as can be seen from Fig. 2, has already reached equilibrium in the first week. Equilibrium of the blood activity is reached just as quickly. Figure 3 shows the mean values of the blood activity of the two rabbits. Despite significant fluctuations we could not detect any regular increase of blood activity after the first day.

After termination of administration total excretion of the third rabbit which was left for a week fell to $\frac{1}{8}$, and excretion in the urine to $\frac{1}{3}$ of the equilibrium level. The total body activity and the distribution in the organs of all three animals were very similar. However a fall of activity was found in the third rabbit in the blood (down to $\frac{1}{3}$ of the equilibrium level) and in the contents of the gastro-intestinal tract (down to $\frac{1}{5}$ of the equilibrium level).

Total body activity and distribution by organs and tissues was also investigated in two other groups of rabbits: in 6 rabbits receiving 3.75 μc ^{60}Co per day (1.25 μc/kg initial weight), and in 10 rabbits receiving 37.5 μc per day (12.5 μc/kg). The first group of rabbits were killed or died in the course of 18–24 months; and the second group between $7\frac{1}{2}$–24 months. In the rabbits of both groups, activity varied within certain limits, regardless of time of death. This can be seen from Table 2, in which data are given

TABLE 2

Body activity of rabbits after administration of 37.5 μc ^{60}Co per day and dying at different intervals

No. of rabbit	Weight (kg)	Time of death (months)	Body activity (excluding the gastro-intestinal tract)	
			μc	percentage of daily administration
9	3.40	7.5	34.2	91.6
7	4.20	9	37.8	101.0
4	3.60	12	19.5	52.0
2	2.70	15	40.0	106.0
1	3.70	18	46.6	124.0
4a	3.43	22	38.0	101.5
10	4.15	23	45.0	119.0
12	3.50	23	31.6	84.0

on the body activity of rabbits of the second group, where times of death ranged over a period of $15\frac{1}{2}$ months. Body activity was calculated from specific activity of the tissues of each rabbit. It is clear that all the rabbits died during the equilibrium period. The same absence of a connection with the duration of the experiment is noticed in the case of excretion, which was measured with 3 rabbits of the first group (Table 3).

TABLE 3

Excretion of ^{60}Co (for 2 days) receiving 3.75 µc per day

Time from commencement of experiment	Excretion as percentage of daily administration		
	urine	feces	total
1 month	9.3	96.0	105.0
2 months	5.7	88.0	93.7
3 ,,	8.4	—	—

Table 4 gives mean values of specific and total activity found in the organs and the whole body of rabbits of each group. The distribution of body weight in the organs and tissues as used for calculation of activity in the whole organ or tissue, is also given. It can be seen that the ratios of specific activities of the tissues are, in general, similar to those found after single administration, but the range of these values is rather less.

In order to prove the validity of the method of calculating body activity according to the specific activity of the main accumulating organs, using the average weight distribution of these organs, and not being able to incinerate the whole corpse, we used the following indirect verification. The external radiation of 3 rabbits of the group receiving 3.75 µc per day was measured with a γ-probe before the animals were killed. The probe was enclosed in a lead jacket 4 cm thick with an opening against which was placed a tight box containing the tightly packed rabbit. Measurements were then taken in four standard positions: the left flank, right flank, head and tail. The average was taken of the measurements from these four positions. After measurement the rabbits were killed, tissue activity measured and body activity calculated (including the gastro-intestinal tract).

In Table 5 are presented the measurements and body activity of each rabbit as calculated by specific activity and weight distribution of organs. The close coincidence of the results obtained with these 3 rabbits by measurement of external radiation and by calculation (to an accuracy of ±5 per cent) confirm the validity of our method of activity calculation. At the same time the possibility of evaluating the level of body activity by external radiation measurement is confirmed.

From Table 4 it can be seen that the level of body activity (without the gastro-intestinal tract) increases disproportionately with increase of ^{60}Co intake. Whereas the ratio of daily administration was 1:10:50 the ratio of body activity, excluding the contents of the gastro-intestinal tract, was 1:2.9:5.7. Figure 4(a) plotted on a logarithmic scale shows the relation

TABLE 4

Specific and total activity of organs (actual figures and as percentage of daily administration) of rabbits receiving ^{60}Co daily

Organs	Weight of organ (g)	3.75 μc/day specific μc/g	3.75 μc/day σ in %	3.75 μc/day total μc	3.75 μc/day percentage of daily administration	37.5 μc/day specific μc/g	37.5 μc/day σ in %	37.5 μc/day total μc	37.5 μc/day percentage of daily administration	195 μc/day specific μc/g	195 μc/day σ in %	195 μc/day total μc	195 μc/day percentage of daily administration
Liver	100*	0.017	±9	1.34	35.6	0.100	±8	9.40	25	0.212	±3	21.15	10.8
Kidneys	20	0.014	±12	0.27	7.2	0.048	±6	0.96	2.5	0.30	±19	6.0	3.0
Lungs		0.007	±15	—	—	0.030	±10	—	—	0.05	±7	—	—
Heart		0.012	±11	—	—	0.056	±7	—	—	—	—	—	—
Spleen and other parenchymatous organs	265	0.007	±13	1.98	53.0	0.017	±10	4.58	12.2	0.022	±10	6.0	3.0
Bone marrow		0.003	—	—	—	0.014	—	—	—	—	—	—	—
Blood	175	0.003	±18	0.53	14.0	0.011	±6	1.71	4.55	0.036	±16	6.30	3.2
Muscle and other organs with similar activity	2450	0.003	±11	—	196.0	0.007	±9	16.5	44.0	0.011	±14	25.75	13.0
Brain		0.004		7.35	—	0.008		—	—	—	—	—	—
Body total excluding the gastro-intestinal tract	3000	0.004	±10	11.5	306	0.011	±9	33.2	88.0	0.022	±10	65.2	33.0
Relative body totals		—	—	1	—	—	—	2.9	—	—	—	5.7	—
Gastro-intestinal tract†	500	0.041		20.5±2%	544	0.24		120±20%	320	0.80		401.0±21%	206.5
Total	3500	—		31.9	850	0.044		153.2	408	0.130		466.2	239.5

* In rabbits of Group I (3.75 μc/day) the average weight of the liver was 81 g.

† In this case σ is given for total activity as total activity of the gastro-intestinal tract was measured and specific activity calculated by weight.

Table 5

Live measurement of body activity of rabbits by external radiation and activity found in the body

No. of rabbit	Mean number of counts measured in four standard positions	Mean body activity (μc)	Value of activity (μc)
14	2800	17.8	1.14×10^{-2}
18	3530	24.9	1.15×10^{-2}
22	1900	13.3	1.24×10^{-2}
Ratios of values found	1 : 1.26 : 0.68	1 : 1.28 : 0.75	1 : 1.02 : 1.09

between the level of activity in the body and the magnitude of daily administration.

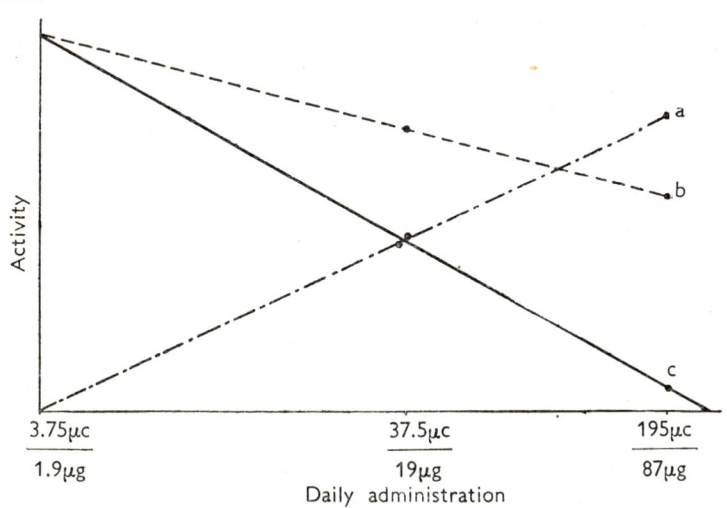

FIG. 4. a—relationship between the equilibrium level of activity in the body of rabbits and the magnitude of daily administration; b and c—relationship between the equilibrium level of activity in the body of rabbits and rats and the quantity of stable cobalt in solution (on a logarithmic scale).

The curve obtained shows that between the equilibrium level of body activity and the amount of ^{60}Co daily administered there is a fixed relationship, expressed by the formula:

$$A_\infty = 6.25 \times a^{0.46} \text{ or approximately } 6.25 \times a^{0.5} \quad (1)$$

where a—administration in μc/day, A—equilibrium level of body activity in μc.

TABLE 6

Activity of organs and whole body of rats as percentage of daily administration of ^{60}Co, as related to content of stable cobalt in the administered solution (mean data for 5 rats)

Organs	Activity found as percentage of daily administration		
	1.9 µg/day	19 µg/day	87 µg/day
Liver	10.8	5.7	2.9
Kidneys	1.8	1.2	1.0
Carcass	11.9	9.0	8.0
Total	24.5±2.5	15.9±1.6	11.9±1.2
Gastro-intestinal tract	7.4	8.0	8.3
Total	31.9	23.9	20.2

The activity retained in the gastro-intestinal tract of rabbits varies within wide limits, but here also the mean value was relatively lower with increase in daily administration (cf. Table 4). However, no such simple correlation as existed for the level of body activity was found.

The disproportionality found between the level of body activity and daily administration may be connected with the fact that the content of stable cobalt in solution increased almost proportionately with administered activity (1:10:46) and absorption or accumulation was relatively decreased. To verify this possibility 3 groups of 5 rats were given 1.4 µc ^{60}Co orally for 40 days. The quantity of stable cobalt received by the rats of each group was the same as that received by the rabbits, namely: 1.9 µg, 19 µg and 87 µg. The rats were killed 1 day after the 40th administration. The activity of the liver, kidneys and the rest of the body, and also of the contents of the gastro-intestinal tract was measured.

The results of these tests are presented in Table 6. It can be seen that with increase of the quantity of the carrier the level of body activity decreases.

This correlation is shown in logarithmic scale in Fig. 4 (b). For comparison, the data for the rabbits, recalculated with regard to the quantity of stable cobalt and presented for the same administered activity, are also shown in Fig. 4 (c).

As can be seen from this figure the correlation is similar for rats, but whereas for rabbits the equilibrium level is approximately inversely proportional to the square root of the daily administration of stable cobalt, for rats it is related to the fourth root of these values. Whether this degree of correlation is connected only with limited absorption in the intestine or whether the change of fixation and excretion of the isotope also has significance we cannot say, as this would require special study. Since there are only 3 points on the curve no general formula can be applied, but within the dose limits studied by us it is obviously fair to assert that they are in close approximation.

TABLE 7

The β-radiation dose of rabbit tissues after daily oral intake of $^{60}CoCl_2$

Organ or tissue	3.75 μc/day		37.5 μc/day		195 μc/day	
	β-radiation dose (rep)					
	per day	for 18–24 months	per day	for 7.5–24 months	per day	for 2 months
Liver	0.100	54–73	0.610	140–430	1.27	76
Kidneys	0.084	45–61	0.290	65–210	1.83	110
Lungs	0.043	23–31	0.180	40–130	0.31	19
Heart	0.074	40–54	0.270	60–195	—	—
Spleen	0.043	23–31	0.110	25–80	0.14	8.5
Bone marrow	0.018	10–13	0.085	19–62	—	—
Blood	0.018	10–13	0.067	15–49	0.22	13
Muscles	0.018	10–13	0.042	9.5–31	0.07	4
Brain	0.024	13–17.5	0.048	11–35	—	—

Table 7 gives the daily doses of β-radiation in particular tissues and the limits of the dose received by the tissues of the rabbits of each group throughout the animals' lives. The liver and kidneys receive the largest β-radiation dose and exhibit the highest specific activity. The dose in the spleen and the other parenchymatous organs is significantly lower. Calculation of the mean β-radiation dose for the whole body is not applicable because of the low penetrative capacity of the β-particles of ^{60}Co.

There is no point on the other hand in calculating the γ-radiation dose for particular tissues and organs. Therefore the mean daily dose of γ-radiation for the whole body is calculated by assuming an even distribution of total activity contained in the body, including the contents of the gastro-intestinal tract. For organs of the abdominal cavity this calculated dose is too low, and for areas remote from the abdominal cavity somewhat too high. We also calculated the mean daily dose in the abdominal cavity, dependent upon the activity of the gastro-intestinal tract contents. This dose is closer to the true value for organs of the abdominal cavity. Although neither is the true dose, as was shown in the previous article they enable an evaluation to be made of the order of magnitude of γ-radiation doses and the relationship between the doses received by the different groups of rabbits. In Table 8 are presented the daily γ-radiation doses and the limits of the total dose received during life for the rabbits of each group. For the groups receiving 3.75 μc/day

Table 8
Mean γ-radiation doses in rabbits after daily oral intake of $^{60}CoCl_2$

Body region	3.75 μc/day per day	3.75 μc/day for 18–24 months	37.5 μc/day per day	37.5 μc/day for 7.5–24 months	195 μc/day per day	195 μc/day for 2 months
	β-radiation dose (r)					
Whole body	0.24	135–185	1.16	250–825	3.4	150
Abdominal cavity	0.57	300–400	3.30	850–2350	11.1	500

and 195 μc/day the radiation doses are approximately the same. For the group which received 37.5 μc/day the dose received by rabbits living for 2 years reaches values greater than 2000 r. Comparing Tables 7 and 8 it is evident that β-radiation doses are in general lower than γ-doses, and even in those organs in which little ^{60}Co accumulates the dose received is nevertheless high on account of γ-radiation. Thus, for a comparison of doses with resulting pathological changes, it is necessary to turn in the main to Table 8. For the liver and kidneys the β-radiation doses must be added to the γ-doses.

The equilibrium which has been shown by us and other writers to arise between administered and excreted activity with chronic administration of radioisotopes is also confirmed by a simple mathematical calculation. If administration of the isotope is equal to a μc/day, the half-life $T_{\frac{1}{2}}$ days, the biological half-life T_b days and the effective half-life $T_{e\frac{1}{2}}$ days:

$$T_{e\frac{1}{2}} = \frac{T_{\frac{1}{2}} \times T_b}{T_{\frac{1}{2}} + T_b}$$

then the radioactivity remaining in the body from the first administration after time t from the commencement of administrations is:

$$a \times \exp\left(-\frac{0.693\,t}{T_{e\frac{1}{2}}}\right)$$

from the second:

$$a \times \exp\left(-\frac{0.693\,(t-1)}{T_{e\frac{1}{2}}}\right)$$

from the third:

$$a \times \exp\left(-\frac{0.693(t-2)}{T_{e\frac{1}{2}}}\right)$$

and so on, up to the activity remaining from the administration on the given day (after t days):

$$a \times \exp\left(-\frac{0.693(t-t)}{T_{e\frac{1}{2}}}\right)$$

The activity A_t, remaining in the body after t days is equal to the sum of the activities remaining from every administration up to that time, and can be represented thus:

$$A_t = \sum_{R=0}^{t} a \times \exp\left(-\frac{0.693(t-k)}{T_{e\frac{1}{2}}}\right) \quad (2)$$

assuming that $T_{e\frac{1}{2}}$ remains constant throughout the experiment. If time t is fairly large by comparison with $T_{e\frac{1}{2}}$, for example $t = 10\,T_{e\frac{1}{2}}$, then the activity remaining in the body after t days from the first administration is less than 1/1000 of the daily dose. Time t can thus be considered infinitely large and the activity remaining from the first administration virtually nil. Thereafter with each following administration ($t+1$, $t+2$ and so on) the first members of the sum can be counted nil and discarded. Therefore the number of members of the sum (2) and consequently the total itself will remain constant and an upper limit of activity is reached, i.e. equilibrium. It is reasonable to consider activity in the body as changing not by discrete steps after each administration but smoothly, as if the isotope is being administered continuously in the same way as it is excreted. In this way the formula for the equilibrium level of activity can be written:

$$A_\infty = a \int_0^\infty \exp\left(-\frac{0.693t}{T_{e\frac{1}{2}}}\right) \times dt = \frac{a \times T_{e\frac{1}{2}}}{0.693} = 1.44\,a T_{e\frac{1}{2}} \quad (3)$$

From the above discussion it can be seen that the time of establishment of equilibrium depends on the magnitude of $T_{e\frac{1}{2}}$ and the degree of accuracy taken. It may be assumed that positive equilibrium is established after a time t equal to 7–10 times the effective half-life. From equation (3) it follows that the level of activity once equilibrium has been established does not depend on time but is proportional to the daily administration of the isotope and the effective half-life. Where the physical half-life is very great by comparison with T_b, as is the case with ^{60}Co, T_b can be substituted for $T_{e\frac{1}{2}}$ in expression (3). If on the other hand $T_{e\frac{1}{2}}$ is substantially less than T_b, $T_{\frac{1}{2}}$ replaces $T_{e\frac{1}{2}}$. If excretion of the isotope is not exactly exponential equilibrium still occurs but its level and time of occurrence have to be established experimentally. In our experiments, which confirm the presence of this equilibrium, it was found that within the limits of the radiation doses the equilibrium level of body activity in rabbits is reached after 1–2 months and is related to daily administration in the ratio:

$$A_\infty - = 6.25 \times a^{0.46} \quad (1)$$

i.e. approximately proportional to the square root of the daily administration. In suggesting that this relationship is connected with the different contents by weight of cobalt of the administered solutions, and reformulated to allow for this variation (cf. Fig. 4c) it was found that for rabbits:

$$A_\infty- = 4.44ad^{-0.58} \qquad (4)$$

where d is the quantity by weight of cobalt daily administered. Thus the equilibrium level of activity established with either magnitude of administered activity is approximately inversely proportional to the square root of the daily intake of stable cobalt.

Comparing the expressions (3) and (4) we find that T_b in equation (3), in the conditions of our experiment, can be replaced by $(4.44/1.44) \times d^{-0.50}$. This is not the biological half-life of ^{60}Co for rabbits, since it is calculated on the basis of body activity, excluding the gastro-intestinal tract, but with its help the time taken to reach equilibrium can be evaluated. This multiplier as it were summarizes those factors on which accumulation and decrease of the isotope in the rabbit's body depend. It may be thought the most important of these factors are the speed at which absorption takes place and the percentage absorbed, as well as the duration of the isotope's stay in the gastro-intestinal tract, in its turn dependent on a whole series of physico-chemical and physiological factors. The study of these problems presents an interesting and important task in itself.

CONCLUSIONS

1. Equilibrium is very rapidly established between the administered and excreted quantities of the isotope in rats and rabbits during daily oral administration of $^{60}CoCl_2$.

2. Body activity of rabbits reaches a constant level, with constant intake of ^{60}Co but with increase of the daily activity administered the body activity increases approximately proportionally to the square root of the amount administered.

3. In rats which had received equal amounts of activity of ^{60}Co with different amounts of stable cobalt a lowering of the equilibrium level of body activity was detected, approximately proportional to the root four of the daily intake of stable cobalt.

4. The mean doses of β- and γ-radiation in the body of rabbits during daily oral administration of $^{60}CoCl_2$ are calculated. The greater part of the total dose is of γ-radiation, especially for organs of the abdominal cavity. For the liver and kidneys the β-radiation dose also acquires material significance and must be taken into account in calculating total radiation dose for these organs.

REFERENCES

Burykina L. N., *Toxicology of Radioactive Substances.* (Materialy po toksikologii radioaktivnykh veshchestv.) Medgiz (1957). English translation published by Pergamon Press (1962).

Burykina L. N., Resumés of reports presented at a *Conference on the Long-term effects of Radiation Injury.* (Referaty dokladov na konferentsii po otdalennym posledstviyam porazhenii, vyzvannykh vozdeistviyem ioniziruyushchikh izlychenii.) 68, Moscow (1956).

Bustad L. K., George L. A., Marks S., Warker D. E. et al., *Radiation Res.* 6, No. 3, 380–413 (1957).

Kurlyandskaya E. B., Beloborodova N. L. and Baranova Ye. F., *Toxicology of Radioactive Substances*, 16, Medgiz (1957). English Translation published by Pergamon Press (1962).

Kurlyandskaya E. B., Beloborodova N. L. and Baranova Ye. F., *Toxicology of Radioactive Substances*, 31, Medgiz (1957). English translation published by Pergamon Press (1962).

Rubanovskaya A. A. and Ushakova V. F., *Toxicology of Radioactive Substances*, 23, Medgiz (1957). English translation published by Pergamon Press (1962).

Rubanovskaya A. A. and Ushakova V. F., *Toxicology of Radioactive Substances*, 13, Medgiz (1957). English translation published by Pergamon Press (1962).

CHANGES IN HEMOPOIESIS DURING PROLONGED INTERNAL ADMINISTRATION OF ^{60}Co

N. L. BELOBORODOVA

RADIOACTIVE cobalt (^{60}Co) is used in various branches of the national economy not only in closed ampoules as a source of external radiation, but also in the form of open preparations. Therefore the study of early signs of damage to hemopoietic activity after internal administration of ^{60}Co is of practical importance.

Changes in hemopoiesis caused by ionizing radiation proceed in phases. But whereas after large acute radiation doses the phases may alternate rapidly, measured in hours and sometimes even in minutes, with chronic administration (external or internal) of small radiation doses the duration of particular phases may be considerable—a year or more (A. P. Yegorov, M. S. Lapteva-Popova, N. L. Beloborodova and E. F. Baranova). With internal application of isotopes, phase duration is dependent not only on dose but also on the physical and chemical properties of the isotope itself; the importance of individual sensitivity is also recognized. The early period of action of small doses of radiation is characterized by unsteadiness in hemopoiesis with fluctuation of particular hematological factors, a phase which is replaced by prolonged stabilization at a level close to normal. Symptoms of suppression of hemopoiesis (the third phase) generally develop late and it is not always possible to observe them under experimental conditions. The scope of this paper is the study of hemopoiesis and the detection of early signs of its impairment during prolonged (22 months) daily administration of ^{60}Co.

For the detection of functional failures of the hemopoietic organs, as well as a monthly examination of the peripheral blood and bone marrow punctures, certain of the physiological stresses on the hemopoietic system used earlier by us were also applied, namely pregnancy and blood loss. At the end of the experiment the morphological composition of the bone marrow and spleen of all the animals killed was studied by contact preparation. The experiment comprised 2 experimental and 3 control groups of rabbits. The details of these groups are presented in the article by

E. B. Kurlyandskaya "Further Research on the Toxicology of Radioactive Substances", included in this collection. As hematological indications in the animals of all three groups acting as controls (one group—biological control and two groups receiving stable cobalt) were alike, the three groups will hereafter be considered as one.

CHANGES IN THE RED BLOOD

In animals of the control group the red blood throughout the 22 months was unchanged; the number of erythrocytes per mm^3 was close to 5,500,000, and hemoglobin varied within 12–14 g per cent. The reticulocyte number was on average about 25⁰/₀₀. No reticulocytosis or reticulopenia was observed.

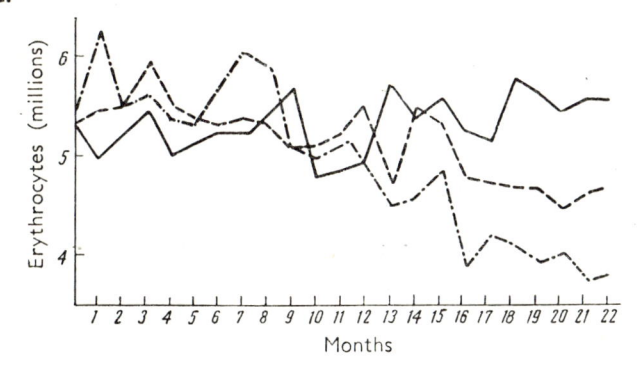

FIG. 1. Changes in the erythrocyte number. —— control; ----- 1.25 µc/kg ^{60}Co; —·—·— 12.5 µc/kg ^{60}Co.

The red blood of animals receiving ^{60}Co differed markedly from the control (Fig. 1). Thus, in animals of both the experimental groups, a temporary increase of reticulocyte number was observed during the early months. In animals of the second group this increase began earlier and was more pronounced: the erythrocyte number, at the start of the experiment, on average 5,500,000 per mm^3, increased after 2–3 weeks to 6,500,000, and in some animals, to 7,000,000 or more. At 7 months, in these same animals, the erythrocyte number again increased, but to a somewhat lesser degree (up to 6,000,000 on average), while at the 12th month a slow but steady fall began. The development of pronounced anemia was observed in the majority of cases between the 16th and 18th months of the experiment. The fall in hemoglobin was sometimes delayed, which produced a temporary increase in the colour index. It should be noticed that the reticulocyte number in the peripheral blood scarcely changed remaining on average at about 20–25⁰/₀₀. This peculiar action of ^{60}Co which appears in the chronic experiment sharply differentiates it from ^{134}Cs and ^{89}Sr, which produce sharp reticulocyte fluctuations, especially in the first year.

TABLE 1

*The morphological composition of rabbit bone marrow 21–22 months after commencement of the experiment**

	Control percentage of the total number of nucleated cells	Control partial myelograms	First group (1.25 μc/kg ^{60}Co) percentage of the total number of nucleated cells	First group (1.25 μc/kg ^{60}Co) partial myelograms	Second group (12.5 μc/kg ^{60}Co) percentage of the total number of nucleated cells	Second group (12.5 μc/kg ^{60}Co) partial myelograms
Hemocytoblasts	0–0.2		0–0.2			
Myeloblasts	0.2–0.4		0.2–1.2		0.2–0.4	
Neutrophils:						
promyelocytes	1.0–3.0	0.4–2.8	0.5–2.6	0.5–2.6	0–2.0	0.2–4.0
myelocytes	3.0–7.0	8.0–15.0	2.2–5.6	2.6–10.5	2.8–6.0	6.0–11
juvenile	3.6–5.4	7.0–18.0	3.8–11.0	6.0–20.0	3.8–8.2	9.0–15.0
stab	10.2–10.5	27.0–40.0	18.0–24.0	27.0–40.0	13.0–15.0	26.0–32.0
segmented	14.0–18.0	46.0–60.0	28.0–30.0	27.0–53.0	21.0–22.0	41.0–51.0
Eosinophils	0.6–3.7		0.4–0.8		0–1.4	
Basophils	1.8–4.0		0.6–1.0		0.6–1.6	
Lymphocytes	15.0–20.0		4.4–7.2		2.0–6.0	
Monocytes	1.6–3.4		0.2–2.2		0.2–0.4	
Proerythroblasts	0.2–0.3	0.5–2.0	0–0.4	0–1.5	0–1.0	0.8–2.2
Basophilic erythroblasts	1.4–3.8	2.0–10.0	0.8–1.6	2.0–7.0	0.2–3.0	2.3–3.2
Polychromatophilic erythroblasts	11.0–17.0	38.0–49.0	9.0–21.0	38.0–58.0	20.0–22.0	42.0–52.0
Normoblasts	14.0–20.0	45.0–57.0	11.0–20.0	40.0–60.0	18.0–26.0	42.0–55.0
Reticular	0.2–0.8		0–1.2		0–0.4	
Plasma	0.2–0.8		1.0–2.4		0.6–1.8	
Megakaryocytes	0–0.4		0–0.4		0–0.2	
White cell division	0.2–0.4		0–0.6		0–0.2	
Red cell division	0.4–1.2		0–0.8		0.2–0.6	
White branch	60.0–75.0		61.0–72.0		50.0–55.0	
Red branch	30.0–32.0		22.0–36.0		43.0–47.0	

* The minimum and maximum values are given for each type of cell.

Increase of the erythrocyte number and hemoglobin as a first reaction to small doses of ionizing radiation has been described in the literature for external radiation (Lacassagne et al.), and also by us for internal radiation of ^{89}Sr (N. L. Beloborodova and E. F. Baranova).

Remembering that the erythrocyte number began to rise in animals of the second group after only 2 weeks, this may be connected with functional shifts in erythropoiesis; mainly a release of mature erythrocytes into the peripheral blood following an apparent acceleration of maturation. Consequently the number of reticulocytes in the peripheral blood does not increase.

Examination of bone marrow punctures showed that the composition of the bone marrow of rabbits of the first group (receiving 1.25 μc/kg ^{60}Co) after 14 months was normal. In the majority of rabbits of the second group (receiving 12.5 μc/kg ^{60}Co), although the number of erythrocytes in the peripheral blood was normal after 14–15 months, the red branch of the bone marrow was 42–49 per cent, i.e. it was on average 15 per cent higher than in the control animals. The ratios of particular types of cells of the red and white series, determined by partial myelo- and erythrograms, remained normal.

Examination of contact preparations of the bone marrow was made in all animals (experimental and control). All rabbits which received 12.5 μc/kg ^{60}Co showed an enlargement of the red branch. The gradual development of erythroid hyperplasia in these animals is apparently the first phase in the development of hypoplastic anemia (I. A. Kassirskii), the comparatively rapid development of which is evidence of profound impairment of erythropoiesis by ^{60}Co. The significant atrophy of the gastric glands, (found in the animals of this group by A. S. Kaplanskii) and also lesions of the liver suggest that one of the causes of impairment of erythropoiesis may be in this case connected with inadequate formation and accumulation of hemopoietic factors in the body. This problem, however, requires a special study. Furthermore, it is known that the spleen plays a part in the regulation of erythropoiesis. It is possible that ^{60}Co impairs not only the lymphopoietic function of the spleen but also its regulatory role.

Thus, changes in erythropoiesis brought about by prolonged administration of ^{60}Co differ from those observed with other radioactive isotopes, and are characterized by the absence of sharp fluctuations of the reticulocyte number and the comparatively early development of anemia.

It should again be emphasized that the impairment of erythropoietic function observed by us cannot be wholly attributed to the action of the metal cobalt as opposed to the radiations from ^{60}Co, since in the rabbits receiving 19 μg/kg/day stable cobalt (i.e. the content of metallic cobalt in the solution with activity of 12.5 ñc/kg ^{60}Co) no deviations in erythropoiesis were observed.

Our observations agree with those reported in the literature (A. O. Voinar), according to which the pronounced effect of cobalt (as opposed to radioactive ^{60}Co) on erythropoiesis (increase of the erythrocyte number, hemoglobin, etc.) is only seen after administration of not less than 1 mg/kg, i.e. in doses exceeding ours more than 700 times.

However, although small quantities of cobalt have no effect on peripheral blood composition, it may perhaps affect the functional capacity of the hemopoietic organs. Thus, K. M. Malenkova and E. V. Koribskaya found that administration of stable cobalt to animals protected them to a significant degree from development of radiation anemia. All the red blood factors of these animals were more stable after irradiation than those of the controls.

Evidently, the combination of the stimulating effect on erythropoiesis of metallic cobalt with the inhibitory effect of ionizing radiation may be the reason for the peculiar changes in erythropoiesis observed in our experiments.

CHANGES IN THE WHITE BLOOD

In animals of the control group the total leucocyte number varied on average from 7000 to 11,000. The absolute number of neutrophils varied from 1500 to 3000, the absolute lymphocyte number from 5000 to 7000.

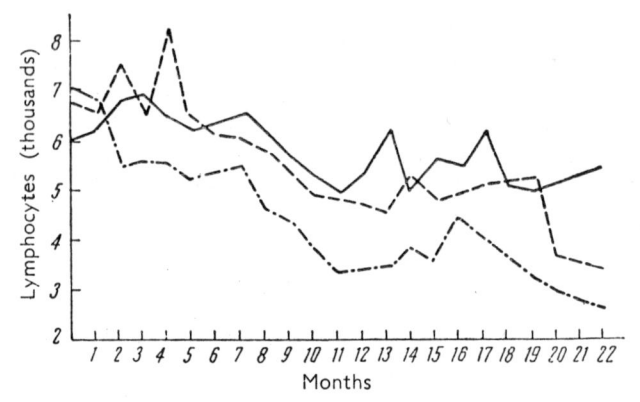

Fig. 2. Changes in the absolute lymphocyte number, ——— control; ----- 1.25 μc/kg ^{60}Co; —·—·— 12.5 μc/kg ^{60}Co.

In all animals to which ^{60}Co was administered variations of the absolute number of neutrophils fell within the limits of the physiological norm. Qualitative changes of cells of this series were not observed.

The main change in the experimental animals of both groups consisted in impairment of lymphopoiesis, the degree of which was dependent upon the amount of ^{60}Co administered (Fig. 2). Thus, in the first months of administration all animals of the first group showed a slight variation in absolute lymphocytosis (7500–8200 lymphocytes per mm^3 blood). Similar symptoms were seen by us after administration of other radioactive isotopes. For 15 months the absolute lymphocyte number remained within normal limits, and some decrease (less than 4000) was noticed only after 19–20 months of ^{60}Co administration. In most cases lymphopenia was unstable and transitory.

In the animals which received 12.5 μc/kg ^{60}Co receiving the larger quantity of cobalt, no absolute lymphocytosis was observed. From the first month of application a gradual progressive decline in the lymphocyte number began. By the end of the experiment (after 21–22 months) the absolute lymphocyte number of the animals of this group comprised only 35 per cent of the initial number and on average was 2600 cells per mm^3 blood. In some cases even lower figures were observed 1500–1800.

The presence in the peripheral blood of pathological forms of lymphocyte and the increase of breakdown (lympholysis) were also symptoms of the impairment of lymphopoiesis in the experimental animals. In the first 6–7 months the number of decayed lymphocytes in these animals was 20–25 per cent, compared with 3–5 per cent in the controls. Subsequently lympholysis declined and remained within normal limits until the end of the experiment. Apparently, the increase of lympholysis is connected with the initial reaction of lymphoid tissue to radiation. At this period in rabbits receiving 12.5 μc/kg ^{60}Co, the appearance of lymphocytes with structureless nuclei was observed due to the breakdown of chromatin (chromatolysis).

At later stages, and also after pregnancy and blood loss, lymphocytes with vacuolated nuclei and protoplasm appeared in the peripheral blood of the test animals. "Budding" of pieces of the nucleus (fragmentosis) or division of the lymphocyte nucleus into two parts was observed. Obviously, the occurrence of such morphological changes in the cells is connected with impairment of the processes of cell division (A. P. Egorov). No similar changes were found in the control animals.

In order to study the nature of the damage to lymphopoiesis caused by ^{60}Co we compared the results of examination of the peripheral blood of the rabbits of the second group with histological data on the quantity of lymphoid tissue in the spleen of these animals, obtained by A. S. Kaplanskii (Table 2).

As can be seen from Table 2 where animals are grouped according to life span, in the 4 rabbits which died during the first year a decrease

TABLE 2

Comparison of changes in the number of lymphocytes in the peripheral blood and spleen of rabbits of the second group (12.5 μc/kg ^{60}Co). Hematological and histological data

Case No.	Life span (months)	Rabbit No.	Changes in the absolute number of lymphocytes in the peripheral blood	Changes in the lymphoid tissue content of the spleen (histological examination)
1	8	9	Lymphopenia in last two months of life. Qualitative changes in the lymphocytes (vacuolization, fragmentosis)	Lymphoid tissue diminished
2	11	7	Lymphocyte number within normal limits	Insignificant diminution of lymphoid tissue (primarily in the pulp)
3	11	8	As above	As above
4	12	4	Constant lymphopenia in last 4 months	Lymphoid tissue sharply diminished
5	17	2	Periodic lymphopenia	Lymphoid tissue diminished
6	19	1	Constant lymphopenia in last 9 months. Atypical lymphocyte forms	Lymphoid tissue well pronounced
7	20	3	Constant lymphopenia in last 9 months	As above
8	21	4a	Lymphocyte number within normal limits	As above
9	21	6	Constant but slight lymphopenia in last 14 months	As above
10	21	10	Constant pronounced lymphopenia in last 15 months	Insignificant diminution of lymphoid tissue
11	22	5	Constant pronounced lymphopenia in last 7 months	Lymphoid tissue well pronounced
12	22	12a	Constant pronounced lymphopenia in last 12 months	Lymphoid tissue moderately pronounced
13	22	14a	Periodic lymphopenia; reinforced during pregnancy	Lymphoid tissue well pronounced

of the amount of lymphoid tissue in the spleen was observed; however, in two rabbits (Nos. 7 and 8) the absolute number of lymphocytes in the peripheral blood remained within normal limits (4400–4900 per mm^3), although it had fallen significantly by comparison with its initial level in these animals (9200–9400 per mm^3).

In some rabbits which died or were killed at later stages absolute lymphopenia in the peripheral blood corresponded to a diminution of lymphoid tissue (rabbits Nos. 2, 10, 12a). However, in 5 animals (Nos. 1, 3, 6, 5, 14a) after 20–22 months, although the amount of lymphoid tissue in the spleen was normal, more or less constant and prolonged absolute lymphopenia in the peripheral blood was observed.

Rabbit No. 4a, is an example of high individual resistance. After almost 2 years of daily administration of ^{60}Co no lymphopenia was observed and the morphological picture of the spleen was unchanged.

A cell count in contact preparations of the spleen, using May–Grunwald–Romanovskii's stain, showed that in the animals which received ^{60}Co, especially 12.5 μc/kg the total number of lymphocytes decreased on average by 20 per cent (Table 3). Most of the cells, as in the control animals, were average lymphocytes, but their number, as also the number of small lymphocytes, had decreased 47–53 per cent compared with 68–80 per cent in the control. A relative increase of prolymphocytes and large lymphocytes was also observed. A similar but less pronounced change in the cellular composition of the spleen was found in rabbits receiving 1.25 μc/kg ^{60}Co.

Consequently, retarded lymphocyte maturation was seen in the spleen of experimental animals, especially in the second group. This circumstance may explain the lymphopenia found in animals with well pronounced lymphoid tissue.

Nor is the possibility excluded that continuous irradiation such as obtained in our experiments may shorten the life of lymphocytes, as occurs with external radiation (A. P. Egorov).

Study of spleen preparations of all the control rabbits disclosed, apart from lymphocytes, 4–5 per cent neutrophils. These were mainly segmented or stab forms, sometimes juvenile, and an insignificant number of neutrophilic myelocytes. No promyelocytes were detected in our preparations. The increase in cells of the neutrophil series in rabbits of both experimental groups was clearly seen in comparison of spleen preparations with the controls. In the group receiving 1.25 μc/kg ^{60}Co, both young and mature forms of neutrophil increase fairly evenly. In the second group the increase in the neutrophil number concerned mainly segmentonuclear; the numbers of myelocytes and juveniles declined relatively. Attention is drawn to the sharp increase (up to 7 per cent) in the number of plasma cells in all the experimental animals, and also in the number of erythro-and normoblasts in the animals of the first group (absent from peripheral blood), which is very rarely observed in rabbits (E. L. Berezov).

On the basis of the data presented above it is concluded that the absolute lymphopenia which develops in rabbits as a result of prolonged admini-

TAB

Morphological composition of contact pre-

Group	Lymphocytes				
	total number	lympho- blasts	prolympho- cytes and large lymphocytes	average	small
Control	92-95	0–0.4	8–14	68–80	10–12
Receiving 1.25 μc/kg ^{60}Co	79–92	0–0.2	5–16	52–70	4–6
Receiving 12.5 μc/kg ^{60}Co	72–75	0–0.2	15–22	47–53	3–9

stration of ^{60}Co may be produced either by a decline in the formative capacity of the spleen in consequence of the destruction of lymphoid tissue (cf. Table 2, rabbits Nos. 2, 4, 9, 10, 12a), or by a retardation of lymphocyte maturation processes while the lymphoid tissue remains well pronounced (cf. Table, 2, rabbits Nos. 1, 3, 5, 6, 14a). Also the possibility of an abbreviation of the life span of lymphocytes in the peripheral blood from the effects of continuous irradiation must not be excluded.

The increase in the number of cells of the myeloid series in contact preparations of the spleen of experimental animals gives ground for suggesting the occurrence of myelopoiesis in the spleen under the influence of ^{60}Co, all the more so since the possibility of reversion to embryonal hemopoiesis in radiation injury is known. However the absence of certain intermediate forms (promyelocytes) prevents us from asserting this categorically.

THROMBOCYTE CHANGES

In no group of animals, including those receiving ^{60}Co, were signs of changes in thrombopoiesis observed. The thrombocyte number varied from 200,000 to 450,000.

BLOOD CHANGES DURING AND AFTER PREGNANCY

In one of our earlier works (The Collection: *The Toxicology of Radioactive Substances*, Vol. 1, Moscow, 1957) in which we investigated the reactivity of the hemopoietic system at different periods in the administration of certain radioactive substances, it was shown that parturition enables the detection of deficiencies in the hemopoietic system of experimental animals.

In the present work we approached this problem 12 months after commencement of the experiment, i.e. at the period before significant

LE 3

parations of the spleen (in percentages)

	Neutrophils					Plasma	Reticular	Erythro- and normo- blasts
total number	myelo- cytes	juvenile	stab	seg- mented			
						cells	
4–5	0.2–0.6	0–0.40	0.2–0.8	3.2–4	0–0.4	2.4–4.2	0–0.2
3–19	0.8–1.2	0.6–3.6	0.2–2.2	1–12	1.4–7.2	0.6–3.4	0.8–3.4
16.8–21.4	0.2–5	0.6–6.0	0.2–3.8	15–18	3–7	0.8–1.8	0

deviations from normal in the peripheral blood have been observed. Twelve females from both groups were taken for the experiment. Pregnancy occurred in only 5 females, in 2 of which it terminated involuntarily and the females died from sepsis. In 3 females, pregnancy and parturition were normal. In 2 of the 3 females, after parturition significant changes in hemopoiesis were observed similar to those found in rabbits which had received ^{89}Sr for more than 2 years. It should be noticed that one of these females received 12.5 µc/kg ^{60}Co and the other 10 times less.

We have found no references in the literature to the character of hemopoietic changes in rabbits in normal pregnancy and parturition.

In our experiments the most characteristic blood change during pregnancy in the control rabbits was the reticulocytosis which arose towards the middle of pregnancy. On the day of parturition the reticulocyte number fell to the lower limit of the norm. The erythrocyte number also fell by 700,000–800,000 and hemoglobin by 10–15 per cent.

Figure 3 shows the changes in reticulocyte and erythrocyte numbers of 2 females, one control and one experimental (12.5 µc/kg). During pregnancy reticulocyte and erythrocyte changes were alike in both animals. On the day of parturition in the control female the reticulocyte number fell to the lower limit of the norm (15⁰/₀₀). In the rabbit receiving ^{60}Co no reticulocytes were found; on the following day there were 0.5⁰/₀₀, then 2⁰/₀₀ and on the 4th day 5⁰/₀₀. The erythrocyte number never fell below 4,000,000 per mm³ in the control female; in the experimental on the 6th day after parturition the erythrocyte number fell to 2,300,000.

The reticulocytosis which was observed in the experimental animal on the 8–12th day and reached 140⁰/₀₀ was not accompanied by an increase of the erythrocyte number which even on the 14th day was less than 4,000,000 per mm³.

During and just after pregnancy white blood changes in the control animals were insignificant and erratic, whereas in the experimental animals more or less constant leuko- and lymphopenia was observed, with the appearance of pathological forms of lymphocytes which were presumably connected with a concealed deficiency of the hemopoietic function of the spleen.

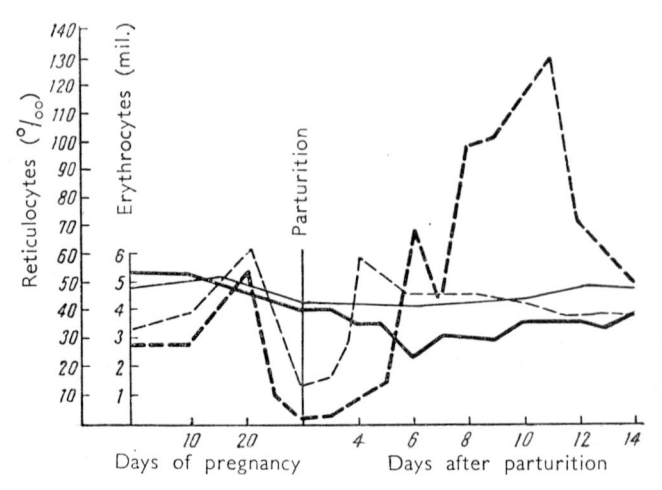

FIG. 3. The erythrocyte and reticulocyte numbers during and after pregnancy. ——— erythrocytes of experimental animals; – – – reticulocytes of experimental animals; ——— erythrocytes of control animals; - - - - reticulocytes of control animals.

Thus observation of hemopoiesis in the experimental animals during and after pregnancy in the period of relative stabilization of peripheral blood factors discloses its weakest points, in this case erythro- and lymphopoiesis. We were unable to study the effect of parturition on the blood picture after more prolonged ^{60}Co administration since pregnancy either failed to occur or terminated.

CHANGES IN HEMOPOIESIS AFTER BLOOD LOSS

In order to study the functional condition of the bone marrow after 16-month administration of ^{60}Co we had recourse to blood loss with subsequent observation of the peripheral blood. The reaction of the bone marrow to blood loss was also studied in rabbits of the control and second groups. One per cent by body weight of blood was removed from 3 rabbits of the first group, 5 rabbits of the second group and 3 rabbits of the control group. Preparatory investigation showed that the peripheral blood was within normal limits in rabbits of the first group (1.25 μc/kg ^{60}Co). In animals of the second group some leukopenia was observed (4000–5000) and pronounced absolute lymphopenia (less than 3000 per mm^3). The erythrocyte number was 600,000–700,000 lower than in the control group. An increased number of cells of the red series was noticed in the bone marrow as compared with the control rabbits (44 per cent instead of 30–34 per cent).

Both in the control and experimental animals blood loss produced a decrease of the erythrocyte number by, on average, 2,000,000 per mm³. In the control animals this decrease was accompanied from the first day by reticulocytosis (on average 60°/₀₀). In the rabbits of the experimental

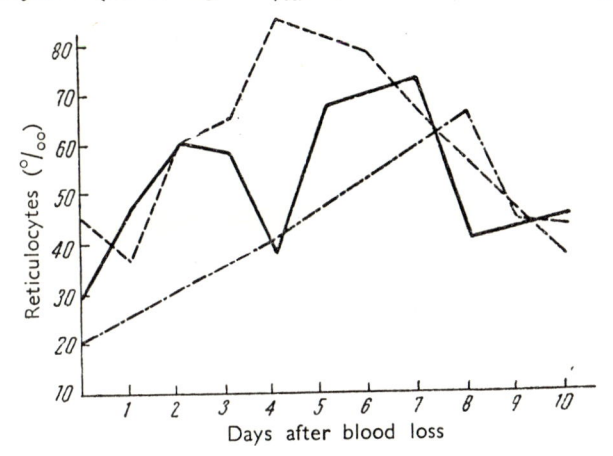

FIG. 4. The reticulocyte number after blood loss. —— Control; —·—· 1.25 μc/kg ⁶⁰Co; —·—·— 12.5 μc/kg ⁶⁰Co.

groups the reticulocyte number increased slowly and reached the above level only on the 4th day (first group) and 8th day (second group) (Fig. 4).

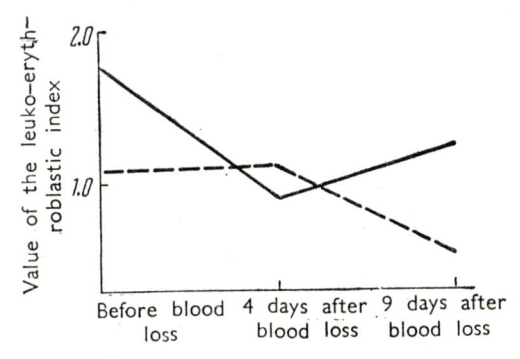

FIG. 5. The leuko-erythroblastic index after blood loss. —— Control animals; ——— experimental animals.

On the 4th day after blood loss a sharp decline of the leuko-erythroblastic index was observed in the control rabbits (Fig. 5). The red branch of the bone marrow increased by 20 per cent, chiefly due to the erythroblasts (Fig. 6). The number of mitoses of cells of the red series significantly increased (up to 2.6 per cent). On the 9th day the number of mitoses declined somewhat but the red branch was still relatively high. Comparison of these shifts with the symptom of reticulocytosis in the peripheral blood suggests a normal regenerative reaction to blood loss in the control animals.

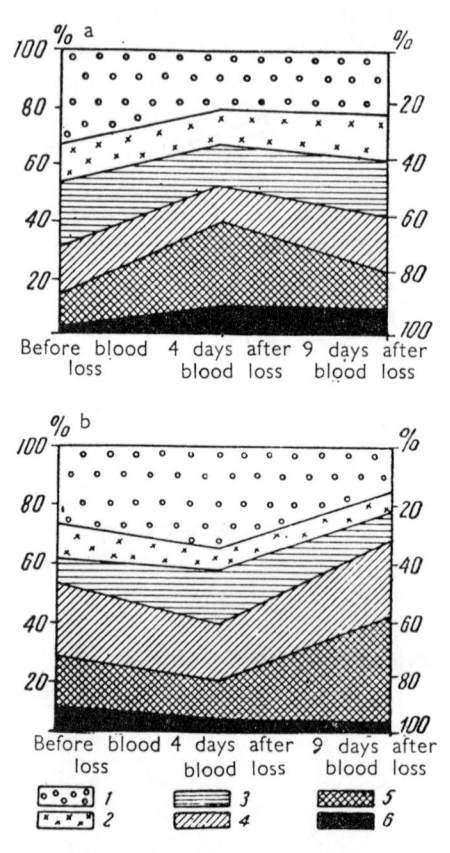

FIG. 6. The morphological composition of the bone marrow after blood loss. The upper figure refers to the control animals, the lower to those receiving 12.5 μc/kg ^{60}Co. 1. stab and segmented neutrophils; 2. promyelocytes, myelocytes and juvenile neutrophils; 3. lymphocytes, monocytes, reticular and plasma cells; 4. polychromatophilic and oxyphilic normoblasts; 5. polychromatophilic erythroblasts; 6. basophilic proerythroblasts and erythroblasts.

In the animals of the second group the leuko-erythroblastic index before blood loss was lower than in the controls because of the enlargement of the red branch due to ^{60}Co. On the 4th day after blood loss the index did not fall, as in the control animals, but remained unchanged (cf. Fig. 5). The number of mitoses of cells of the red series did not increase. A lowering of the leuko-erythroblastic index was observed in the experimental animals only on the 9th day. The red branch at this point reached 65 per cent of all nucleated bone marrow cells. The number of mitoses somewhat increased—up to 1 per cent.

The absence of enlargement of the red branch, the low mitotic activity of the red blood cells (no more than 1 per cent), and the absence of reticulocytosis in the peripheral blood during the first days after blood loss, are all factors pointing to a functional weakness of the erythroblastic part of the bone marrow in the experimental animals.

Differences in reaction to blood loss in the control and experimental animals were also observed concerning the white blood. In the control rabbits the total leukocyte number during the first days after blood loss rose from 9000 to 13,000. The absolute lymphocyte number also increased to the upper limits of the norm or a little higher (on average 9300 per mm^3).

In the rabbits of the first group leukocytosis was of the same order as in the control rabbits, but its maximum was reached on the 3rd–4th day. The lymphocyte number was little changed.

In the second group the total leukocyte number rose very slowly and reached maximum (8000) only on the 8th–9th day. It increased mainly due to the neutrophils, corresponding to which, on the 9th day, a relative increase in the bone marrow of young cells of the neutrophilic series was noticed (promyelocytes, myelocytes, juveniles) (Fig. 7).

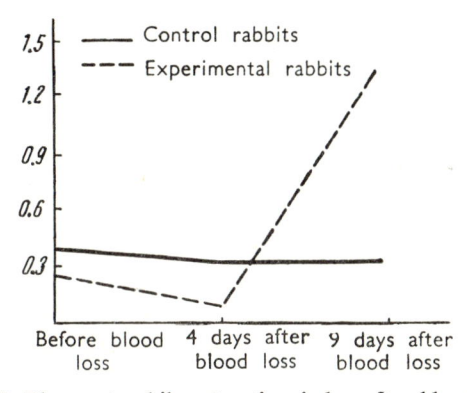

FIG. 7. The neutrophil maturation index after blood loss.

The absence in the experimental animals of an increase in the absolute lymphocyte number confirms our observations on the impairment of the lymphopoietic processes (Fig. 8).

Thus investigation of the peripheral blood and bone marrow after blood loss has confirmed the impairment of erythro- and lymphopoiesis by ^{60}Co.

On the basis of the experimental results set out above we have reached the conclusion that the lymphoid and erythroblastic tissue of the bone marrow is particularly sensitive to internal administration of ^{60}Co in doses one hundred and one thousand times the maximum permissible level.

Lymphopoietic changes in the animals of the first group were comparatively insignificant, chiefly concerning the processes of lymphocyte

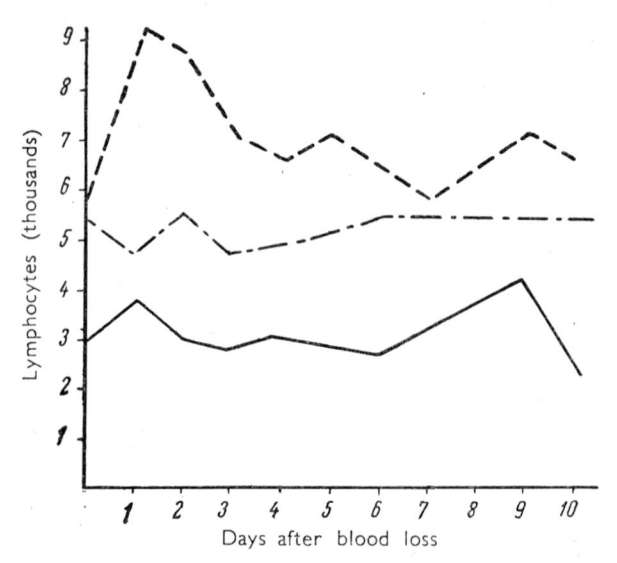

Fig. 8. The absolute lymphocyte number after blood loss. --- Control. —·— 1.25 µc/kg ^{60}Co. ——— 12.5 µc/kg ^{60}Co.

maturation, and were only slightly reflected in the peripheral blood picture. No constant lymphopenia was observed in these animals. There was only a slight decrease of lymphoid tissue in the animals of this group (A. S. Kaplanskii). However, the development of lymphocytosis in the first months of administration and the acceleration of lymphocyte decay indicate the early involvement of the spleen in the pathological process. Similar symptoms were observed by us with administration to rabbits of the radioactive isotopes ^{134}Cs and ^{89}Sr. The decrease of lymphopoietic activity in the animals receiving 1.25 µc/kg ^{60}Co, despite the normal lymphocyte number in the peripheral blood, is confirmed by the absence in these animals of lymphocytosis after blood loss and by the lymphopenia which arises during and after pregnancy.

In the second experimental group, receiving the larger quantity of ^{60}Co, a gradual decline of the absolute lymphocyte number was observed from the very beginning of the experiment. In animals living for more than a year pronounced constant lymphopenia developed. In all animals which died at an earlier period a diminution of lymphoid tissue in the spleen was found (A. S. Kaplanskii). In the animals which lived 20–22 months lymphoid tissue was very pronounced and changes in lymphopoiesis were confined to a retardation of lymphocyte maturation.

Erythropoietic changes in the animals of both experimental groups are distinguished by the absence of initial fluctuations of the reticulocytes. Such fluctuations have always been observed by us during administration of other isotopes. It is possible that the insignificant changes in the reticulocyte number are connected with the presence of the metal cobalt.

Profound impairment of erythropoiesis in the form of gradually developing hyporegenerative anemia was noticed only in animals of the second group. In animals of the first group impairment of erythropoiesis was detected only by application of functional stresses. After parturition sharp inhibition of erythropoiesis was observed and after blood loss a retarded increase of reticulocytes.

The absence of visible quantitative and qualitative changes concerning the neutrophils and thrombocytes suggests that the significantly more rapid impairment of erythropoiesis by ^{60}Co in comparison with other radioisotopes (even with bone selecting ^{89}Sr) is connected not only with direct irradiation of the bone marrow but also perhaps with the impairment of the functions of certain other organs which participate in the regulation of erythropoiesis including the spleen, liver and gastric glands.

CONCLUSIONS

1. With prolonged daily administration of ^{60}Co impairment of erythro- and lymphopoiesis was observed, the degree of which was proportional to the quantity of isotope administered.
2. In the first experimental group of rabbits, which received 1.25 $\mu c/kg$ ^{60}Co, impairment of lymphopoiesis was expressed in a certain retardation of lymphocyte maturation which under ordinary experimental conditions did not produce a decline of the absolute lymphocyte number in the peripheral blood. Lymphopoietic activity in the form of lymphopenia was detected by application of functional stresses (blood loss, parturition). Impairment of erythropoiesis in this group was also only detected with functional stresses.
3. In the second experimental group, which received 12.5 $\mu c/kg$ ^{60}Co, the absolute lymphocyte number began to decline from the first month of administration and after 6–7 to 10 months steady absolute lymphopenia developed. Retardation of the lymphocyte maturation processes in the spleen was more pronounced than in the animals of the first group.

Impairment of erythropoiesis had the character of gradually developing hyporegenerative anemia. Blood loss disclosed the functional weakness of the erythroblastic part of the bone marrow.

REFERENCES

BELOBORODOVA N. L. and BARANOVA YE. F. *The Toxicology of Radioactive Substances* (Materialy po toksikologii radioactivnykh veshchestv.) Vol. 1, Moscow (1957). English translation published by Pergamon Press (1962).

BEREZOB E. L., *The Functions of the Spleen.* (O funktsiyakh selezenki.) Moscow (1925).

KASSIRSKII I. A., Prob. gematol. i pereliv. krovi **5** (1957).

LACASSAGNE A., *Le progrés Medical* **26** 1077 (1928).

MALENKOVA K. M. and KARIBSKAYA YE. V.. *The Reaction to Penetrating Radiation of Animals on an Additional Cobalt Diet.* (Reaktsiya zhivotnogo organizma na pronikayushcheye izlucheniye pri podkormke kobal'tom.) Proceedings of the 30th Anniversary Session of the Central Research Institute of Rontgenology and Radiology, Moscow (1954).

VOINAR A. O., *The Biological Role of Microelements in Animals and Man.* (Biologicheskaya rol' mikroelementov v organizme zhivotnykh i cheloveka.) Moscow (1953).

YEGOROV A. P. and BOCHKAREB V. V., *Hemopoiesis and Ionizing Radiation.* (Krovotvoreniye i ioniziruyushchaya radiatsiya.) Moscow (1954).

HEMOPOIESIS IN THE OFFSPRING OF RATS WHICH HAVE UNDERGONE PROLONGED ^{60}Co ADMINISTRATION

N. L. BELOBORODOVA, V. L. VIKTOROVA and E. K. RED'KINA

THE effect of irradiation of a mother on her offspring has been very inadequately studied despite the urgency of the problem. References to the changes in hemopoiesis in the offspring of irradiated animals, as treated here, are particularly few. After a single X-ray dose of 300 r, A. Yu. Svigris found acute inhibition of the hemopoietic processes in the fetus and newborn. T. A. Ivanova has investigated hemopoiesis in the offspring of dogs administered with uranium decay products in a concentration of 1 mc/kg. Retardation of erythroblast maturation, inhibition of lymphopoiesis and delay in the transition of reticular cells to blood cells were found in the pups.

In the present paper are presented the results of investigation of hemopoiesis in the offspring of rats which have received orally 150 μc/kg ^{60}Co per day in the form of a 1 ml. solution of cobalt chloride. The calculation of ionizing doses made by G. A. Abrunina has shown that the amount of ^{60}Co administered to the rats was sufficient to create a body dose of on average about 1 rep per day. Since administration commenced 21 days before pregnancy, continued for the 20–22 days of pregnancy and after, the experimental animals were subjected to the affects of ^{60}Co from the very beginning of uterine life.

By measurement of the radioactivity of young rats in the first days after birth (G. A. Abrunina) greatest activity was found at birth (0.03–0.07 μc/g weight). Subsequently it declined (on the 6th day 0.02–0.03 μc/g), although the mother's milk contained a certain quantity of ^{60}Co. In this respect ^{60}Co differs from those isotopes which form a reservoir in the body, as, for example, radioactive strontium, administration of which to lactating females sharply increases radioactivity of the offspring (A. A. Rubanovskaya, L. N. Burykina *et al.*).

The quantity of ^{60}Co administered produced no pronounced symptoms of radiation sickness in the females either during or after pregnancy. The beginning of pregnancy was established by vaginal smear, by which we were able to demonstrate that the duration of pregnancy was the same in the experimental animals as in the controls—21, or rarely, 22 days.

In view of references in the literature to the increase under usual conditions of the average weight of the offspring of irradiated animals (E. G. Lomovskaya and E. I. Vorob'yeva, E. A. Kakushkina) the comparison of the weights of control and experimental animals presented considerable interest. Although some young rats were killed each day and consequently the feeding conditions of the remaining rats changed, it was not impossible to study increase of weight by growth of the animals. Data are given only for newborn rats: 88 control and 127 experimental animals. In analysis of weight changes all the young rats were killed in groups depending on the size of the litter (Table 1).

TABLE 1

The weight of newborn rats born to control and experimental females

Size of litter	Group	Number of litters	Average weight of litter (g)	Mdif = mdif	Number of newborn in group	Average weight of newborn (g)	Mdif = mdif
Up to 5	Control	1			2	5.0	
	Receiving ^{60}Co	3			12	4.4	
6–8	Control	3	42.6		23	5.5±0.63	
	Receiving ^{60}Co	6	40.6	2.0±2.05	44	5.4±1.21	0.1±1.4
10–12	Control	6	53.5		63	5.1±0.9	
	Receiving ^{60}Co	5	61.1	7.6±4.5	55	5.5±1.0	0.4±1.35
13 and above	Control	0					
	Receiving ^{60}Co	1			16	5.8	

In view of the small number of rats in the first and fourth groups a statistical analysis was carried out only for the second and third groups. It can be seen from Table 1 that there is no statistically valid difference in the average weight of the whole litter and each newborn rat of control and experimental mothers. The average weight of young rats of both groups was normal (P. P. Sakharov). However, it is noticeable that in the column "Average weight of rat" the standard deviation in the experimental offspring was higher than in the controls, especially in the second group (0.63 and 1.21). This is evidence of the large weight variation of offspring of rats receiving ^{60}Co.

The development of experimental offspring (eye opening, growth of fur, and so on) occurred at the same intervals as in the controls.

Investigation of hemopoiesis in the young rats was carried out mainly during the first 11 days of post-natal life, i.e. during the period of adjustment to new conditions of existence.

Both control and experimental offspring were killed each day in groups of 4–6 animals.

The figures given below are averages of 4–6 analyses.

Peripheral blood analysis was carried out by the usual methods. Blood was taken from incisions of vascular fascicles in the neck.

The hemopoietic processes of the liver and spleen were studied by contact preparation. Because of the small volume of bone marrow in newborn rats it was necessary to mix it with serum and produce thin smear preparations. May–Grunwald–Romanovskii stain was used for all preparations.

THE PERIPHERAL BLOOD

Table 2 gives the mean values of red blood factors in the control and experimental offspring. It can be seen that the animals of both groups were born with a low erythrocyte number and comparatively high percentage hemoglobin as a result of which the colour index was considerably higher than in adult rats. Almost all the erythrocytes in the peripheral blood had a reticulocytic substance. The number of nuclear forms of erythrocyte was very great.

TABLE 2

Red blood changes with age of control and experimental newborn rats

Age (days)	Group	Erythrocyte number (mil.)	Hemoglobin (g $^o/_{oo}$)	Colour index	Reticulocytes ($^o/_{oo}$)	Number of normoblasts per 100 leukocytes
1	Control	2.3	14.1	1.68	950	155
	Receiving ^{60}Co	2.5	13.9	1.62	998	140
5	Control	2.2	11.0	1.5	484	60
	Receiving ^{60}Co	2.5	10.9	1.3	180	129
10	Control	2.9	11.0	1.14	200	3
	Receiving ^{60}Co	2.8	10.9	1.16	430	30
15	Control	3.9	11.0	0.84	108	0–1
	Receiving ^{60}Co	3.5	11.7	1.00	276	10–15
20	Control	3.9	9.7	0.74	72	0
	Receiving ^{60}Co	3.4	9.0	0.79	223	1–1.5

During the first five days the erythrocyte number in both control and experimental rats remained unchanged but a lowering of hemoglobin by an average 2 per cent was noticed, which produced some decline in the colour index. Increase of the erythrocyte number in both groups of young rats began only between the 10th and 15th days. Beginning from the 10th day in the control rats a decline and gradual disappearance of normoblasts from the peripheral blood was observed. By the 20th day the reticulocyte number had decreased considerably. Among the experimental rats the decrease of young forms of erythrocyte proceeded more slowly and normoblasts were found even on the 30–35th day. The reticulocyte number was also somewhat higher. Measurement of the total leukocyte number was made very difficult by the presence of normoblasts which it was not possible to differentiate accurately from lymphocytes in fresh blood. Therefore the sum of leukocytes and normoblasts was taken; after calculation of the leukocytic formula and the normoblasts number in a stained blood smear the requisite correction was made. According to our results the leukocyte number in young rats during the first postnatal days is from 1200 to 4500 per mm^3 blood. These low leukocyte figures are also confirmed by the general appearance of the smear used in calculation of the leukocytic formula.

Leukocytic formulae at birth for control and experimental animals were similar. A preponderance both relative and absolute of neutrophils was observed. In the experimental rats neutrophils comprised on average 60 per cent, or 1750 cells per mm^3 blood; in the controls—52 per cent, or 1250 cells per mm^3 blood. In the experimental animals there were 40 per cent lymphocytes, or 1400 cells per mm^3 blood, and in the controls—48 per cent, or 1150 cells per mm^3 blood. Young forms of neutrophil—promyelocytes and myelocytes—were found in the control rats only during the first 2 days after birth, whereas in the experimental animals they were found for somewhat longer—5–6 days. On the 4–5th day in both groups an increase of the relative lymphocyte number began. In the rats of the control group during the first days vacuolization of lymphocytes was often observed. In the experimental rats, apart from vacuolization, chromatin breakdown in the lymphocyte nucleus and significant neutrophil nuclear fragmentosis (up to 10 per cent) was observed, something not seen in the control group.

THE BONE MARROW

Examination of bone marrow cells was carried out in a number of preparations. The numerical results of analyses are presented in Table 3. On the first day of post-natal life of the control rats more than 50 per cent of all nucleated cells were of the white series. The red branch of the bone marrow comprised on average 16 per cent. About 20 per cent of all red cells were proerythroblasts and basophilic erythroblasts. A very large

TABLE 3

The morphological composition of the bone marrow of rats in the first days of life (in percentages)

Day of life	Group	Hemocytoblasts	Myeloblasts	Promyelocytes and myelocytes	Neutrophils Juveniles	Neutrophils Stab	Neutrophils Segmented	Eosinophils	Basophils	Proerythroblasts	Basophilic erythroblasts	Polychromatophilic erythroblasts	Normoblasts	Reticular cells	Lymphocytes	Monocytes	Cell division White	Cell division Red
1	Control	0.9	1.7	1.4	2.8	21.0	19.0	2.0	0.5	1.0	2.2	8.5	3.5	24.5	10.5	0.5	0-0.4	0-0.8
1	Receiving ⁶⁰Co	0.1	1.6	1.7	0.6	15.8	12.8	0.4	0.4	1.7	3.6	9.8	6.6	30.0	14.8	0.1	0-0.4	0.2-1.0
2	Control	0.7	2.4	3.1	3.3	16.8	30.6	1.4	0.3	3.4	2.8	10.5	4.9	9.8	9.4	0.6	0.6-1.0	0.4-1.4
2	Receiving ⁶⁰Co	0.6	1.8	2.9	2.6	21.0	22.2	1.8	0.3	1.9	2.9	5.9	4.9	16.9	13.9	0.4	0-0.4	1.1-0.1
3	Control	0.6	1.0	4.1	2.8	14.6	22.2	0.3	0.1	0.6	4.0	17.8	19.8	6.4	5.5	0.2	0.2-0.4	0.4-2.4
3	Receiving ⁶⁰Co	0.3	1.5	2.6	2.8	10.2	19.0	0.4	0.3	2.3	2.5	25.8	8.2	8.2	15.6	0.3	1.0-1.6	1.0-2.2
4	Control	0.3	0.8	4.6	1.0	3.0	15.0	0.1	0.3	1.0	5.3	31.3	27.0	7.0	3.3		0.2-0.8	2.6-4.4
4	Receiving ⁶⁰Co	0.1	0.8	2.3	2.0	5.7	12.9	0.1	0.2	1.6	2.2	26.8	29.8	6.9	8.2	0.4	0.4-0.8	1.4-2.8
5	Control	1.0	1.0	3.0	2.7	12.0	6.0	0.1	0.2	0.9	2.5	49.6	11.9	3.0	5.9	0.2	0.6-1.2	2.2-2.8
5	Receiving ⁶⁰Co	0.5	2.0	3.3	3.0	8.4	14.9	0.2		1.4	4.8	24.7	22.8	4.0	9.5	0.2	0.2-2.0	1.2-2.4
6	Control	0.8	0.8	2.6	2.0	11.8	10.3			1.6	4.3	31.8	23.8	3.8	6.3	0.2	0-1.0	1.0-2.6
6	Receiving ⁶⁰Co		0.9	3.3	1.9	3.7	5.8			1.5	5.3	35.2	32.1	3.3	6.8	0.2	0-1.6	1.2-4.4
11	Control	0.3	0.8	5.2	2.3	7.8	5.9	1.1	0.2	0.8	2.2	40.9	17.6	1.2	13.4	0.3	0.6-4.4	1.2-2.2
11	Receiving ⁶⁰Co	0.5	1.0	4.7	3.9	10.5	7.3	0.5	0.1	0.8	2.4	26.7	28.8	2.8	9.8	0.2	0.4-2.4	1.4-3.0

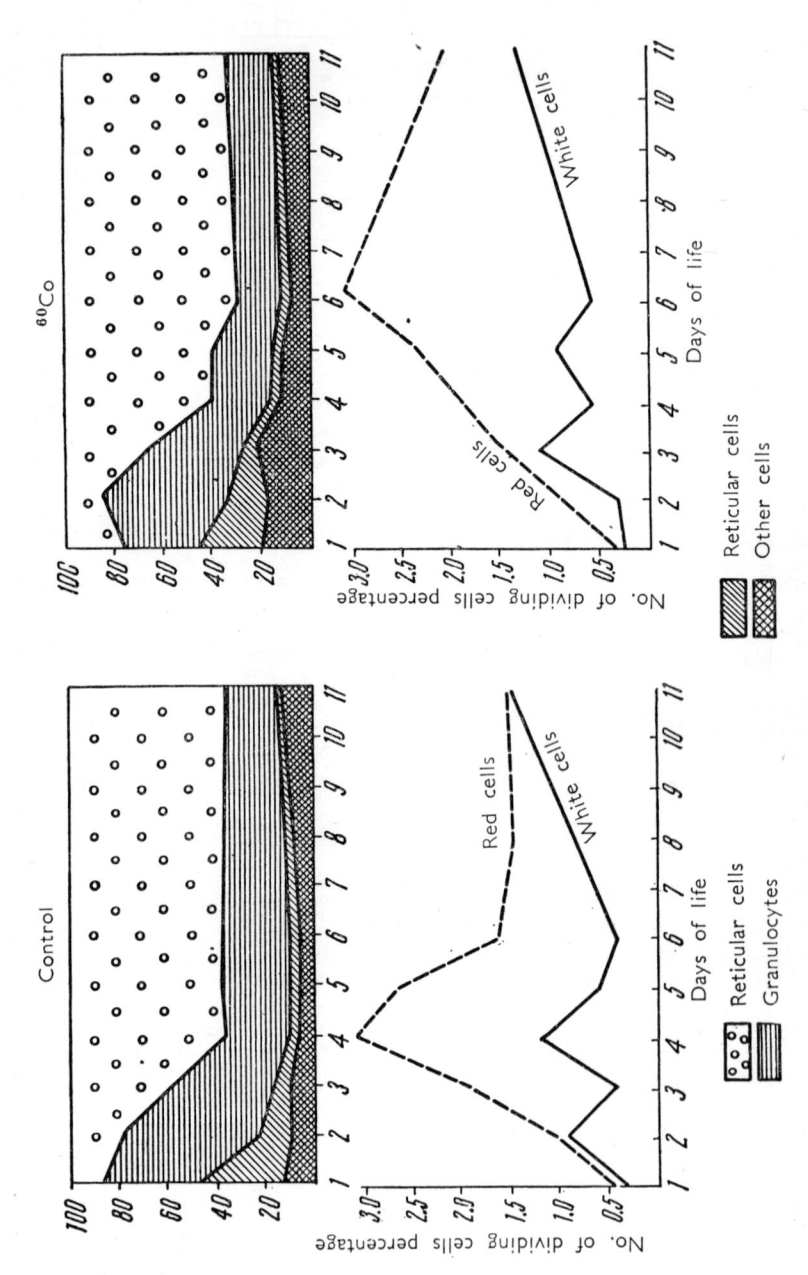

FIG. 1. The morphological composition of the bone marrow of rats in the first days of life and mitotic activity.

number of reticular cells were noticed (from 15 to 38 per cent). In the following days of post-natal life the greatest changes were observed in the red branch. From the first day red cell division increased and the red branch increased continuously (Fig. 1). By the 4th day about 65 per cent of all bone marrow cells were of the red series. The increase in the number of hemoglobin-containing cells (polychromatophilic erythro- and normoblasts) had begun by the 3rd, and was particularly intensive on the 4th day.

Changes in the white branch had a less definitive character; a fluctuating increase in mitotic activity was noticed, and a gradual increase on the 3–4th day of the number of young forms of neutrophils (Table 3).

The bone marrow of the experimental rats at birth differed from that of the controls, showing some enlargement of the red branch (on average 22 per cent). Subsequent bone marrow development comprised a gradual enlargement of the red branch, although somewhat retarded during the first two days. Corresponding to this is the slower increase in mitotic activity of the red cells as compared with the controls (cf. Fig. 1). The number of red cells in division began to increase only on the 3rd day and reached its maximum, not on the 4th day as in the controls, but on the 6th day. However, following days red cell division in the experimental rats was more active. The deposition of hemoglobin in the red cell protoplasm was as intensive, and occurred at the same time, in the experimental rats as in the controls, as a result of which the red cell maturation index in both groups was alike.

THE SPLEEN

The morphological composition of the spleen was studied with contact preparations counting 500 cells (Table 4).

In the newborn control rats the total number of lymphocytes in the spleen was on average 60 per cent. In the main these were average lymphocytes. There were 1 per cent of lymphoblasts, 8 per cent of large lymphocytes. Small lymphocytes were not counted separately as there were so few of them. Apart from the lymphocytes a significant number of cells of the red series (17 per cent) were found in spleen preparations and also, rather fewer, granulocytes. As Table 4 shows, all the young forms of the granulocytic series were found in the preparations (with the exception of the myeloblasts which proved impossible to differentiate from lymphoblasts). The presence of young myeloid cells, and the significant number of mitoses indicate that the spleen pulp in newborn rats participates actively in myelopoiesis. As is known, even in adult rats the erythropoietic capacity of the spleen is low.

Figure 2 shows the development of the main cellular groups of the spleen from the 1st to the 11th day in control and experimental rats, and also

Table 4

The morphological composition of the spleen of rats in the first days of (life percentage)

Day of life	Group	Lymphocytes					Cells of the red series						Granulocytes				Division of cells	
		total number	lymphoblasts	large lymphocytes and prolymphocytes	average lymphocytes	total number	Proerythroblasts and basophilic erythroblasts	Polychromatophilic erythroblasts	Normoblasts	Reticular cells	total number	immature cells	mature cells		red	white
1	Control	60.4	1.2	9.0	50.2	17.8	0.6	6.2	11.0	6.6	15.2	2.0	13.2		0.2	0.4
	Receiving ⁶⁰Co	54.8	0.6	8.8	45.4	26.0	0.8	10.0	15.2	11.6	7.6	1.0	6.6		0.4	0.4
2	Control	46.6	1.0	5.4	40.2	37.8	0.8	18.6	18.4	9.2	6.4	1.8	4.6		0.6	
	Receiving ⁶⁰Co	44.4	1.0	4.0	39.4	31.8	0.8	14.2	16.8	16.8	7.0	1.4	5.6		0.6	0.2
3	Control	55.4	0.8	4.4	50.2	28.4	0.8	11.6	16.0	5.6	10.6	2.2	8.4		0.6	0.2
	Receiving ⁶⁰Co	36.7	1.0	2.9	32.8	41.6	0.4	13.4	27.8	12.2	9.0	2.8	6.2		0.6	
4	Control	60.6	0.8	2.8	57.0	25.4	1.6	11.2	12.6	6.2	7.4	1.6	5.8		1.0	0.8
	Receiving ⁶⁰Co	23.8	0.6	0.4	22.8	50.2	0.4	17.0	32.8	10.0	16.0	6.4	6.6		1.4	0.2
5	Control	49.6	0.8	2.8	46.0	35.4	0.2	11.4	23.8	7.0	8.0	1.8	6.2		0.8	0.2
	Receiving ⁶⁰Co	34.6	0.8	1.8	32.0	51.2	0.4	20.6	30.2	9.6	4.6	0.8	3.8		1.0	0.2
8	Control	46.6	0.8	1.6	44.2	43.0	0.3	18.5	24.2	7.0	3.4	1.4	2.0		1.2	0.2
	Receiving ⁶⁰Co	32.6	0.6	1.2	30.8	55.8	0.4	22.0	33.4	8.6	3.4	2.2	1.2		1.2	0.4
11	Control	56.8	0.6	1.6	54.6	33.0	0.2	11.2	21.8	4.8	5.4	2.2	3.0		0.4	0.2
	Receiving ⁶⁰Co	26.4	1.0	1.8	23.6	56.0	0.5	21.0	34.6	9.6	8.0	2.6	5.4		1.2	0.2

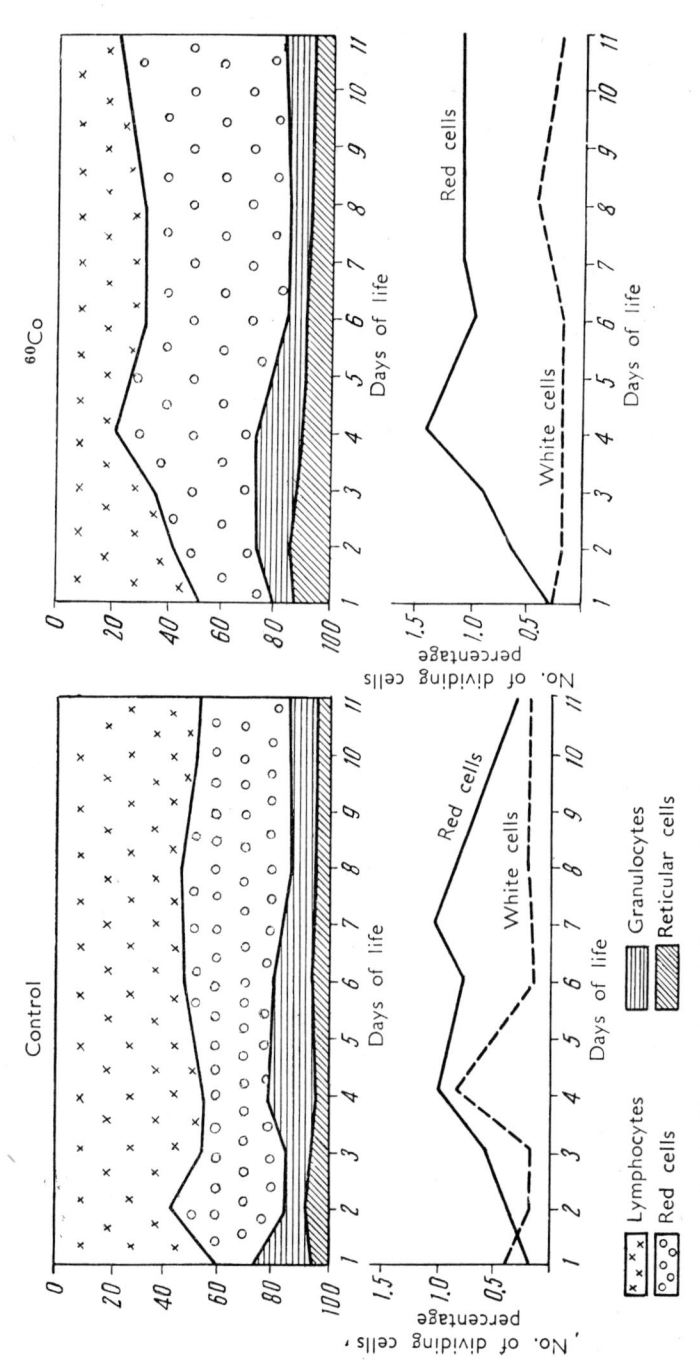

FIG. 2. The morphological composition of the spleen of rats in the first days of life and mitotic activity.

the changes in mitotic activity of white and red cells. It can be seen that in the control rats the ratios of lymphocytes, erythroblasts and granulocytes did not materially change throughout the 11 days. The lymphocytes comprised approximately 50 per cent. On the 4th day an increase in the number of dividing cells of the granulocytic and red series was noticed.

In the spleen of the experimental rats from the first day of post-natal life the number of red cells began to increase sharply, accompanied by an acceleration in their division. This indicates the presence of "active" hyperplasia of the erythroblastic tissue in the spleen of these animals. The lymphocyte number declined by more than half (down to 24 per cent). However, this decrease was apparently only of a relative character as the number of lymphoblasts and prolymphocytes remained unchanged. No increase in the number of mitoses of cells of the granulocytic series was observed in the experimental rats.

THE LIVER

In studying the liver's hemopoietic functions during the first post-natal days of young rats we were interested both in the characteristics of hemopoiesis in the control and experimental animals and in the degree of its

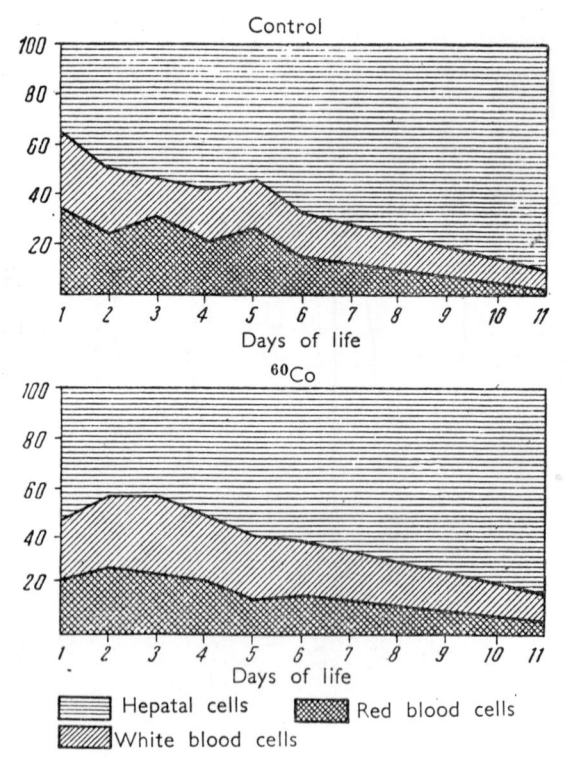

FIG. 3. The morphological composition of the liver of rats in the first days of life.

activity. Therefore hepatal cells and blood cells were counted separately for every factor measured and their ratios calculated. As in our study of the bone marrow not less than 500 blood cells, taking all forms into account, were counted.

For a fairly long time after birth the liver of young rats takes an active part in erythro- and leukopoiesis. With increase in age the number of blood cells in the liver gradually declines.

Figure 3 shows changes in the numbers of hepatal and blood cells from the 1st to the 11th days.

In the control rats during this period a fairly even decline of the total number of blood cells was observed, particularly of the red series. The number of these was around 1 per cent on the 11th day, i.e. the liver's erythropoietic function had virtually ceased. The diminution of red cells proceeded more slowly in the experimental rats and they still comprised 6 per cent on the 11th day. Among the red cells of rats of both groups hemoglobin-containing cells predominated (98 per cent of all red cells), and the maturation index did not materially change throughout the 11 days.

The leukopoietic function of the liver lasted somewhat longer and to the same degree in both groups. On the 11th day the number of cells of the granulocytic series in liver preparations was on average 10 per cent. Throughout the whole observation period the majority of white cells (approximately 70 per cent) of both groups consisted of young forms of neutrophil—promyelocytes, myelocytes and juveniles. The ratio of these to mature neutrophil forms changed little.

THE LUNGS AND KIDNEYS

Since during the embryonal period in mammals various organs possess a hemopoietic capacity, contact preparations of the lungs and kidneys, using May–Grunwald–Romanovskii stain, were studied. In one-day-old rats of both groups a significant number of all the young forms of the granulocytic and red series, numerous mitoses and cells of hemocytoblast type were found.

From the study of many preparations it is suggested that the lungs and kidneys of rats have a hemopoietic capacity up to the time of birth. The duration of this capacity in the control rats was very short: one day in the kidneys and 1–2 days in the lungs. In the experimental rats hemopoiesis in the lungs lasted significantly longer and young blood cells (erythroblasts, myeloblasts, promyelocytes and myelocytes) were found in lung preparations up to the 5–6th day. Hemopoiesis in the kidneys of experimental rats was of the same duration as in the controls.

Analysis of our experimental results indicates that systematic ^{60}Co intoxication of rats in a dose corresponding to 1 rep per day has little material effect on the general condition of their offspring. The number per litter was normal, they were born at term and birth weight was the same as in the controls. The development of young rats was normal. In this respect our results agree with those of S. P. Voskresenskii and A. P. Novikova who also found no abnormalities of development and weight in the offspring of rats to which ^{90}Sr had been administered. The sole difference noted by us consisted in a large weight fluctuation in the experimental rats. A similar observation, although based on very little material, was made by M. Ya. Chaikovskaya investigating the offspring of irradiated dogs.

More clear-cut results were obtained when the hemopoietic processes were studied. Abnormalities found in the experimental rats concerned mainly erythropoiesis, the biggest changes being found in the spleen in the form of progressive hyperplasia of erythroblastic tissue and accelerated red cell division.

Rather more active cell division was also seen in the red branch of the bone marrow from the 6th day, although the general character of bone marrow development was similar to that of the controls.

The erythroblastic function of the liver of experimental rats was not impaired, although it took longer to disappear than in the control rats.

As concerns the general character of impairment to erythropoiesis in the experimental group, although the erythrocyte number and hemoglobin level were normal for age, a more prolonged circulation of young nucleated forms of erythrocyte in the peripheral blood was observed. It is possible that this was connected with the pathological hyperplasia of the erythroblastic tissue in the spleen, but it may also have been a result of impairment of the barrier functions of the hemopoietic organs.

Thus no pronounced inhibition of erythropoiesis, such as has been observed after external radiation (A. Yu. Svigris) or during internal administration of uranium breakdown products (T. A. Ivanova) was produced by ^{60}Co in our experiments. This is possibly because of the stimulating effect on erythropoiesis of the element cobalt.

CONCLUSIONS

1. After daily ^{60}Co administration (150 μc/kg) to rats before, during and after pregnancy the level of radioactivity in the newborn rats was 0.03–0.07 μc/kg. This level declined slowly.
2. The number of young rats in the litter, duration of pregnancy, weight, and their general condition and development were normal.
3. Study of the hemopoietic processes disclosed the impairment of erythropoiesis, mainly in the spleen, in which progressive "active" hyperplasia of the erythroblastic tissue was observed.

REFERENCES

BURYKINA L. N., ZAKUTINSKII D. I., KRAYEVSKII N. A. and KURLYANDSKAYA E. B., *The Long-term Effects of Radiation Injury with Small Doses in the Chronic Experiment*. (Otdalennyye posledstviya porazheniya malymi dosami radioaktivnykh veshchestv v khronicheskom eksperimente.) Report from the 2nd UNO International Conference on the Peaceful Uses of Atomic Energy, Geneva (1958).

CHAIKOVSKAYA M. YA., *Vest. rentgenol. i radiol.* **4**, 34–37 (1955).

IVANOVA T. A., *The Peripheral Blood and Hemopoietic Organs of the Offspring of Dogs intoxicated with Uranium Decay Products*. (Osobennosti perifericheskoi krovi i organov krovotvoreniya u potomctva sobak, otravlennykh produktami deleniya urana.) Proceedings of a Conference on the Effects of Ionizing Radiation on Pregnancy and Development of Fetus and Newborn, Leningrad (1957).

KAKUSHKINA YE. A. and PLODOVSKAYA L. A., *The Development of Offspring of Rats X-irradiated before, during and after Pregnancy*. (Nekotorye dannye o pazvitii potomstva krys, obluchennykh vne i vo vremya beremennosti rentgenovymi luchami.) Proceedings of a Conference on the Effects of Ionizing Radiation on Pregnancy and Development of Fetus and Newborn, Leningrad (1957).

LOMOVSKAYA E. G. and VOROB'YEVA YE. I., *Biofizika* **2**, No. 4, 502–512 (1957).

RUBANOVSKAYA A. A. and USHAKOVA V. F., *The Toxicology of Radioactive Substances*. (Materialy po toksikologii radioaktivnykh veshchestv.) Vol. 1. Moscow (1957). English translation published by Pergamon Press (1962).

SAKHAROV P. P., *Laboratory Animals*. (Laboratornyye zhivotnyye.) Moscow, Leningrad (1937).

SVIGRIS A. YU., *The Sensitivity of the Hemopoietic Organs of Pregnant Females and their Offspring to Ionizing Radiation*. (Chuvstvitel'nost' krovotvornykh organov beremennykh zhivotnykh i ikh plodov k ioniziruyushchemu izlucheniyu.) Proceedings of a Conference on the Effects of Ionizing Radiation on Pregnancy and Development of Fetus and Newborn, Leningrad (1957).

VOSKRESENSKII S. P. and NOVIKOVA A. P., *Certain Characteristics in Development of Offspring of Rats and Dogs subjected to the Effects of Uranium Decay Products*. (O nekotorykh osobennostyakh razvitiya potomstvo krys i sobak, podvergshikhsya vozdeistviiu produktov deleniya urana.) Proceedings of a Conference on the Effects of Ionizing Radiation on Pregnancy and Development of Fetus and Newborn, Leningrad (1957).

CHANGES IN THE FRACTIONAL COMPOSITION OF THE SEROUS PROTEINS AND RESIDUAL NITROGEN CONTENT OF RABBITS DURING CHRONIC INTERNAL ADMINISTRATION OF ^{60}Co

Ye. D. Grishchenko

It is known that many forms of radiation—heat (Colvin), visible light with a colour sensitizer, ultra-violet radiation, α-, β-, γ- and X-rays—all produce *in vitro* denaturization and sometimes destruction of proteins (I. I. Ivanov, V. S. Balabukha *et al.*, P. N. Kiselev *et al.*). The serous proteins are an important component of the blood. Some of them are composed of a more or less inert, non-specific material from which any fall in protein content of organs and tissues is made up, while others form part of the protective immunity mechanism.

Exposure to ionizing radiation produces a series of changes in the blood which may result especially from processes of denaturization, degradation or complete destruction of the tissue proteins. In this case shifts in the total nitrogen content of the blood, primarily of the albumins and residual nitrogen, are produced.

Ionizing radiation may also exert a direct effect on the serous proteins.

The inactivation of such vitally important proteins as the enzymes (although their resistance to ionizing factors is not alike—Barron *et al.*) leads to disturbance of the normal course of synthesis, including the processes of formation and breakdown of protein substances. The direct bombardment of the nucleic components of the cytoplasmic structures, which are the centres of these processes, must also be reflected in the course of the latter.

Metabolic disturbances can lead to general weakness of the animal necessitating the reinforcement of the protective mechanisms, as a consequence of which there is a significant increase of globulins. Finally, by selectively attacking the nervous, neuroendocrine and other systems, ionizing rays are also capable of producing shifts in the protein composition of the serum. Thus, changes in the composition of the nitrogen fractions of the blood serum can reflect the most diverse processes of the body, especially of the blood stream under the influence of some agent or other.

There are accounts in the literature* concerning changes in the protein complement of the blood after acute external irradiation. The effects of chronic irradiation, particularly during internal administration of ^{60}Co, have never been investigated. With administration of ^{60}Co the animal is subjected to the continuous internal irradiation by both β-particles and hard γ-rays. Because of this the picture of damage must differ from that produced by external irradiation with X- or γ-rays.

Below are described the changes occurring in the protein composition of the blood serum of rabbits which for 2 years received ^{60}Co orally in a dose of 1.25 and 12.5 μc/kg per day, and also the changes following the application of a physiological stress (bloodloss). Three groups of rabbits served as a control.

METHODS

The animals were kept in normal conditions in a vivarium. The experiments were carried out on young rabbits of both sexes which had reached a more or less constant weight.

Blood serum was obtained by separation in a centrifuge of the blood clot from the remainder of the blood, which was taken from the marginal auricular vein.

Bloodloss

Where bloodloss was used as a physiological stress blood was taken from the auricular vein in an amount of 10 ml./kg weight, which comprises about 10 per cent of the total volume circulating. Coagulation was prevented with heparin.

Nitrogen fraction (total nitrogen, residual nitrogen and albumin nitrogen) was determined, after acidification of the appropriate fraction with sulphuric acid, by the colour intensity produced with Nessler's reagent.

The globulins were separated from the albumins with a 26 per cent solution of sodium sulphate and not 22–23 per cent as is usual. Passaro and Passalacqua, using an electrophoretic control, have established that a 26 per cent concentration of sodium sulphate gives the most clear and complete separation of these two fractions. This can probably be explained by the much lower A/G ratio (0.8–1.2) found in our healthy rabbits than is described in the literature. It must be mentioned that the A/G found by us from analysis of paper electrophoretic studies varied within the same low limits (0.80–1.20).

Paper Electrophoretic Study

During the later months of the experiment changes in the fractional composition of the serous proteins were investigated with paper electrophoretic studies. The method described by A. E. Gurvich was used.

An 0.04 per cent solution of "amidoblack 10-B" in methyl alcohol was used for staining the electrophoretogram. The unadsorbed stain was washed from the bands with 10 per cent acetic acid containing a 4 per cent solution of phenol. As a rule only four completely differentiated bands were obtained: albumin and α-, β- and γ-globulin. For quantitative measurement of the fraction ratios the stain was eluted from these four bands with 0.1 N NaOH, after the paper had dried at room temperature. Stain

* A. A. Oganezova; G. Shilinsh; Andreoni et al.; Fischer et al.; Frieden et al.; Gjessing et al.; Hohne et al.; Stender et al.; Supplee et al.; Volkin et al.; Winkler et al.

intensity was measured with a photoelectric colorimeter PEC-M with a red filter. The quantity of stain fixed to each protein fraction was taken as directly proportional to the quantity of protein. In a few cases curves were taken with a densitometer (A. A. Sokolov, V. I. Vlasenko, A. E. Gurvich, L. K. Starosel'tseva).

RESULTS

The Nitrogen Fractions of the Blood Serum at Different Periods of ^{60}Co Intoxication

A change in the A/G ratio is considered one of the signs of serious disturbance in the body. The effect of any sort of infective process, physical factors of unusual strength or character, inadequate physiological conditions—all this usually leads to a lowering of the A/G, i.e. to an increase in the globulin fraction in the overall protein content.

Our rabbits reacted in just this way to chronic oral administration of ^{60}Co.

Only curves of total protein content and A/G are presented in Fig. 1, as the albumins and globulins can easily be deduced from these figures.

TAB

Total protein, A/G ratio and residual nitrogen content of

	Group	Before administration mean	σ	number of rabbits	2 months mean	σ	number of rabbits	4 months mean	σ	number of rabbits
Total protein (%)	Control	6.87	0.16	12	6.42	0.20	11	6.39	0.12	11
	Receiving 12.5 μc/kg	6.89	0.08	10	7.45	0.11	10	7.27	0.08	10
	Receiving 1.25 μc/kg	6.86	0.10	8	7.42	0.11	8	7.34	0.15	9
	Receiving stable cobalt	6.77	0.08	4	6.38	0.26	5	6.33	0.14	5
A/G	Control	1.17	0.10	12	0.93	0.10	11	1.10	0.12	11
	Receiving 12.5 μc/kg	1.24	0.17	10	0.65	0.06	10	0.77	0.12	10
	Receiving 1.25 μc/kg	1.29	0.18	8	0.76	0.14	8	0.71	0.05	9
	Receiving stable cobalt	1.23	0.14	5	1.07	0.21	5	0.96	0.15	5
Residual nitrogen (mg %)	Control	35	3.7	12	42	3.0	11	39	0.5	11
	Receiving 12.5 μc/kg	40	1.7	10	27	3.8	10	47	3.8	10
	Receiving 1.25 μc/kg	36	1.6	8	35	2.3	8	40	1.2	8
	Receiving stable cobalt	27	1.2	4	45	3.7	5	—	—	—

CHANGES OF SEROUS PROTEINS AFTER ^{60}Co 77

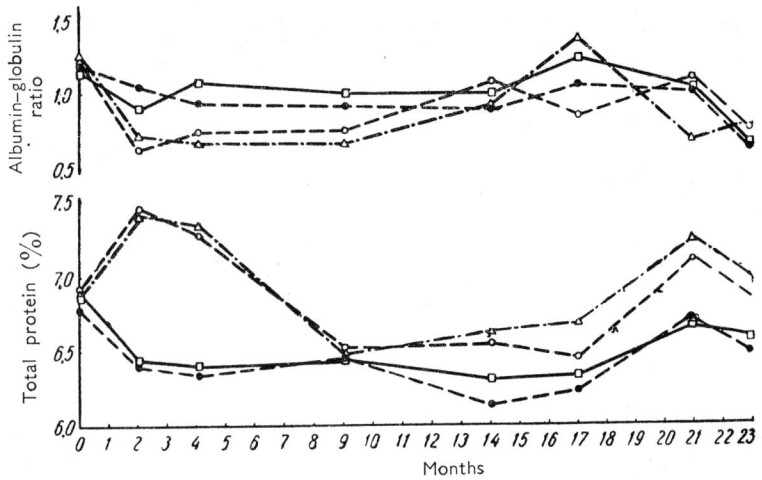

FIG. 1. Total serous protein and the A/G ratio during chronic radiocobalt intoxication.
□—□ control rabbits; △—·—△ rabbits receiving 1.25 μc/kg per day; o---o rabbits receiving 12.5 μc/kg per day; ●---● rabbits receiving stable cobalt.

LE 1

rabbits at different periods of chronic ^{60}Co intoxication

of administration														
9 months			14 months			17 months			21 months			23 months		
mean	σ	number of rabbits	mean	σ	number of rabbits	mean	σ	number of rabbits	mean	σ	number of rabbits	mean	σ	number of rabbits
6.42	0.19	11	6.30	0.15	8	6.32	0.18	8	6.64	0.15	3	6.57	0.04	2
6.49	0.21	10	6.54	0.18	9	6.43	0.3	8	7.10	0.12	5	6.92	0.10	1
6.47	0.16	8	6.69	0.10	8	6.64	0.08	8	7.26	0.09	6	6.98	0.11	6
6.43	0.14	5	6.13	0.34	4	6.23	0.19	4	6.70	0.11	4	6.48	0.16	4
1.05	0.09	11	1.03	0.09	8	1.27	0.24	8	1.10	0.07	3	0.72	0.04	2
0.79	0.05	10	1.11	0.15	9	0.89	0.15	8	1.16	0.11	5	0.81	0.00	1
0.73	0.11	8	0.94	0.06	8	1.42	0.07	8	0.74	0.08	6	0.85	0.09	6
0.95	0.15	5	0.90	0.09	4	1.10	0.09	4	1.08	0.07	4	0.69	0.03	4
41	3.4	11	41	2.7	8	35	3.6	8	—	—	—	—	—	—
40	2.4	10	42	1.9	9	40	3.5	8	—	—	—	—	—	—
30	1.7	8	35	2.5	8	34	2.6	8	—	—	—	—	—	—
38	1.0	5	35	2.4	4	30	1.2	4	—	—	—	—	—	—

It is clearly seen (upper curves) that, for at least 9 months of ^{60}Co administration to rabbits, the A/G of these animals remains at a significantly lower level than in the controls (rabbits either receiving no treatment or an equivalent dose of stable cobalt). This difference is statistically significant as the standard deviation of the A/G for all the groups is approximately a third of the difference between them (Table 1).

The decrease of the A/G ratio in the first 9 months is due not to an absolute decrease of albumins but to a fairly sharp increase in the quantity of globulins in the blood serum, in consequence of which there is a corresponding increase in the total protein content (lower curves of Fig. 1). Whereas during this period (2–9 months) in the control rabbits and in those receiving stable cobalt it does not exceed 6.3–6.5 per cent, in the rabbits receiving the smaller and larger doses of ^{60}Co it does not fall below 7.25 per cent, with a maximum standard deviation of 0.2 per cent. At the 9th month the total protein content in both experimental groups becomes normal, agreeing completely with the controls. Subsequently, at the 14th and 17th months, the total protein content of the control and experimental rabbits again diverges, that of the latter increasing. At the end of the experiment, at the 21st–23rd months, the difference becomes fairly large (about 0.5 per cent), although not so large as during the first months of the experiment. The A/G ratio in all four groups at 14th months is alike and it is impossible to detect any clear regularity by chemical analysis at later periods.

In the last months of the experiment (21st–23rd) the fractional composition of the serous proteins of the rabbits of all four groups was investigated by paper electrophoresis. The results obtained by analysis of electrophoretograms relating to parallel serum tests and tests on individual rabbits at the same periods showed marked similarity.

In Table 2 are presented mean values each one of which is based on at least 10 electrophoretograms. The small number of rabbits used in electrophoresis by comparison with the number with which the experiment began is explained by the fact that from the 18th month animals were being killed for pathomorphological examination and measurement of the enzyme activity of the carbohydrate–phosphorus metabolism of the liver. At the 18th month about 80 per cent of all rabbits were still living. Only the group receiving the larger ^{60}Co dose was an exception: in this group only 7 rabbits out of 13 lived for 18 months.

In contrast to the results obtained by chemical analysis, which from the 17th month of administration showed no consistent change in the A/G, even although the increase in total protein content in the experimental rabbits was clearly pronounced by comparison with the controls (cf. Fig. 1, Table 1), electrophoretograms show that a depressed A/G was

TABLE 2

The serous protein fractions in rabbits at the 21st and 23rd months of ^{60}Co intoxication (established by electrophoresis on paper)

Period of intoxication (months)	Group	Number of animals	albumin	α	β	γ	A/G
21st	Control	3	46.4	19.7	17.2	16.7	0.87
	Receiving 12.5 μc/kg	5	43.5	19.6	17.1	19.8	0.72
	Receiving 1.25 μc/kg	3	43.4	18.9	16.5	21.8	0.77
	Receiving stable cobalt	4	47.5	20.0	15.0	17.5	0.90
23rd	Control	2	59.2	13.3	13.3	14.2	1.45
	Receiving 12.5 μc/kg	1	52.4	14.8	14.1	18.7	1.10
	Receiving 1.25 μc/kg	6	41.8	16.5	19.0	22.7	0.72
	Receiving stable cobalt	4	54.3	14.3	14.5	16.9	1.19

(Protein fractions (%); globulins: α, β, γ)

characteristic for rabbits receiving ^{60}Co, even in the last months of the experiment. Thus, whereas for the physiological control and the stable cobalt control the A/G ratios at the 21st month were respectively 0.87 and 0.90, and at the 22nd 1.45 and 1.19, for the groups receiving the larger and smaller dose of ^{60}Co the A/G values were respectively 0.72 and 0.77 at the 21st month, and 1.10 and 0.72 at the 23rd. This difference in the A/G ratio is chiefly due to the increase of the γ-globulin content in rabbits receiving ^{60}Co (Table 2, Fig. 2).

The reasons for the divergence between the results obtained by chemical and electrophoretic analysis should be sought, presumably, in the sharp changes in dispersity of the serous proteins, chiefly of the α-globulins, during the later stages of administration. In fact, the A/G values of the control groups at the 17th and 20th months underwent much less fluctuation (cf. Fig. 1).

As far as residual nitrogen content is concerned, in all cases it remained within normal limits (cf. Table 1). At the 4th month some increase was noticed in the animals receiving ^{60}Co but the variations of individual values are such that it can only be said that there is a tendency to increase.

Changes in the Composition of the Serous Proteins Produced by Blood Loss

One of the ways of measuring gravity of injury is by the application of so-called physiological stresses.

Since blood loss makes increased demands not only on the hemopoietic system but also on the organs which determine the protein composition of the blood this stress was used. Blood was withdrawn from the auricular vein in an amount of 10 ml./kg weight after 14–18 months both in the control rabbits and in those receiving ^{60}Co (12.5 μc/kg). In the rabbits receiving 1.25 μc/kg blood was withdrawn after 11 months. The resulting changes and restorative processes were investigated for 3–7 months following the loss of blood. The results are presented in Table 3 on the basis of which the curves given in Fig. 3 were constructed.

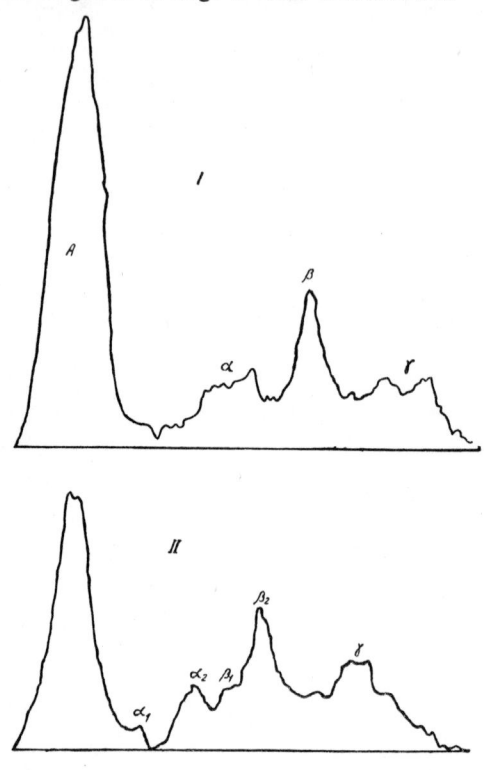

FIG. 2. Electrophoretograms of rabbit serum. I—control rabbits; II—rabbits receiving 12.5 μc/kg ^{60}Co per day (23rd month of experiment).

In examination of these curves the uniformity of the reactions of the normal rabbits becomes apparent (the curves on the left of Fig. 3). In the first 1–2 months the total nitrogen content fell by 0.5–1.25 per cent. Despite this, the absolute albumin content in the same period significantly increased, which also led to a sharp increase of the A/G ratio. Thus, in rabbit No. 12 the total protein content at 2 months after blood loss fell from 6.43 to 5.25, whereas the albumin content increased from 3.44 to 3.9 per cent. As a result the A/G ratio increased from 1.15 to 3.12. In rabbit No. 37 during the same period the total protein content fell from 7.93 to 6.7 per cent but the albumin content rose from 3.56 to 4.04 per cent. In rabbit No. 34 the fall in total protein reached its maximum a month after blood loss—from 6.84 to 6.47 per cent. By this time the albumin

TABLE 3

The effect of chronic ^{60}Co administration in a dose of 12.5 µc/kg for 15 months on the shifts in total protein content and its fractions produced by blood loss

No. of rabbit	Interval after blood loss (months)	% age content total protein	% age content albumin	% age content globulins	A/G
		Control animals			
12	0	6.43	3.44	2.99	1.15
	1	5.90	3.72	2.18	1.71
	2	5.15	3.90	1.25	3.12
	3	5.72	3.20	2.52	1.27
	4	6.61	2.68	3.93	0.63
37	0	7.93	3.56	4.37	0.81
	1	7.20	4.04	3.16	1.27
	2	6.70	2.98	3.72	0.80
	3	6.86	2.81	4.05	0.69
	4	7.25	3.20	4.06	0.79
	5	7.83	4.05	3.78	1.07
34	0	6.84	2.07	4.77	0.43
	1	6.47	3.50	2.97	1.18
	2	7.12	2.77	4.35	0.64
		Animals receiving 12.5 µc/kg per day			
	0	7.04	3.80	3.24	1.17
3	1	6.20	4.64	1.56	2.98
	1.5	6.89	3.35	3.54	0.95
	2	7.20	3.38	3.82	0.88
	3	7.24	3.33	3.91	0.85
5	0	6.26	3.32	2.94	0.84
	1	6.79	3.33	3.46	0.96
	2	6.97	3.24	3.73	0.87
	3	6.78	3.50	3.29	1.06
	4	6.67	3.66	3.01	1.22
10	0	6.03	3.03	3.00	1.01
	0.5	6.00	3.36	2.64	1.27
	1.5	6.18	3.16	3.02	1.05
	2.5	6.26	3.52	2.74	1.28
	3.5	6.12	3.22	3.00	1.04
12a	0	7.04	4.93	2.11	2.34
	0.5	6.86	3.58	3.28	1.09
	1.5	6.62	3.18	3.44	0.92
	2.5	6.02	3.54	2.50	1.42
	3.5	6.16	3.50	2.66	1.32
	5.5	6.80	4.24	2.56	1.66
	7	7.04	3.73	3.31	1.13
14a	0	6.88	3.22	3.66	0.88

No. of rabbit	Interval after blood loss (months)	% age content			A/G
		total protein	albumin	globulins	
	1	6.95	3.20	3.75	0.85
	2	6.55	2.38	4.17	0.57
	3	6.31	2.85	3.46	0.82
	5	6.85	3.52	3.33	1.06
	Animals receiving 1.25 μc/kg per day
21	0	6.68	2.77	3.91	0.71
	1	6.70	2.95	3.75	0.78
	2	6.74	3.16	3.58	0.89
	3	6.74	3.47	3.27	1.06
	4	6.60	3.82	2.78	1.38
22	0	6.70	3.35	3.35	1.00
	1	5.89	3.72	2.17	1.72
	2	6.62	3.18	3.44	0.92
	3	6.72	3.45	3.27	1.06

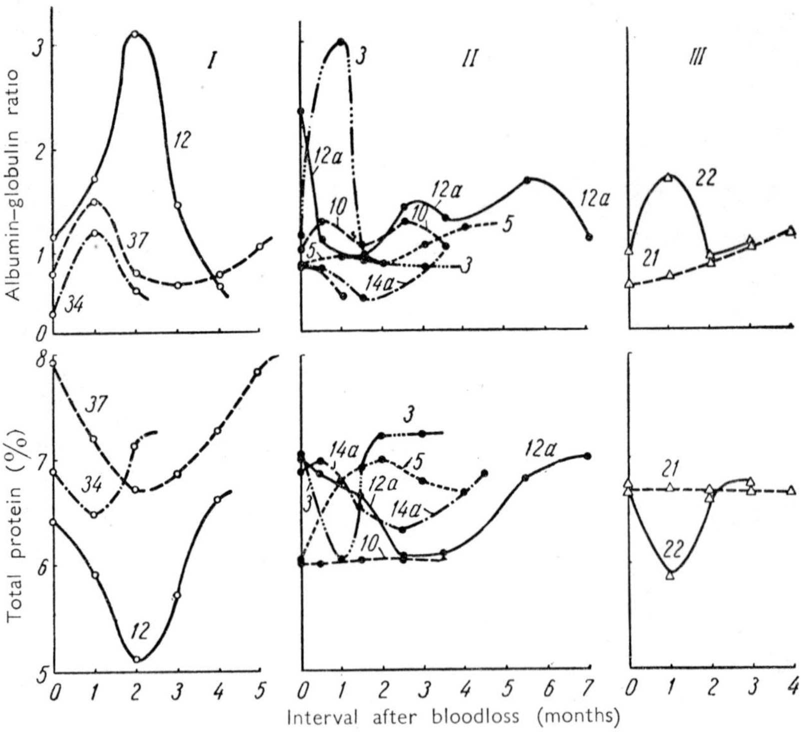

FIG. 3. Total protein (lower curves) and A/G ratio (upper curves) in rabbits after blood loss. I—control rabbits; II—rabbits receiving 12.5 μc/kg per day; III—rabbits receiving 1.25 μc/kg per day. In groups I and II blood loss occurred at the 15th month of the experiment; in group III—at the 11th month. 0—time of blood loss. The figures against the curves give the rabbit No.

content, 2.07 per cent before blood loss, had risen to 3.5 per cent. Subsequently, 2-5 months after blood loss, total protein and A/G reached approximately their initial values. The corresponding results for the rabbits receiving the larger ^{60}Co dose present an extremely variegated picture. In 3 rabbits of this group (Nos. 3, 12a and 14a) a decrease of the total protein content with subsequent restoration was observed in response to blood loss, as in the healthy rabbits. In one (No. 5) a lasting increase was observed and in another (No. 10) the total protein content remained unchanged for 3 months after blood loss.

Great disparities were also observed in changes in the A/G ratio. In only one rabbit (No. 3) was the normal course established: at one month after blood loss with total protein reduced from 7.04 to 6.2 per cent the albumin content increased considerably from 3.8 to 4.6 per cent, which produced an increase of the A/G from 1.17 to 2.98. By the 2nd month total protein had already begun to rise again (to 7.2 per cent) and the albumin level and A/G consequently fell to 3.38 per cent and 0.88. In the remaining rabbits the A/G ratio after blood loss fluctuated within fairly narrow limits (Table 3, Fig. 3). In rabbit No. 5 it remained at the initial level for 2 months after blood loss (0.84) and then increased, reaching 1.22 at 4 months.

In rabbit No. 10 the A/G ratio twice rose and fell in the course of $3\frac{1}{2}$ months (1.01-1.28). In rabbit No. 12a after a sharp fall (from 2.34 to 0.92) the A/G fluctuated twice within 5 months: 0.92-1.42-1.32-1.66-1.13. In rabbit 14a changes the reverse of the normal occurred in the A/G ratio: the A/G fell at 2 months from 0.88 to 0.57, after which it increased to 0.82 at 3 months and 1.06 at 5 months. The absolute albumin content as a rule (with the exception of rabbit No. 12a) was not materially changed.

DISCUSSION

Throughout the period (2 years) of administration of ^{60}Co to rabbits, substantial shifts in total protein content and the fractional composition of the serous proteins were observed. The changes detected were similar to the disturbances produced by acute radiation sickness (cf. Table 4).

The total protein content after fatal and close to fatal X-ray doses generally falls (G. Shilinsh *et al.*; Stender *et al.*; Supplee *et al.*); sometimes, however, it rises because, it is suggested, of hemoconcentration (I. I. Ivanov *et al.*), or it sometimes remains at a normal level (Andreoni *et al.*). The absolute and relative albumin content falls and the globulin content increases, as a result of which there is a significant decrease of the A/G ratio (G. Shilinsh, Fischer *et al.*; Gjessing *et al.*; Volkin *et al.*). The increase of the globulin content is due according to some results to the α-globulins (Gjessing), according to others to the β-globulins (Andreo-

TABLE 4

The fractional composition of the serous proteins after acute X-irradiation (published results)

Subject of investigation	Dose (r)	globulins α	globulins β	globulins γ	albu- min	A/G	total protein	Authors
Patients with tumours	Therapeutic	+(α_1) −(α_2)	+	—	—	—	—	V. D. Blohkina, G. Shilinsh et al.
,,	,,	0	0	0	0			Frieden and White
Dogs	1250	+	+	—	—	+		et al. V. S. Balabukha, V. D. Blokhina
Rabbits	500–1000	+	+	—	—	—		Stender, Elbert
,,	1000		+(β_3)	+	0		0	Andreoni, Dompe and Russo
Rats	200			+	—			Winkler et al.
,,	500–7000	+(α_1 α_2)	+	—	—	—	—	A. A. Oganezova; G. Shilinsh; Gjessing and Chanutin; Hohne et al.; Volkin et al.; Chanutin; Winkler et al.
,,	800	0	0,+ (β_1)— −(β_2)	—	—			Fischer, Magee and Coulter

Footnote: + increase; − decrease; 0—unchanged by comparison with the control; the figures in parentheses indicate which fractions of the α- and β-globulins were responsible for the change.

ni et al.; Fischer et al.) or again, to both these fractions at once (A. A. Oganezova, Stender et al.). Most investigators are agreed that the γ-globulins after irradiation are diminished (Fischer et al.; Gjessing et al.; Winkler et al.) or at best are unchanged (Frieden). Reports on increase of the A/G ratio, absence of any substantial shifts in the fractional composition of the serous proteins (Frieden) or an increase of the γ-globulins (Andreoni et al.; Winkler et al.) after irradiation are rare.

Under the conditions of our chronic experiment of oral administration of ^{60}Co a sharp 15–20 per cent increase of the total protein content is observed; the albumin level remains normal for more than 4 months. Thus the decrease of the A/G ratio at this period is caused simply by the sharp increase of the globulin content (cf. Fig. 1, Table 1). The total protein content reverts to normal at the 9th month, but the A/G remains depressed. The total protein level becomes normal at this period by virtue of a proportional decline of the albumins and globulins which accounts for the continued depression of the A/G ratio. Subsequently, total protein again increases slightly and remains raised up to the 22nd–23rd month when the experiment was terminated.

The differences in changes of the protein composition of the serum in the control and experimental animals after blood loss, carried out at the 14th–16th month of administration, indicate the impairment of albumin synthesis.

Examining the literature, both Russian and foreign, we have been unable to find any reports dealing with the effects of radiation on the processes of restoration of total protein and the protein fractions of the blood serum after blood loss. In healthy animals, however, and also in donors, changes of total protein, albumins and globulins have been investigated in the first hours or days after removal of 10–25 per cent of the circulating blood. All the investigators without exception report the significant dilution of the blood remaining in the blood stream because of the increased flow of interstitial fluid and lymph (K. F. Bogdanov; M. A. Volin and S. N. Sorochkina; Calvin; Lands and Johnson), as a result of which the total protein content falls sharply (by 1½–2 times and more) (B. Yu. Andrievskii and I. S. Tkachenko; A. Kh. Babaeva; N. A. Gorbunova; R. E. Messik; Brandhendler; Elman *et al.*). After some time, certain proteins, chiefly the albumins, begin to increase, which leads to a gradual increase of the A/G ratio (B. Yu. Andrievskii *et al.*; I. T. Volynets; Elman *et al.*; Calvin). Some authors find that this protein consists of albumins and globulins in the same proportion as found in the blood before blood loss (N. A. Gorbunova; Elman).

We find this conclusion doubtful. Depending on the quantity of blood lost and on the object of study, total protein and the albumins and globulins revert from pathologically low levels to normal within one day (Ebert *et al.*), 7–10 days (A. Kh. Babaeva; K. F. Bogdanov; I. T. Volynets; N. A. Gorbunova; R. E. Messik; Brandhendler; Elman *et al.*) or even several weeks (K. F. Bogdanov). From this it can be concluded that there is in the body no reservoir of reserve serous proteins in a state of readiness: time is needed for their formation (Elman). Careful examination of the results of different writers persuades us that total protein and albumins never reach their initial magnitude in the periods indicated but remain 10–20 per cent below, although within normal limits. Since it seemed that a return to the initial level indicated complete restoration of the blood proteins, only partly achieved in the first hours or days after blood loss, we measured changes at a later period—after half a month or more.

In our tests on the control rabbits after blood loss, a significant decline of the total protein level occurred but despite this, a sharp absolute increase of albumins, which can only be attributed to newly formed albumin. The ratio of albumin to globulins increases. Total protein level approaches normal after 2–5 months, the A/G after 2–3 months. In the rabbits receiving ^{60}Co the decline in total protein is less pronounced and is sometimes even undetectable. The absolute albumin content as a rule changes little. As a result the A/G ratio either declines or fluctuates within narrow limits for 2–7 months after bloodloss (cf. Table 3, Fig. 3). Blood was removed from the rabbits receiving 1.25 µc/kg ^{60}Co at the 11th month of administration. In some the reaction was normal (decline of total protein, increase of A/G with comparatively rapid return of both factors to their initial levels), in others no changes were observed.

Fischer and Coulter consider that the decline of albumin and increase of β-globulins in irradiated rats (800 r) result from the emaciation of the animal, whereas the γ-globulin content falls as a result of continuous irradiation, since in irradiated and non-irradiated hungry animals the levels of albumin, α-globulins and β-globulins are alike and only the γ-globulins decrease in the irradiated rats. On the basis of the observations described above it is suggested that in our rabbits the decrease of albumin is also the result of continuous irradiation either on the protein itself or on the enzyme system which regulates its synthesis, especially since comparison of animal weights in the control and experimental groups gives no indication of any wasting away of the experimental animals.

In the later periods of administration at the 21st and 23rd months the A/G ratio determined chemically by separation of albumins and globulins with sodium sulphate differs little from the control groups. However, paper electrophoretic studies disclose a definite variation: in the experimental animals of both groups (receiving 12.5 and 1.25 µc/kg per day) the A/G ratio is below normal. Thus it should be recognized that even at this period the increase in total protein after temporary normalization is achieved by increase of globulins.

The disparity in the A/G ratios obtained chemically and by electrophoresis at the 21st and 23rd months of administration can possibly be explained by the presence in the serum of a factor of unknown origin produced by radiation. Determination of the A/G ratio in the presence of this factor both chemically and by ultracentrifugation gives artificially high results, whereas it has no effect on electrophoretic results. If it is extracted from the serum of the irradiated animal with a mixture of alcohol and ether the A/G value obtained chemically and by ultracentrifugation falls to the level in healthy animals.

Judging by the data in Table 2, at 21 and 23 months the globulin content increases by virtue, not of the α- and β-fractions as in acute radiation sickness (Table 4), but of the γ-globulins. In this connection it is interesting to note the observations of the Italian writers (Andreoni *et al.*) where they show that rabbits given a single radiation dose of 1000 r produce some increase of the α- and β-globulins, which quickly disappear. When the animals which have received this dose are subjected again to smaller doses a significant increase of γ-globulins is observed in the serum. An increase of the γ-globulins after relatively small X-ray doses has also been reported in another paper (Winkler *et al.*), whereas large doses produced an increase of β-globulins and, especially, of α-globulins. The ratio of α-globulins to γ-globulins increased with increase of the radiation dose.

In view of these reports it seems that accumulation of α- or β-globulins is an initial, transitory reaction of the body to irradiation producing acute radiation sickness. Subsequently, a steady increase of γ-globulins occurs and is particularly clearly detected in chronic radiation sickness.

In examining the experimental material mentioned above and comparing it with the already known data on changes in the levels of total protein, albumin and A/G after exposure to lethal or near lethal doses of ionizing radiation a similarity becomes apparent between the changes of these fractions in the acute and chronic forms of radiation sickness. Furthermore, definite phases in the development of chronic radiation sickness can be detected. In the first period, lasting several months, total protein increases because of the globulin increase. At 7–9 months of intoxication the total protein content falls back to normal. In the second period (months 9–14) a normal A/G is re-established apparently as a result of increased formation of albumin and globulins. After the 14th month changes occur caused by the more serious, progressive impairment of vital activity. From this period the total protein content increases to a higher level than before due to the γ-globulins and the A/G ratio again falls. There is also deterioration in other factors: with each month the glycogen-forming capacity of the liver declines (N. I. Vinogradova; E. D. Grishchenko), the blood picture deteriorates sharply (N. L. Beloborodova), the permeability of the blood vessels increases to a significant degree (A. A. Rubanovskaya) and, from the flattening of the T wave and the change in the S–T interval, the intensity of metabolic processes, important for cardiac activity, declines (A. O. Saitanov; I. N. Golovshchikova).

Thus chronic administration of ^{60}Co to rabbits produces periodic disturbances which are typical for many forms of intoxication for example, lead poisoning (E. D. Grishchenko; V. V. Nikitenko). These are: (1) initial, transitory disturbances; (2) a period of temporary remission maintained by significant strain on compensatory mechanisms (detected by application of physiological stresses); (3) the gradual development of irreversible pathological processes as a consequence of the inadequacy of adaptive measures.

The specific character of these changes is determined however by the nature of the causal agent.

No substantial changes in residual nitrogen content of the blood serum could be detected throughout the experiment, apart from a slight increase at the 4th month.

In conclusion the following two important circumstances must be emphasized. Firstly, changes in the levels of total protein, albumin, globulins and A/G in the serum of rabbits receiving stable cobalt were in all respects identical with those in the pure control. This is not surprising, since even much larger doses of stable cobalt are not harmful to the body (A. O. Voinar), and even confer some protection against X-radiation (Parr, O'Neill, Krebs). Secondly, changes in the levels of total protein, albumin, globulins and A/G in each of the experimental groups (receiving 12.5 and 1.25 μc/kg ^{60}Co) differ little from each other.

CONCLUSIONS

1. Changes in the content and composition of the protein fractions of the blood serum in rabbits were investigated during daily oral administration of ^{60}Co in doses of 12.5 and 1.25 μc/kg for 23 months.
2. In the first 7–9 months the total serous protein content increases significantly due to the globulin fraction (approximately from 6.40 to 7.40 per cent), as a result of which the A/G ratio falls. In the period from the 9th to the 14th months of administration total protein returns to its normal level (probably as a result of hemoconcentration), and then also the A/G ratio. Subsequently, total protein again rises to a higher point than before and the A/G falls as a result of an increase of the γ-globulin fraction, demonstrated by paper electrophoretic studies. The character of the changes produced by physiological stress (blood loss) at the 15th month indicates a weakening of the albumin synthesizing processes.

No substantial changes in the residual nitrogen content of the blood serum could be detected throughout the experiment apart from a slight increase at the 4th month.

REFERENCES

A. *Russian*

ANDRIYEVSKII B. YU. and TKACHENKO I. S., *Novyi khir. arkh.* **33**, No. 1, 56 (1935).
BABAYEVA A. KH., *Zdravookhraneniye Turkhmenistana*, No. 1, 27 (1957).
BOGDANOV K. F., *The Effect of Venous Bloodloss on Hemodynamics and Blood Composition.* (O vliyanii venoznogo krovopuskaniya na gemodinamiku i sostav krovi.) Proceedings of the Krasnoyarsk Medical Institute **4**, 117 (1955).
VOINAR A. O., *The Biochemistry of Cobalt.* (Usp. sovr. biol.) **30**, No. 5, 345 (1950).
VOLIN M. A. and SOROCHKINA S. N., *Terap. arkh.*, **13**, No. 5, 77 (1935).

VOLYNETS I. T., *Medichnyi zh.*, No. 3, 783 (1938).
GORBUNOVA N. A., *The Restoration of the Fluid Part of the Blood and Protein following Bloodloss*. (O vosstanovlcnii zhidkoi chasti krovi i belka v blizhaishiye sroki posle krovopoteri.) Proceedings of the 11th Conference of the Student Society of the Stalinabad Medical Institute, Stalinabad (1955); Proceedings of the 1st Conference of Physiologists, Biochemists and Pharmocologists of Central Asia and Kazakhstan, Tashkent (1956).
GRISHCHENKO YE. D. and NIKITENKO V. V., *Vopr. med. khim.* **2**, No. 5, 328 (1956).
GURVICH A. E., *Lab. delo* **3**, 3–9 (1955).
IVANOV I. I., BALABUKHA V. S., ROMANTSEV YE. F. and FEDOROVA T. A., *Metabolic Processes in Radiation Sickness*. (Obmen veshchestv pri luchevoi bolezni.) Medgiz (1956).
KISELEV P. N., BUSINI P. A. and SEMINA V. A., *Vest. rentgenol. i radiol.* **3**, 3 (1955).
MESSIK R. E., *The State Institute of Clinical and Experimental Hematology and Blood Transfusion*. (Gosudarstvennyi institut klinicheskoi i eskperimental'noi gematologii i perelivaniya krovi.) **4**, 106 (1932).
OGANEZOVA A. A., *The Effect of X-irradiation on the Protein Fractions of the Blood of Animals on Different Diets*. (Kharakter izmenenii belkovykh fraktsii krovi pri rentgenovskom obluchenii zhivotnykh na fone razlichnogo pitaniya.) Medgiz, 54 (1956).
SHILINSH G., *The Effect of X-rays on Total Protein and the Protein Fractions in the Blood*. (Vliyaniye luchei Rentgena na obshcheye kolichestvo belka i fraktsii belkov krovi.) Riga (1952).

B. *Foreign*

ANDREONI O., DOMPE M. and RUSSO A. M., *Ricerca scient.* **25**, No. 6, 1393 (1955); No. 13, 12804 (1956).
BARRON E. S. G., DICKMAN S. and MUNTZ J. A., *J. Gener. Physiol.* **32**, No. 4, 537 (1949).
BLUM H. F., *Photodynamic Action and Diseases Caused by Light*, New York (1941).
BRANDHENDLER W., *Bull. Biol. et Med. exper.* **8**, 326 (1939).
CALVIN D. B., *J. Lab. Clin. Med.* **26**, 1144 (1941).
COLVIN J. R., *Arch. Biochem. Biophys.* **46**, No. 2, 385 (1953).
ELMAN R., *Amer. J. Physiol.* **128**, No. 2, 332 (1940).
ELMAN R., LISCHER C. E. and DAVEY H. W., *Amer. J. Physiol.* **138**, No. 4, 569 (1943).
FISCHER M. A., MAGEE M. Z. and COULTER E. G., *Arch. Biochem. and Biophysiol.* **56**, No. 1, 66 (1955).
FRIEDEN J., WHITE A., *Yale J. Biol. Med.* **22**, No. 5, 395 (1950).
GJESSING E. C. and CHANUTIN A., *Arch. Biochem.* **27**, No. 1, 191 (1950).
HOHNE G., KUNNEL H. A. and ANGER R., *Klin. Wschr.* **11–12**, 284 (1955).
LANDS A. M. and JOHNSON W., *Proc. Soc. Exper. Biol. Med.* **49**, No. 2, 123 (1942).
PARR W., O'NEILL T. and KREBS A., *Science* **117**, No. 3033, 153 (1953).
PASSARO G. and PASSALACQUA W., *Boll. Soc. ital. Biol. sperim.* **29**, No. 2, 243 (1953); No. 15, 36249 (1954).
RUZDIC I. and PUCAR Z., *Acta pharmacol. jugosl.* **3**, No. 1, 130 (1953); No. 13, 12188 (1956).
STENDER H. S. and ELBERT O., *Strahlentherapie* **89**, No. 2, 275 (1952).
SUPPLEE H., HAUSSCHILDT J. D. and ENTENMANN C., *Amer. J. Physiol.* **169**, No. 2, 483 (1952).
VOLKIN E. and KOHN H. J., *Arch. Biochem.* **30**, No. 2, 326 (1951).
WINKLER C. and PASCHUE G., *Klin. Wschr.* **41–42**, 1011 (1955).

THE EFFECT OF ^{60}Co ON CARBOHYDRATE METABOLISM IN RAT LIVER

N. I. VINOGRADOVA

IN RECENT years much has been published on the effect of ionizing radiation on carbohydrate metabolism in experimental animals (I. I. Ivanov, V. S. Balabukha *et al.*). It has been established that irradiation of rats with X-rays in a dose of 110,000 r leads to a diminution of glycogen reserves in the liver (Levy *et al.*). According to B. M. Grayevskaya the glycogen content of the liver of rats is halved on the second day after X-irradiation (500 r) but returns to normal after 4 days.

F. I. Rivosh has shown that irradiation of dog liver with large X-ray doses impairs the synthesis of glycogen; small doses stimulate it. In rats starved before and after X-irradiation (300 r) the glycogen content of the liver increases. This effect is obtained by administration of cysteine before irradiation (Fischer, Ross *et al.*). Fisher has shown that the glycogen of rat liver is synthesized for 24 hr after irradiation from two or three carbon compounds, the breakdown products of proteins and fats brought to the liver in the blood. In guinea pigs 6–8 days after irradiation glycogen in the liver is being synthesized from carbon chains of a different order than in the first day after irradiation (Ord *et al.*). This would seem to explain the glycogen deficit at the 12th–14th day after irradiation at a dose of 500 r in the experiments of Lourau and Lartigue, *et al.*

The effect of X-rays on the animal body is to lower the assimilation of sugar by the muscles and liver (N. I. Kochneva, N. I. Kochneva and E. S. London). In dogs the concentration of lactic acid in the blood decreases probably as a result of blockage of the enzymes of carbohydrate metabolism (Ingram, Dobrovolskaya-Zavadskaya *et al.*).

Published results indicate that irradiation produces changes in the carbohydrate metabolism of dog liver. The character of these changes depends to a considerable degree on the dose received.

However, most of the information in the literature on changes in carbohydrate metabolism following irradiation relate to large doses of X- and γ-rays. There is little material on the effect on carbohydrate metabolism of small doses of radioactive substances, particularly ^{60}Co, administered internally.

In this paper are presented the results of study of the glycogen-forming capacity of rat liver after administration (intraperitoneal and oral) of different amounts of ^{60}Co. The glycogen content of the liver and its structure at different intervals after ^{60}Co administration, and the phosphorylytic and amylolytic activity of liver extracts were measured. Under our experimental conditions changes in the glycogen-forming function of the liver were to be expected since ^{60}Co accumulates predominantly in the liver (M. G. Petrovnin, G. A. Abrunina), and may exercise a direct effect on its functions.

METHODS

Our experimental animals were white rats weighing 100–240 g (weight was the same in the experiment as in the control) maintained in usual conditions in a vivarium. Radioactive cobalt chloride was administered in a quantity of 15–900 μc per rat either orally or intraperitoneally in a 1–2 ml. solution. At different intervals after administration rats were killed by decapitation.

Glycogen content of the liver was determined in the following way. A weighed portion of the liver (about 500 mg) was quickly hydrolyzed on a boiling water bath for 30 min with 1 ml. 60 per cent KOH. The glycogen was precipitated with alcohol and twice reprecipitated from water, after which it was dissolved in 9 ml. of water, 1 ml. of 25 per cent HCl was added, and hydrolyzed for 3 hr on a boiling water bath. The solution was neutralized with 35 per cent KOH, transferred to a measuring flask, diluted and glycogen content determined by Hagedorn–Jensen's method. The figures obtained were transposed for glycogen content of the liver (in milligrams per 1 g tissue). Glycogen was isolated from the liver by Ostern's method.

The ease of breakdown of glycogen by β-amylase was determined as follows: 10 mg of glycogen was dissolved in 2 ml. of freshly boiled and cooled acetate buffer (pH 4.8). 3 ml. of a 1 per cent solution of β-amylase of high activity, obtained from soya flour by Baurne and Peat's method and free from α-amylase and maltase, was added. The mixture was incubated under toluene in a thermostat at 37°. After one day and again after 5 days the quantity of maltose formed was measured by Somodyi's method and glycogen breakdown calculated as a percentage. Enzymic hydrolysis of all the preparations was carried out at the same time with one and the same solution of β-amylase. The maximal breakdown of glycogen occurred in the first day.

Liver water extract was prepared from the exsanguinated liver by shaking it in water in a 1:1 ratio for 5 min. After centrifugation the liquid obtained was used as an extract for determining phosphorylytic and amylolytic activity (A. N. Petrova).

For examination of the phosphorylytic activity of liver extracts 0.75 ml. 0.04 M NaF, 10 mg glycogen and 0.25 ml. phosphate buffer were added to 2 ml. of the extract.

Amylolytic activity was determined by adding 10 mg glycogen, 55 mg sodium chloride and 1 ml. water to 2 ml. liver extract. Tests were selected to determine the reducing agents in the incubated mixtures before and after acidic hydrolysis. The incubated mixtures were placed in a thermostat at 37°. After 30 and 60 min the increase of reducing agents was tested. On the basis of the results obtained glycogen breakdown during incubation was calculated. The reducing agents were determined by Somodyi's methods.

RESULTS

The tests set out above showed that at 1 and 5 days after a single intraperitoneal injection of rats with ^{60}Co in an amount of 22–44 μc per rat (liver tissue activity was 200–570 counts per min per 100 mg tissue) glycogen content in the liver is unchanged and indistinguishable from the control. On average the quantity of glycogen is 54 mg/g liver (variation between 34 and 60).

After an intraperitoneal injection of 100 μc ^{60}Co (liver activity 446–703 counts per min per 100 mg) the glycogen content of the liver falls to 28–25 mg/g. The average for the control was 42 mg/g liver (Table 1).

It is interesting to observe that where the same quantity of ^{60}Co (100 μc per rat) is administered orally the glycogen content of the liver falls to 18 mg/g liver, while the control figure is 47 mg/g (Table 2). In some rats after administration of 107 μc per rat the quantity of glycogen declined sharply (0.5–4 mg/g) and was still not restored after 5 days (18–30 mg/g liver).

A possible cause of this phenomenon may be that the direct irradiation of the liver is supplemented by radiation from the intestine, since cobalt is poorly absorbed (about 35 per cent in rats) and a large part remains in the feces thus creating a focus of radiation in the intestine. Nevertheless, as can be seen from Table 2, resynthesis of glycogen takes place at this dosage.

Intraperitoneal injection of rats with a large ^{60}Co dose (886 μc per rat) has sharp repercussions on the glycogen-forming function of the liver. Glycogen almost completely disappears from the liver and even 5 days after injection the glycogen level is still depressed (1–2 mg/g tissue). Under these experimental conditions the radioactivity of 100 mg of liver at this period is high: 1558–1738 counts per minute (Table 3).

TABLE 1

Glycogen content of the liver and its ease of breakdown by β-amylase in control rats and after a single intraperitoneal injection of ^{60}Co

No. of rat	Amount of ^{60}Co injected (μc per rat)	Period after injection	Tissue radioactivity (imp/min/100 mg)	Glycogen content mg/kg tissue)	% age glycogen breakdown by β-amylase
			Experimental animals		
1	22	1	202	47	31
2	22	1	270	34	39
3	22	1	289	60	33
			Control animals		
4	0	0	0	38	44
5	0	0	0	49	38
6	0	0	0	48	49
			Experimental animals		
7	22	5	71	58	28
8	22	5	97	59	31
9	22	5	118	60	27
			Control animals		
10	0	0	0	60	49
11	0	0	0	60	47
			Experimental animals		
12	44	1	221	61	27
13	44	1	439	—	29
14	44	1	573	59	33
			Control animals		
15	0	0	0	60	—
16	0	0	0	47	—
17	0	0	0	54	—
			Experimental animals		
18	80	1	800	—	—
			Control animals		
19	0	0	0	—	47
			Experimental animals		
20	100	1	446	25	28
21	100	1	703	28	26
22	100	1	763	32	25
			Control animals		
23	0	0	0	42	52

TABLE 2

Glycogen content of rat liver and its ease of breakdown after oral administration ^{60}Co

No. of rat	Amount of ^{60}Co administered (μc per rat)	Period after administration (days)	Tissue radioactivity (imp/min/100 mg)	Glycogen content (mg/kg tissue)	% age glycogen breakdown by β-amylase
24	0	0	0	47	48
25	100	1	272	18	—
26	100	1	275	17	30
27	100	1	301	18	25
28*	107	1	227	4	—
29*	107	1	156	0.5	—
30*	107	5	42	18	—
31*	107	5	60	30	—

* Rats of another group.

TABLE 3

Glycogen content of rat liver 5 days after administration of 886 μc ^{60}Co and a corresponding quantity of stable cobalt (956 γ)

No. of rat	Cobalt	Tissue radioactivity (imp/min/100 mg)	Glycogen content (mg/g tissue)
32	Radioactive	1558	2
33	,,	1738	1
34	Stable	0	31
35	,,	0	19

Thus, the results show that glycogen content of the liver depends on the amount of ^{60}Co administered. Although after administration of 22–44 μc ^{60}Co per animal, glycogen content is almost unchanged, its synthesis in the liver is impaired. This is indicated by the results of investigation on the ease of breakdown by β-amylase of glycogen preparations isolated from the liver at different intervals after ^{60}Co administration. It was demonstrated in these conditions that the ease of breakdown of glycogen by β-amylase was on average 28.6–34 per cent, as against 43–48 per cent in the control, which indicates formation of glycogen with shortened side chains, i.e. with a changed structure.

As has already been pointed out above, no diminution of the glycogen level in the liver was detected after intraperitoneal injection of 22 μc ^{60}Co. However, it was found that if a smaller dose (14.7 μc) was administered orally not once but for 12 days the glycogen level falls to 28–33 mg/g liver (Table 4). The total dose of ^{60}Co administered is 176.4 μc per rat.

TABLE 4

Glycogen content of rat liver and its ease of breakdown by β-amylase after daily oral administration of ^{60}Co in a dose of 14.7 μc for 12 days

No. of rat	Liver radioactivity (imp/min/100 mg)	Glycogen content (mg/g tissue)	% age glycogen breakdown by β-amylase
36	242	33	31
37	278	33	30
38	309	34	29
39	359	28	30
40	549	—	25

TABLE 5

The phosphorylytic and hydrolytic effect of rat liver extracts on glycogen after a single intraperitoneal injection of $^{60}CoCl_2$ (100 μc)

Tissue radioactivity (imp/min/100 mg)	Phosphorolysis 30 minutes	Phosphorolysis 60 minutes	Hydrolysis 30 minutes	Hydrolysis 60 minutes
Control				
0	1.60	2.36	1.04	2.99
0	3.14	4.21	0.74	2.53
0	2.70	5.30	1.23	2.57
0	2.32	3.15	—	3.77
0	2.74	4.08	2.66	3.57
0	1.60	3.17	1.30	2.13
Average				
0	2.35 (100%)	3.71 (100%)	1.40 (100%)	2.99 (100%)
One day after $^{60}CoCl_2$ injection				
1022	1.73	2.99	0.65	1.39
1047	1.45	2.11	1.94	2.84
1173	—	1.87	1.01	1.63
—	1.26	1.97	—	2.62
—	—	2.66	1.64	2.36
Average				
1082	1.45 (61%)	2.32 (64%)	1.31 (94%)	2.16 (74%)
5 days after $^{60}CoCl_2$ injection				
228	1.72	2.61	1.43	2.18
250	1.95	3.05	1.11	2.36
336	1.80	3.16	1.04	2.87
182	2.08	3.88	—	3.05
—	2.00	2.87	—	2.00
Average				
243	1.91 (81%)	3.19 (86%)	1.19 (85%)	2.49 (85%)
20 days after $^{60}CoCl_2$ injection				
20	2.60 (111%)	3.89 (105%)	1.84 (132%)	2.64 (88%)

decrease of glycogen (mg/ml.) after incubation of

As Tables 1 and 4 show, liver activity after both single intraperitoneal injection of 22 μc ^{60}Co and repeated oral administration of 14.7 μc is similar although the duration of exposure and consequently the total tissue doses received by the liver in the latter case are much greater.

As well as glycogen content of the liver and its ease of breakdown by β-amylase, the phosphorylytic and hydrolytic activity of rat liver extracts was determined after intraperitoneal injection of 100 μc of ^{60}CoCl$_2$. The methods used are described above. The results are presented in Table 5.

The initial glucose content in all the tests was found within limits of from 2.17 to 5.66 mg/ml., average 3.30 mg/ml. The glycogen content was 5.76–15.61 mg/ml., average 9.62 mg/ml.

In a series of experiments, as well as increase in the quantity of reducing agents in the incubated mixture, changes of organic phosphate content were determined by Fiske and Subbarou's methods. In phosphorolysis tests a diminution of inorganic phosphate was always observed. In amylolysis tests the inorganic phosphate content was unchanged.

The data presented in Table 5 show convincingly that a day after an intraperitoneal injection of rats with ^{60}Co the phosphorylase activity of the liver decreases to 61–64 per cent, recovering after 5 days from injection to 81–86 per cent. Amylase activity a day after injection declines to 84 per cent, being completely restored after 20 days. Similar results have been obtained by R. Ya. Keilina. X-irradiation (500 r) of rats produced a depression in phosphorylase activity of the liver but amylase activity increased. It is possible that the change observed in the glycogen-forming function of the liver is connected with impairments of enzymic activity, chiefly of the phosphorylase.

CONCLUSIONS

1. After a single intraperitoneal injection of 22–44 μc ^{60}Co per rat (100–250 μc/kg weight) the glycogen content of the liver is unchanged.
2. A day after administration of 100 μc/kg and more (500 μc/kg and more) the glycogen content of the liver declines and phosphorylase activity is depressed.
3. Oral and intraperitoneal administration to rats of 100 μc/kg ^{60}Co and more, produces formation in the liver of glycogen with shortened side chains.

REFERENCES

BAURNE E. and PEAT W. J., *J. Chem. Soc.* **160**, 61 (1945).
DOBROVOLSKAYA-ZAVADSKAYA W. and MACCHI L., *J. Radiol. Electrol.* **33**, 237 (1952).
FISCHER P., *Arch. Inter. Physiol.* No. 62, 134 (1954).
GRAYEVSKAYA B. M., KEILINA R. YA. and MANOILOV YE. S., *Vest. rentgen. i radiol.* No. 6, 22 (1953).

INGRAM M., MASON W. B., WHIPPLE H. and RAVILAND J. W., *Univ. Rochester Atom. Energy Proj.* 196 (1952).
IVANOV I. I., BALABUKHA V. S., ROMANTSEV E. F. and FEDOROVA T. A., *Metabolic Processes in Radiation Sickness.* (Obmen veshchestv pri luchevoi bolezni.) Medgiz (1956).
KEILINA R. YA., *Biokhimiya* No. 20, 421 (1955).
KOCHNEVA N. I., *Vest. rentgenol. i radiol.* No. 20, 90 (1936).
KOCHNEVA N. I. and LONDON YE. S., *Vest. rentgenol. i radiol.* No. 14, 388 (1953).
LEVY B. and RUGH R., *Proc. Soc. Exper. Biol. Med.* No. 82, 223 (1953).
LOURAU M. and LARTIGUE O. J., *J. physiol.* (Paris) No. 43, 593 (1951).
ORD M. G. and STOCKEN L., *Physiol. Rev.* **33,** 356 (1953).
OSTERN P. and HUBE S., *Acta biol. exper.* **13,** No. 8, 89 (1939).
PETROVA A. N., *Biokhimiya* **20,** 718 (1955).
RIVOSH F. N., *Vest. rentgenol. i radiol.* **18,** 163 (1937).
ROSS M. H. and ELY J. O., *J. Cell. Comp. Physiol.* **37,** 163 (1951).
SOMODYI M. J., *Biol. Chem.* **160,** No. 161, 69 (1945).

IMPAIRMENT OF SOME ASPECTS OF CARBOHYDRATE-PHOSPHORUS METABOLISM IN RABBITS AFTER PROLONGED ADMINISTRATION OF ^{60}Co

N. I. VINOGRADOVA and Ye. D. GRISHCHENKO

THE regulation of carbohydrate-phosphorus metabolism is accomplished by the activity of a series of organs and systems.

A number of reports are to be found concerning the effect of acute radiation injury on carbohydrate metabolism but comparatively few on the disturbances caused by chronic irradiation. This paper presents the results of investigations on the phosphorolytic and amylolytic activity of liver homogenates and glycogen structure in rabbits during chronic oral administration of ^{60}Co. The liver was chosen as the object of investigation because as well as being a reservoir of glycogen it is in this organ that most ^{60}Co is concentrated. The liver is also chosen as a critical organ in calculations of maximum permissible concentrations of ^{60}Co in water (G. A. Abrunina; N. G. Gusev).

METHODS

The experiments were carried out on 21 young rabbits. A sixth group of rabbits was included as well as the 5 groups of animals mentioned in earlier articles. The 4 rabbits of this sixth group each received orally 65 μc/kg ^{60}CoCl$_2$ per day for 2 months. This group was used to obtain pronounced changes in carbohydrate metabolism for comparison with the effects obtained in the other groups.

The enzymic activity of amylase and phosphorylase and glycogen structure were investigated as described by N. I. Vinogradova.

The rabbits were killed by aeroembolism.

In studying hepatal amylase and phosphorylase activity we made a determination of not only reducing agents but also inorganic phosphorus, which, in conditions conducive to phosphorylase activity always decreased and in the tests on amylase activity remained unchanged.

Blood sugar was determined by Hagedorn and Jensen's method.

Sugar loading: glucose in the form of a 50 per cent solution was administered orally in an amount of 2 g/kg live weight.

RESULTS

The blood sugar level in the control rabbits throughout the first 14 months varied from 129 to 138 per cent. Subsequently, it fell somewhat and from the 15th to the 22nd month varied from 112 to 129 mg per cent showing no consistent trend.

In the rabbits receiving 12.5 μc/kg ^{60}Co, the blood sugar level was 126–137 mg per cent in the first 4 months, and then gradually declined, falling to 107 mg per cent at the 15th month. This level was maintained up to and including the 19th month, but at the 21st–22nd month it returned to its initial value (up to 130–138 mg per cent). In the group which received an equivalent dose of stable cobalt the blood sugar level varied for the first 14 months, as in the controls, within the narrow limits of 130–137 mg per cent, and from the 15th month to the 23rd month within 105–128 mg per cent.

In the rabbits receiving 1.25 μc/kg ^{60}Co a noticeable decline of the blood sugar level occurred a month after commencement of administration (112$\pm$4 mg per cent, as compared with the initial value of 129$\pm$5 mg per cent). By the 15th month it had fallen to 98$\pm$2 mg per cent, after which it rose again, varying from the 16th to the 23rd month within the limits 118–136 mg per cent.

It is difficult to suggest on the experimental data available a reason for the variations of blood sugar level found in this group of rabbits.

Sugar Curves

From the 15th month sugar curves of animals of all 5 groups were studied. In Fig. 1 only the curves relating to the control group and to the rabbits receiving 12.5 and 1.25 μc/kg ^{60}Co are presented. The curves of animals receiving stable cobalt differ little from those of the controls.

As is seen in Fig. 1, after oral glucose administration at 15 months to the rabbits receiving the large ^{60}Co dose the reducing substances were leaving the blood much more rapidly than in the controls. Their maximum level in the control animals was 167 mg per cent, returning to its initial level after 2 hr; in the experimental animals it was 141 mg per cent, returning to its initial value after 2½ hr. A similar picture is observed at the 16th month, when the sugar curves of rabbits receiving the smaller dose of ^{60}Co occupy a position intermediate between the control curves and the large dose curves. However, by the 18th month of the experiment the withdrawal of glucose from the blood is proceeding at the same speed in all 3 groups. At the 21st month symptoms of carbohydrate impairment appear: the sugar curves acquire a diabetic character. This deviation from normal becomes progressively larger with increase of the administration period; the body becomes steadily less able to cope with the sugar load.

Glycogen content of the liver in the different groups is given in the second column of Table 1.

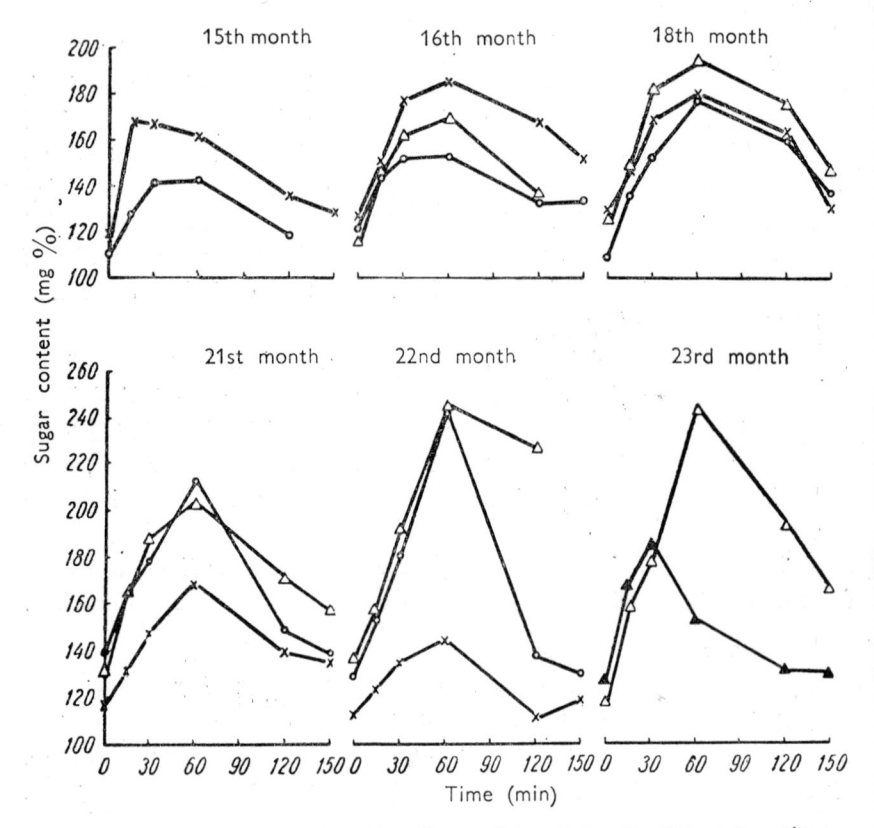

FIG. 1. Blood sugar content of rabbits. (°)—receiving 12.5 µc/kg ^{60}Co daily; (△)—receiving 1.25 µc/kg ^{60}Co daily; (ˣ)—controls. Glucose was orally administered in a dose of 2 g/kg weight.

It should be noticed that in no group of rabbits does chronic administration of ^{60}Co produce exhaustion of glycogen reserves, as is the case after a single very large dose of this isotope (1 mc per rabbit) (N. I. Vinogradova).

The incubated mixture for testing phosphorolysis comprises 4 ml. water-soluble extract of the liver +20 mg glycogen +0.5 ml. phosphate buffer +1.5 ml. 0.04 M NaF.

The incubated mixture for conducting hydrolysis comprised 4 ml. liver extract +20 mg glycogen +100 mg NaCl +2 ml. water.

The initial glucose content in all tests of phosphorylase and amylase activity fell within the limits 0.9–6.25 mg/ml., average 3.66 mg/ml.; glycogen content was 3–15.8 mg/ml., average 9.15 mg/ml.

TABLE 1

Glycogen content and structure and phosphorolytic and amylolytic activity of the liver of rabbits undergoing chronic ^{60}Co intoxication

Tissue activity (counts/min per 100 mg wet weight)	Glycogen content (mg/g liver)	Glycogen breakdown by β-amylase (%)	Phosphorylase 30 minutes	Phosphorylase 60 minutes	Amylase 30 minutes	Amylase 60 minutes
	1.25 µc/kg daily for 21–23 months (first group)
25	40	50	0.65	1.59	1.00	1.27
—	10	40	1.23	2.10	0.93	—
17	11	45	0.78	1.91	—	1.61
18	22	50	0.68	1.97	—	1.66
25	24	42	1.03	2.60	1.13	1.84
	Average
21	21	45	0.87	2.04	1.02	1.59
	12.5 µc/kg daily for 21–22 months (second group)
—	14	28	0.81	1.58	0.78	1.54
156	5	30	0.78	1.30	0.85	2.17
161	13	27	0.45	1.38	1.49	2.04
—	24	14	0.64	1.39	1.46	2.01
	Average
158	14	25	0.67	1.42	1.15	1.94
	The smaller stable cobalt dose (1.9 γ) for 21–25 months (third group)
0	15	52	1.19	2.28	0.66	1.08
0	17	400	0.84	1.84	0.56	1.27
0	6	33	0.40	1.33	1.02	1.65
0	21	53	1.03	2.50	0.50	1.15
	Average
0	15	44	0.87	1.99	0.68	1.29
	The larger stable cobalt dose (19 p) for 23 months (fourth group)
0	—	42	1.20	2.44	—	—
	Control (fifth group)
0	17	49	0.94	2.30	0.86	1.80
0	15	47	1.03	2.11	0.74	1.70
0	20	46	1.70	3.80	—	2.50
0	32	—	1.06	2.38	1.27	1.84
0	25	47	0.76	1.60	1.20	1.74
	Average
0	22	47	1.10	2.44	1.04	1.92
	65 µc/kg daily for 2 months (sixth group)
285	24	7	2	0.32	0.42	0.70
270	37	5	—	0.36	0.77	1.6
	Average
277	30	6	—	0.34	0.60	1.03

Glycogen structure in the liver underwent significant changes during chronic administration of ^{60}Co, the greater the higher the dose administered. Thus, glycogen breakdown by β-amylase in rabbits receiving 65 μc/kg ^{60}Co per day for 2 months (sixth group) was 6 per cent (cf. Table 1). This indicates that under these experimental conditions glycogen with shortened side-chains is being formed. No such severe glycogen degradation was observed in either of the other groups receiving smaller doses of ^{60}Co for a much longer period (first and second groups), nor in those submitted to acute ^{60}Co intoxication (N. I. Vinogradova). Percentage breakdown of glycogen by β-amylase in the second group of rabbits (those receiving 12.5 μc/kg ^{60}Co daily for 21–22 months) was 25, whereas 42–47 per cent of hepatal glycogen is hydrolyzed in the control animals (third, fourth and fifth groups). Glycogen breakdown in the first group, receiving 1.25 μc/kg ^{60}Co daily for 21–23 months is normal.

The Glycogenolytic Activity of Water-soluble Liver Extracts

It can be seen from Table 1 that hepatal phosphorylase is significantly more sensitive to ionizing radiation than amylase. Whereas phosphorylase activity in the rabbits of the first and second groups declines with prolongation of the experimental period to 14 per cent and 58 per cent respectively by comparison with the controls, amylase activity falls only to 56 per cent in rabbits of the sixth group which received 65 μc/kg ^{60}Co daily for 2 months, and in all the other groups remains within normal limits.

DISCUSSION

The effects of radiation sickness on carbohydrate metabolism has chiefly been investigated in cases of single, large, sublethal doses. In these cases the exhaustion of glycogen reserves has often been observed (G. Kh. Bunyatyan, B. M. Grayevskaya et al., R. Ya. Keilina, V. S. Balabukha, Fischel, Lelièvre et al.).

There are several viewpoints concerning this problem. Some writers consider it to be the effect of direct irradiation of the enzymic systems of the liver (V. P. Fedotov); others suggest a reaction of neuro-humoral origin (R. E. Kavetskii, Levy); and, finally, yet others believe that irradiated animals suffer loss of appetite and that energy requirements of the body are supplemented by hepatal glycogen.

Clearly the last proposition is nearest the truth. In starved rats with depressed glycogen content radiation, instead of producing further diminution of glycogen reserves, leads to a significant increase, the greater the higher the dose (Denson, Gray et al., Lowman, Nims et al.). Under these conditions glycogen synthesis may be dependent on a strengthening of protein metabolism giving supplementary material for glycogenesis (Louran). This possibly also explains the increased blood sugar content of animals subjected to large (up to 5000 r) X-ray doses (Kay and Entenman) or small, trace doses (5 μc per rabbit) of ^{32}P (R. E. Kavetskii et al.).

The increase of hepatal glycogen in starved animals can hardly be the result of any changes in activity of the hepatal enzymes because shielding of the liver does not alter this effect (Ross and Ely), and the intensity of incorporation of radioactive carbon in hepatal glycogen given in the form of glycine and acetate does not differ from normal (S. F. Epshtein). Shielding (Ross et al.) or removal (Denson) of the suprarenals also does not alter the character of the reaction of hungry rats to radiation; thus the possibility that the suprarenals affect the glycogen-forming function of the liver indirectly, through the chromaffin system, is excluded. Analysing the data in the literature of recent years on this problem we come to the same conclusion as I. I. Ivanov, V. C. Balabukha, E. F. Romantsev and T. A. Fedorova, that, "it is impossible to detect by normal methods the sharp and severe changes in carbohydrate metabolism caused by lethal or sublethal X-ray doses."

It should be noticed however that this conclusion can only be applied to cases of acute damage by external X- or γ-irradiation, or to internal administration of radioactive elements which become diffusely distributed in the body (e.g. ^{32}P) or, at any rate, do not become concentrated in the centres of carbohydrate metabolism (e.g. ^{210}Po) (V. P. Fedorov).

This is not the case with ^{60}Co. As is known, ^{60}Co absorbed in the intestine is accumulated in the liver. It is evident that administration of this isotope primarily affects the liver. In fact, as the experiments of N. I. Vinogradova have shown, intraperitoneal injection of ^{60}Co sufficient to create in the liver on the fifth day radioactivity of 1500 counts/min per 100 mg tissue and more, leads to the complete exhaustion of the glycogen reserves of the liver, whereas corresponding doses of stable cobalt do not have this effect. With doses of this size—and also with smaller ^{60}Co doses—glycogen breakdown declines from the normal value of 50 per cent to 25–30 per cent after ^{60}Co administration, indicating significant abbreviation of glycogen side-chains. Amylase activity under these conditions is little changed but phosphorylase activity one day after administration falls to 63 per cent of its initial value.

In the chronic experiment, the results of which are presented in the previous section, the damage to the glycogenolytic enzymes is still more marked. After daily administration of ^{60}Co to rabbits for 2 months in a dose of 65 μc/kg weight phosphorylase activity falls to 14 per cent and amylase to 56 per cent (cf. Table 1). Smaller quantities of ^{60}Co given over a much longer period (12.5 μc/kg daily for 21–22 months) have no effect on the course of hydrolytic breakdown of glycogen by water-soluble liver extracts, although phosphorylase activity falls to 59 per cent. A quantity of 1.25 µc/kg ^{60}Co daily, administered orally for a similar period, has no effect on the glycogenolytic enzymes.

The structure of glycogen isolated from the liver of rabbits which have received ^{60}Co differs from normal in that the side chains are shortened. In the sixth group glycogen breakdown by β-amylase comprises in all 6 per cent, in the second group 25 per cent. These changes cannot possibly be explained by a lessened demand for food by the experimental animals since firstly, their weight increased at the same rate as that of the controls and secondly, the glycogen content of the liver differed little from normal. Thus the effect of radiation is for the hepatal enzymic system, partially or wholly dose-dependent in the chronic experiment, to lose the capacity to form the glycogen side chains. A peculiarity of the effect of ^{60}Co is that amylase activity is suppressed to a far less degree than phosphorylase activity. In this connection the fact that acute irradiation produces a sharp decline of oxidizing phosphorylation acquires special importance (L. V. Mytareva). Incidentally, in alloxan diabetes the converse phenomenon is observed: significantly greater depression of amylase activity than of phosphorylase (A. N. Petrova). This is a definite indication that the depression of the glycogenolytic hepatal enzymes during chronic ^{60}Co administration is not connected with injury to the pancreas.

The suppression of the enzyme systems which catalyse glycogen conversion must unavoidably lead to the impairment of the sugar-fixing function of the liver. The study of sugar curves confirms this conclusion: at the 21st–22nd month of ^{60}Co administration they have a clearly pronounced hyperglycemic character (cf. Fig. 1). Furthermore, the content of reducing agents in the blood of rabbits of the first and second groups (which received 1.25 and 12.5 µc/kg daily for 21–23 months) was somewhat increased.

A similar type of hyperglycemia develops not immediately but only in the concluding period of intoxication. As indicated above, study of sugar curves after loading with glucose was begun from the 15th month of intoxication. For 15–16 months the curves have a clearly expressed hypoglycemic character. At the 18th month they are more or less normal and only later, at the 21st–23rd months, does the sugar-fixing function of the liver become disturbed, so that it is then unable to overcome artificially produced hyperglycemia as rapidly as is normal.

In examining the chronic experiments with oral administration of ^{60}Co the effect of the element cobalt on the liver should be taken into account. It is known that cobalt chloride in a single dose of 3 mg, or in repeated doses of 3 mg per day for 18 days, produces significant increase of the glycogen content of the liver (Gabe and Guillet). 50 mg doses of this salt after 1½–2 hr raise the blood sugar level by 60 mg per cent (Volk et al.). In the first of the mentioned works the changes observed are explained by the writers as the selective toxic effect of cobalt on the A cells in the islets of Langerhans, in the second as the extrapancreatic toxic effect of cobalt on the liver. However, it must be said that in our experiments the stable cobalt doses were clearly insufficient to exert any toxic effect on carbohydrate metabolism. In the animals which received the larger stable cobalt dose both the activity of hepatal enzymes and the content of reducing agents in the blood after oral administration of glucose remained at the same levels as in the controls. Hyperglycemia after powerful γ-ray doses has been observed by a number of writers (R. Ya. Keilina; Kay et al.).

Thus, the changes in carbohydrate metabolism observed by us in the chronic experiment are attributable only to the effect of ^{60}Co. Comparing the results in the literature with our own, it would seem that this effect is connected chiefly with damage to the hepatal enzymic systems.

In our investigations on the fractional compositon of the serous proteins during chronic ^{60}Co administration (E. D. Grishchenko) it was said that in some respects the chronic effect of ionizing radiation is similar to acute radiation injury. Data drawn from the literature incline us to a similar conclusion with respect to carbohydrate metabolism. According to Soldatenkov et al. in the first day after irradiation from a betatron of 20 MeV the blood sugar content declines by 20–30 mg per cent by comparison with the initial values but on the 2nd–3rd day increases and hyperglycemia develops.

As has already been pointed out, in our experiments the hypoglycemic character of the sugar curves for 16–18 months is replaced by a hyperglycemic reaction with administration of glucose. It is possible that it is the differing reactions of the body and the different radiation doses which explain the significant disparity in the results of a number of writers.

CONCLUSIONS

1. During chronic oral administration of ^{60}Co to rabbits in a dose of 12.5 and 1.25 µc/kg per day the blood sugar level is little changed, exhibiting only a tendency to rise towards the end of the experimental period of 21–23 months.
2. At the 15th–16th month after loading with glucose the sugar curves have a clearly hypoglycemic character. At the 18th month they become normal but at the 21st–23rd month significant hyperglycemia develops.

3. Hyperglycemia results from direct damage to the enzymic systems of the liver. In contrast to diabetes (according to A. N. Petrova) phosphorylase activity is primarily affected, whereas amylase is harmed much less by radiation energy.
4. The glycogen content of the liver differed little from the control in all the experiments.
5. Glycogen structure is significantly modified: in the rabbits subjected to 65 μc/kg ^{60}Co it is almost completely divested of side chains (breakdown by β-amylase is 6 per cent); in the rabbits receiving 12.5 μc/kg ^{60}Co the side chains are shortened by half (breakdown by β-amylase is 25 per cent); in the rabbits receiving 1.25 μc/kg ^{60}Co the glycogen side chains are of normal length (glycogen breakdown by β-amylase is 45 per cent; in the control 47 per cent).

REFERENCES

BUNYATYAN G. KH., *Proceedings of the All-Union Scientific-Technical Conference on the Uses of Radioactive and Stable Isotopes and Radiation in the National Agriculture and Science*. (Tezisy dokladov na Vsesoyuznoi nauchno-tekhnicheskoi konferentsii po primeneniyu radioaktivnykh i stabil'nykh izotopov i izluchenii v narodnom khozyaistve i nauke.) p. 130, Medgiz (1957).

DENSON J. R., GRAY E. J., GRAY J. L., HERBERT E. J., TEW J. T. and JENSEN H., *Proc. Soc. Exper. Biol. Med.*, No. 82, 707 (1953).

EPSHTEIN S. F., *Proceedings of the All-Union Scientific-Technical Conference on the Use of Radioactive and Stable Isotopes and Radiation in the National Agriculture an Science*, p. 49, Medgiz (1957).

FEDOTOV V. P., *Proceedings of the All-Union Scientific-Technical Conference on the Uses of Radioactive and Stable Isotopes and Radiation in the National Agriculture and Science*, p. 129, Medgiz (1957).

FISCHEL E., *Schweiz. med. Wrsch.*, No. 71, 764 (1941).

GABE M. and GUILLET G., *Compt. rend. Soc. Biol.*, No. 149, 319 (1955).

GRAYEVSKAYA B. M., KEILINA R. YA. and MANOILOVA S. YE., *Vest. rentgenol. i radiol.* **6**, 22 (1953).

GRAYEVSKAYA B. M. and KEILINA R. YA., *Problems of Radiobiology*. (Voprosy radiobiologii.) Leningrad, p. 352 (1956).

GUSEV N. G., *A Reference Book to Radioactivity and Protection*. (Spravochnik po radioaktivnym izlucheniyam i zashchite.) Medgiz (1956).

IVANOV I. I., BALABUKHA V. S., ROMANTSEV YE. F. and FEDOROVA T. A., *Metabolism in Radiation Sickness*. (Obmen veshchestv pri luchevoi bolezni.) Medgiz (1956).

KAY R. E. and ENTENMAN C., *Proc. Soc. Exper. Biol. Med.*, No. 91, 143, (1956).

KAVETSKII R. YE., STOLYAROVA L. B., NIKITENKO R. D. and AMDURSKAYA N. M., *Proceedings of the All-Union Scientific-Technical Conference on the Uses of Radioactive and Stable Isotopes and Radiation in the National Agriculture and Science*, p. 125, Medgiz (1957).

KEILINA R. YA., *Problems of Radiology*. (Voprosy radiologii.) p. 347, Leningrad (1956).

KURLYANDSKAYA E. B. *et al.*, *Proceedings of the All-Union Scientific-Technical Conference on the Uses of Radioactive and Stable Isotopes and Radiation in the National Agriculture and Science*, p. 49, Medgiz (1957).

Lelievre P., *Compt. rend. Soc. Biol.*, No. 149, 1296 (1955).
Levy B. and Rugh R., *Prac. Soc. Biol. Med.*, No. 82, 223 (1953).
Louran M., *Compt. rend. Acad. Sci.*, No. 236, 422 (1953).
Louran M. and Lartique O., *Experimentia*, No. 232, 1144 (1951).
Mytareva L. V., *Med. radiol.* **1,** No. 1, 35 (1956).
Petrova A. N., *Biokhimiya*, No. 20, 718 (1955).
Ross M. and Ely J. O., *J. Cell. Comp. Physiol.* **37,** 163 (1951).
Volk B. W., Lazarus S. S. and Goldner M. G., *Proc. Soc. Exper. Biol. Med.*, No. 82, 406 (1953).

CHANGES IN CAPILLARY PERMEABILITY OF EYES AND SKIN OF RABBITS DURING CHRONIC INTERNAL ADMINISTRATION OF ^{60}Co

A. A. Rubanovskaya

One of the responses of the body to exposure of ionizing radiation is a variation in capillary permeability. An increase in the permeability of the blood vessels is one of the symptoms of the hemorrhagic syndrome which develops after acute radiation injury (Cronkite, 1947, 1950; Hempelmann, Lisco and Hoffman, 1954; *et al.*).

There are in the literature many experimental results and clinical observations concerning the permeability of the blood vessels of the skin and organs after X-irradiation. These results were obtained after a single general or local irradiation in most cases of large dosage.

Some writers have observed experimentally a sharp increase in capillary permeability after X-irradiation (B. N. Mogil'nitskii, 1949; P. N. Kiselev, 1950; McCutcheon, 1952; *et al.*), others—a decline.

This disagreement can be explained by the fact that these writers used different radiation doses, different methods of investigating vascular permeability and had different objectives. The observation period was in most cases short.

Clinical investigation has been carried out on patients undergoing X-ray therapy for malignant growths (Veksler, 1955). In most patients impairment of vascular permeability was observed after irradiation but the character of the changes varied: in some permeability increased, in others it declined.

In a few works the course of changes in vascular permeability over long and short periods following a single irradiation is examined (N. I. Arlashchenko, 1956; P. N. Kiselev, 1953; S. I. Itkin, 1940). The phasic character of changes was elucidated; after an initial increase in permeability a phase of apparent normalization occurs which, according to dose, makes way for a phase of decline or terminal increase of permeability.

Almost no work has been done on vascular permeability during chronic internal administration of small doses of ionizing radiation. The investigation of changes thus produced and their connection with disturbances of other systems and organs is of practical and theoretical interest. It has material significance in any explanation of the pathogenesis of radiation injury and in the detection of early symptoms of chronic radiation sickness.

The subject of the present work concerns the capillary permeability of the eyes and skin during chronic oral administration of ^{60}Co.

The experimental animals were 13 rabbits receiving 12.5 μc/kg weight ^{60}Co daily for 19½ months.

Radioactive cobalt is an isotope which becomes diffusely distributed in the body and accumulates primarily in the parenchymatous organs. In oral administration to rabbits from 13 to 30 per cent of the daily dose is absorbed. With prolonged daily intake by the blood and organs a more or less constant ^{60}Co content is established. Thus, all the organs and tissue of the animal are subjected to continuous irradiation.

Ten rabbits served as a control: 5 were given a solution of $CoCl_2$ containing an amount of stable cobalt corresponding to the content by weight in the ^{60}Co solution, while the other 5 were kept as a pure control group.

The permeability of the hemato-ophthalmic barrier and the skin were studied as guides to the general condition of vascular permeability. According to the literature the capillary permeability of the eye reflects to a known degree the general state of capillary permeability throughout the body (Amsler and Huber, 1949; N. I. Arlashchenko, 1956; A. V. Lebedinskii, 1956).

Two tests were used for investigating capillary permeability of the eye: permeability to fluorescein and the protein content of the aqueous humour of the anterior chamber. Normally the capillaries of the eye are scarcely permeable to protein. The protein content of the aqueous humour is negligible compared with its concentration in the plasma. However, under conditions which modify the normal permeability of the blood vessels of the eye significant penetration of protein from the plasma into the aqueous humour occurs (O. A. Romanova-Bokhon, 1937; Yu. A. Petrovich and E. P. Dmitriyeva, 1955; Wesselkin, 1929).

VASCULAR PERMEABILITY OF THE EYE TO FLUORESCEIN

A 5 per cent solution of fluorescein was injected intravenously in an amount of 20 mg/kg weight. Half-an-hour after injection the anterior chamber of the eye was punctured and 0.2 ml. of aqueous humour withdrawn. At the same time blood was taken from the marginal auricular vein for determination of fluorescein content in the plasma.

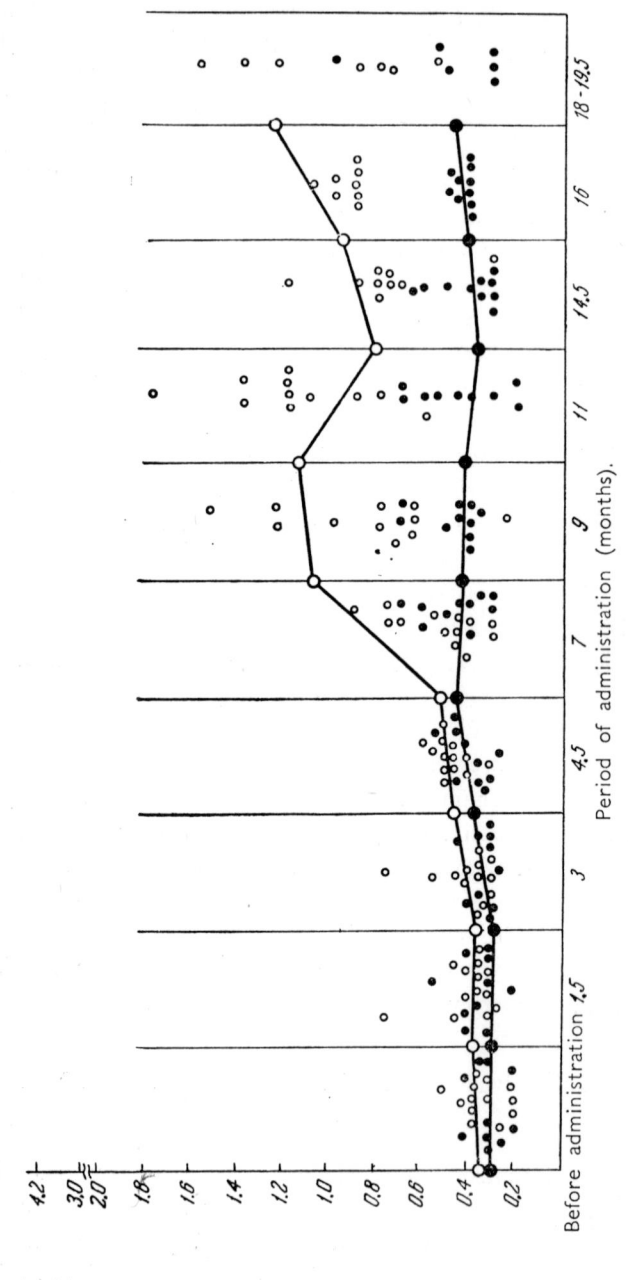

FIG. 1. Fluorescein content of the aqueous humour of the anterior chamber of rabbits at different periods of ^{60}Co administration (γ/ml.) ●——● average values for controls; ○——○ average values for experimental rabbits. ● control rabbits; ○ experimental rabbits;

The aqueous humour and plasma were transferred to thinwalled tubes of 0.6 cm diameter. Fluorescein content was determined by comparison in ultra-violet light with a previously prepared scale of standard fluorescein solutions. The tests were made in a darkened room specially equipped for luminescent analysis with a stationary quartz lamp with a Wood filter.

After determination of the quantity of fluorescein present, 0.2 ml. 20 per cent trichloracetic acid was added to the aqueous humour to precipitate the proteins. Quantitative measurement of protein nitrogen was carried out with Nessler's reagent and a photoelectric colorimeter.

Preliminary (prior to ^{60}Co administration) determination of the permeability of the hemato-ophthalmic barrier enabled us to select rabbits in which this permeability varied within fairly narrow limits. The fluorescein concentration 30 min after intravenous injection in the aqueous humour of the rabbits chosen for the experiments varied from 0.2 to 0.42 γ per 1 ml. Capillary permeability of the eye was examined before ^{60}Co administration and at different intervals for 19½ months from commencement of intoxication.

Figure 1 shows results of investigations on vascular permeability of the eye to fluorescein at various intervals from the commencement of ^{60}Co administration.

It can be seen that up to 7–9 months of administration the penetration of fluorescein in the aqueous humour of the anterior chamber in the majority of the experimental rabbits remains within the same limits as in the control rabbits. Only in individual experimental animals is some increase in fluorescein content in the aqueous humour observed at 3–4½ months. At 7–9 months penetration of fluorescein increases in the majority of the experimental rabbits. At 11 months fluorescein content in almost all the experimental animals is greater than at the beginning of the experiment and than in the controls. At all subsequent periods fluorescein concentration was greater in the experimental animals than in the controls.

In all the control rabbits, both those receiving stable cobalt and the pure controls, only small variations in fluorescein penetration with a slight tendency to increase were observed throughout the experimental period.

The tendencies described above were also observed when the fluorescein content of the aqueous humour of the anterior chamber was compared with its concentration in the plasma (Fig. 2).

Thus, it was found that capillary permeability of the eye to fluorescein in the majority of the rabbits was impaired only after 7–9 months of daily oral administration of ^{60}Co in the doses indicated above. Later, after 14½–16 months, permeability declines somewhat increasing again after

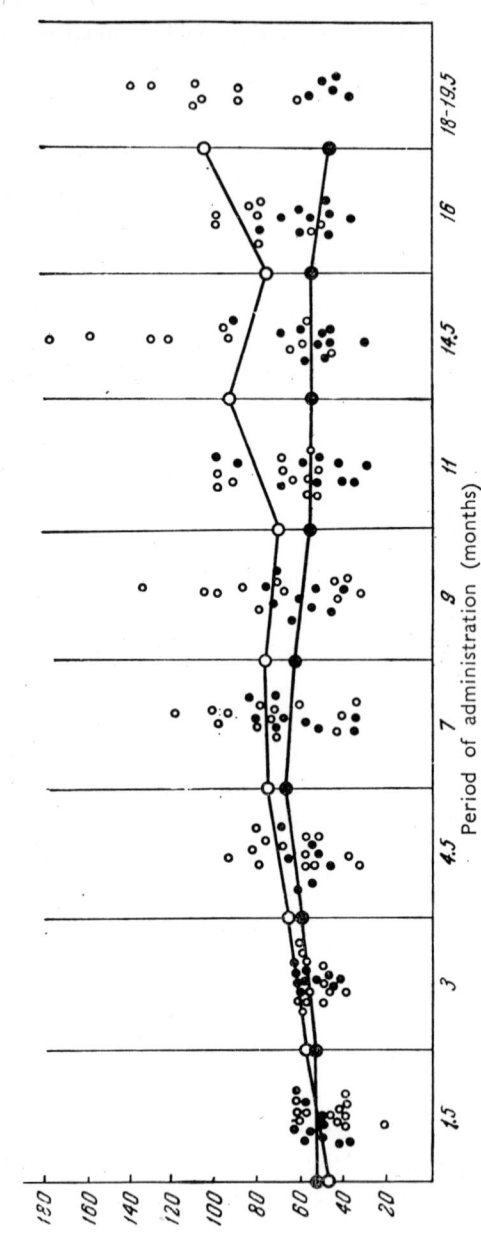

Fig. 2. Fluorescein content of the aqueous humour of the anterior chamber of rabbits at different periods of ^{60}Co administration (percentage of the blood plasma content). ●—● control rabbits; ○—○ experimental rabbits; ●—● average values for controls; ○—○ average values for experimental rabbits.

18–19½ months and remaining high by comparison with the controls. The intervening decline in permeability was not observed in some animals.

THE PROTEIN CONTENT OF THE AQUEOUS HUMOUR OF THE ANTERIOR CHAMBER

The protein content of the aqueous humour of the anterior chamber was subject to fairly significant individual variation. The limits of physiological variation of protein content in the aqueous humour of the anterior chamber in rabbits are, according to various writers, from 19 to 72 mg per cent (Yu. A. Petrovich and E. P. Dmitriyeva, 1955).

One-and-a-half months after commencement of ^{60}Co administration the protein content of the aqueous humour of control and experimental rabbits varied within similar limits (from 22 to 52 mg per cent) and thus did not exceed normal limits. Throughout the observation period in almost all the control rabbits protein content remained within normal limits. In the experimental rabbits up to 7–9 months of intoxication the protein content changed little; at 7–9 months a marked increase going beyond normal limits was observed.

Subsequently, the protein content in the experimental rabbits remained at a higher level than in the controls. A particularly sharp divergence was observed at 18–19½ months. In some of the experimental rabbits which survived to this time the amount of protein in the aqueous humour was 90–140 mg per cent, while the equivalent figure for the controls was 37–56 mg per cent. No consistent movements in protein content were observed in 3 of the experimental rabbits throughout the observation period (Fig. 3).

Thus, the changes in vascular permeability of the eye to plasma proteins were less pronounced than to fluorescein. This is presumably because the fluorescein dose used both free fluorescein and fluorescein fixed to the plasma proteins penetrating into the anterior chamber (I. A. Oivin and V. I. Oivin, 1950). Apart from this the large size of the protein molecule is significant.

An increase of filtration of plasma proteins through the capillary walls of the eye is evidence of more profound impairment of permeability. A sharp increase of protein concentration in the aqueous humour has been observed in derangement of the neuro-regulatory processes and trophical system of eye tissue produced by extirpation of the cervical sympathetic ganglion, neurotomy of the trigeminal nerve, stimulation of the appropriate section of the cerebral cortex, and so on (O. A. Romanova-Bokhon, 1937; Yu. A. Petrovich, and E. P. Dmitriyeva, 1955; Wesselkin, 1929; *et al.*).

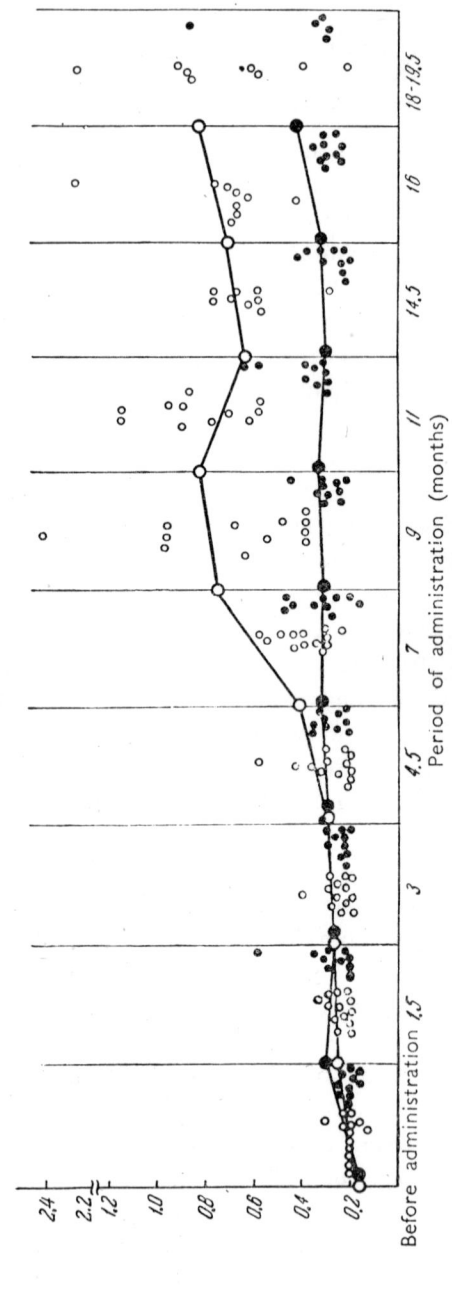

Fig. 3. Protein content of the aqueous humour of the anterior chamber of rabbits at different periods of ^{60}Co administration (mg%). ● control rabbits; ●—● average values for controls; ○ experimental rabbits; ○—○ average values for experimental rabbits.

It is clear that the effect of the chronic internal irradiation of our experiments on vascular permeability is less severe than that of the above indicated stimulants.

PERMEABILITY OF THE SKIN

A skin trypan test was used for study of cutaneous permeability. The method of carrying out this test was as follows. The fur was removed from an assigned area of the abdomen. A day later 2 subcutaneous injections of 0.2 ml. 1 per cent trypan blue were made, one on each side of a line bisecting this area. Immediately after injection, and again 24 hr later the circumference of the stain was measured and the area calculated by the ellipse formula. The ratio of the mean area of staining 24 hr after injection to the mean area immediately after injection was taken as an index of skin permeability. Skin permeability was determined at the same intervals as was the permeability of the hemo-ophthalmic barrier (Fig. 4).

The results obtained are presented in Fig. 4. It can be seen that up to 9 months of administration skin permeability to trypan blue in the control and experimental rabbits varied approximately within the same limits.

Some of the increase in skin permeability observed in both groups at 4½ months is possibly due to seasonal effects (mid-August). At 9–11 months a tendency for skin permeability to increase was observed in the experimental rabbits. At this period in most experimental rabbits, (9 of 11) skin permeability was somewhat higher than in the controls. This tendency, although less pronounced, was still evident after 14½ months. At 16 and 19½ months the skin permeability of the experimental rabbits no longer differed from that of the controls.

Thus, throughout 19½ months of daily administration of 12.5 μc/kg ^{60}Co the skin permeability of rabbits undergoes small variations similar in character to those concerning the vascular permeability of the eye. The changes in skin permeability, however, occur a little later and are much less pronounced.

The occurrence of changes in skin permeability, although only slight, together with the changes which take place in the vascular permeability of the eye lead to the conclusion that chronic ^{60}Co administration results in a general impairment of vascular and tissue permeability.

The degree of stain diffusion in the skin in the trypan test characterizes the permeability of the skin capillaries and connective tissue, chiefly its intercellular substance. The smallness of changes in skin permeability is presumably connected with the lower sensitivity of the connective tissue to ionizing radiation.

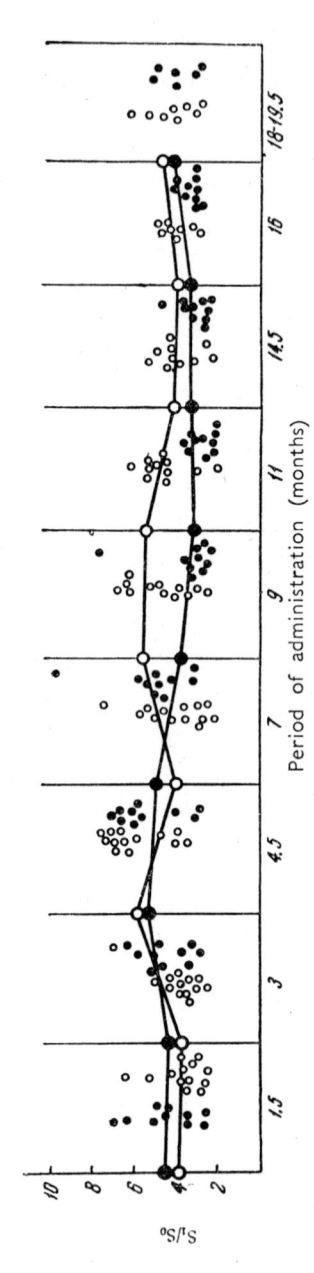

FIG. 4. Skin permeability of rabbits at different periods of ^{60}Co administration. S_1/S_0—ratio of the stain area one day after injection to the stain area immediately after injection. ● control rabbits; ○ experimental rabbits; ●—● average values for controls; ○—○ average values for experimental rabbits.

DISCUSSION

The results obtained have shown that small doses of ionizing radiation impair capillary permeability only with rather prolonged chronic administration. The impairment of vascular permeability is one of the later manifestations of chronic radiation sickness. Changes in the peripheral blood and in some sorts of protein metabolism occurred much earlier in chronic ^{60}Co administration than did changes in vascular permeability.

In view of the mildness of these changes it may be supposed that these impairments have a functional character and are not accompanied by gross morphological changes in the vascular walls.

In comparing changes in vascular permeability with the peripheral blood picture at various periods of ^{60}Co intoxication it is noticeable that no consistent changes of thrombocyte number were observed in the peripheral blood throughout the entire experimental period (N. L. Beloborodova). Peripheral blood changes were expressed chiefly in a fall of the leukocyte number due to a direct decline of the absolute lymphocyte number, which began from the first month of administration.

Thus, variation in vascular permeability in chronic radiation sickness was observed although the thrombocyte content of the peripheral blood was normal. This to some degree confirms the results of writers who have shown that at a certain stage of radiation sickness changes in vascular permeability and the blood coagulation system may not coincide (Cronkite, 1947; A. S. Petrova, 1956; *et al.*).

CONCLUSIONS

1. The permeability of the eye capillaries to fluorescein and protein is impaired only after 7–9 months of daily administration of 12.5 μc/kg ^{60}Co.
2. A pronounced tendency for skin permeability to increase is detected only after 9–11 months of chronic internal ^{60}Co irradiation.
3. The impairment of vascular permeability is one of the later manifestations of chronic radiation sickness produced by internal administration of ^{60}Co.
4. Changes in vascular permeability under conditions of chronic internal irradiation by ^{60}Co are slight and presumably consist in functional disturbances.

REFERENCES

ARLASHCHENKO N. I., *Med. radiol.* **3** (1956).

AMSLER M. and HUBER A., *Arch. f. Ophthalmologie* **6,** 149 (1949).

CZONKITE E. P. The Hemorrhagic Syndrome of Acute Ionizing Radiation Illness Produced in Goats and Swine by Exposure to the Atomic Bomb at Bikini, 1946, *Blood (J. Hematol.)* **5,** 1 (1950).

CRONKITE E. P., *Amer. J. Path.* **23**, 891 (1947).
GEMPEL'MAN L., LISKO G. and GORMAN D., *The Acute Radiation Syndrome.* (Ostryi luchevoi sindrom.) (1954).
ITKIN S. I., *Byull. eksper. biol.*, No. 10, 4, (1940).
KISELEV P. N., *The Effect of X-rays on Permeability and the Barrier Functions of the Body Tissues.* (Vliyaniye rentgenovykh luchei na pronitsayemost' i bar'yernye funktsii tkanei organizma.) Dissertation (1950).
KISELEV P. N., *Vest. rentgenol. i radiol.* **5** (1953).
LEBEDINSKII A. V., *Med. radiol.* **2** (1956).
MCCUTCHEON M., *J. Cell. Comp. Physiol.* **39** (1952).
MOGIL'NITSKII B. N., *The Increase of Vascular Permeability after X-Irradiation.* (Povysheniye sosudistoi pronitsayemosti pod vliyaniyem rentgenovykh luchei.) Proceedings of the Scientific Institute of Roentgenology and Radiology (1949).
OIVIN I. A. and OIVIN V. I., *Byull. eksper. biol. i med.* **29**, 5 (1950).
PETROVA A. S., *Med. radiol.* **4** (1956).
PETROVICH YU. A. and DMITRIYEVA YE. P., *Ophthal. zhur.* **3** (1955).
ROMANOVA-BOKHON O. A., *Vest. ophthal.* **2**, 10 (1937).
VEKSLER YA. I., *Voyenno-med. zhur.* **9** (1955).
WESSELKIN W., *Zschr. f. d. ges. exp. Mediz.* **66** (1929).

ELECTROCARDIOGRAPHIC INVESTIGATIONS OF RABBITS DURING PROLONGED INTERNAL ADMINISTRATION OF SMALL DOSES OF STABLE AND RADIOACTIVE COBALT

A. O. SAITANOV

THERE is in the literature little work on the peculiarities of action of small doses of radioactive substances during prolonged internal administration (inhalation, oral administration or cutaneous injection), despite the practical and theoretical significance of the problem. Certain writers (A. P. Egorov, V. A. Sanotskii *et al.*) consider that radioactive substances have more pronounced effects when administered internally than with external application. Unfortunately, no tissue doses are given in these works. Radioactive substances which have a long half life and so act on the tissue for a long period and produce the most serious disturbances present a special danger.

The damage done to individual organs depends on the distribution and properties of the radioactive substances administered and on the specific characteristics of the tissue. The method of administration, rate of excretion, physical and chemical state of the substance and the initial condition of the animal all have a defined significance.

We have not found any reports in the literature concerned with a systematic study of the heart by electrocardiographic methods during chronic administration of small doses of ^{60}Co. Such reports as there are deal mainly with heart changes after external irradiation with large and medium doses.

It was established soon after the discovery of radioactivity that radon baths containing hundreds of Roentgen units of activity have a beneficial effect on a series of diseases, particularly of the cardio-vascular system. In the opinion of most writers (K. M. Bykov, A. N. Arzhilas, F. I. Midtsev *et al.*, 1939) radon produces a change in vascular tone. At the moment of vasoconstriction the flow of blood to the heart and other organs increases, so improving their function (V. K. Modestov and A. Valedinskii, 1939).

A. L. Myasnikov (1939) considers that radioactive substances in small doses acting on the heart affect the neuro muscular apparatus and metabolic activity, as a result of which the contractile function of the myocardium improves. The body's reaction changes with increase of dosage. Large doses produce pathological changes of a functional and morphological character (M. I. Karlin and B. N. Mogil'nitskii, 1933, *et al.*).

Yu. I. Arkusskii (1955) has studied the effect of γ-rays on cardiac activity by irradiation of the head of dogs and rabbits with ^{60}Co. On the scalp the radiation dose comprised 1000 r, at 50 r per min. Irradiation was repeated (1–3 times) in a series of cases. Each time the dose was 1000 r. Electrocardiograms were taken several times before irradiation as a control, and afterwards, immediately after removal of the radioactive cobalt and daily for the following week, then not less than twice a week. Thirty to sixty minutes after irradiation of 1000 r significant changes in the electrocardiogram were observed in the form of a frequency decrease and a heightening of the T_{I-II} waves. The writer connects these changes with the stimulation of the retarding fibres of the efferent nerves of the heart.

Subsequently, large-scale wave deformation occurred; the T_I wave declined and became biphasic, and after the second irradiation the negative wave $T_{I-II-III}$ appeared. These changes were consolidated after a day and maintained for 1–2 months.

In studying the electrocardiogram of patients submitted to X-irradiation of the head and skin in a total fractional dose of 5000, 6000 and 10,000 r the levelling down and inversion of the T waves and the appearance of ventricular extrasystoles were observed. The writer ascribes the latter to the myocardial dystrophy which results from irradiation. Yu. I. Arkusskii considers that the heart can be affected not only by the direct irradiation of that region but also by irradiation of the skin of remote parts of the body and head. He explains these changes as a reflex effect on the heart and also as the effect of ionizing radiation on the body cells.

F. A. Fanardzhyan, K. A. Kyandaryan and co-workers (1954) confirmed Yu. I. Arkusskii's results in an experiment on 10 rabbits and also by observations on 10 patients who had been submitted to X-irradiation (for various growths in the region of the head). The total X-ray dose varied between 5000 and 10,000 r.

Fulton *et al.* (1954) have found in golden hamsters, after a total X-ray dose of 1000 r, electrocardiographic changes in the form of a decline of the P and T waves, deformation of the $QRST$ complex and inversion of the T wave. These electrocardiographic changes were accompanied by the impairment of the K and Na content of the blood serum.

Yu. I. Arkusskii and K. T. Volkova (1938) have shown in work on 30 rabbits that irradiation of the heart region even with small X-ray doses and with radium and radon produces a change in cardiac activity. Bradycardia was observed (in one case extrasystolism) and wave deformation, inversion of the T wave and so on, was seen on the electrocardiogram. These changes arose immediately after irradiation and lasted for 10–12 days. The writers attribute these effects to metabolic disturbances in the cardiac muscle. No lesions were found in microscopic examination of the heart of these rabbits.

Yu. I. Arkusskii and M. M. Mints (1937) detected in patients with malignant growths of the chest undergoing X-ray therapy electrocardiographic changes in the form of a voltage decline and deformation of the wave complex, especially of the T wave. The writers connect these changes, as in the previous work, with dystrophic processes produced by irradiation.

T. E. Seletskaya (1954), during X-ray therapy of a similar group of patients, detected identical changes. Bedyurftig and Gryusner* have observed in a similar group electrocardiographic changes which endured throughout the period of X-irradiation.

Whitfeld and Kunkler (1957) have described in 4 patients the appearance of pronounced clinically asymptomatic electrocardiographic changes in radiotherapy of the neck and chest. These changes were maintained for 2 months after cessation of treatment.

M. N. Fateyeva, V. S. Klimov *et al.* (1956) indicate that under conditions of prolonged ionizing irradiation in industry probationary workers made many complaints concerning the cardio-vascular system; their electrocardiograms exhibited pronounced changes in frequency disturbance, retardation of conduction, wave changes and a large number of sinistralgrams.

A. V. Kozlova, K. M. Malenkova, E. V. Karibskaya and T. S. Seletskaya (1957), and also E. D. Semiglazova (1958), on the basis of clinical and roentgenokymographic investigation of almost 50 per cent of patients with different degrees of chronic radiation sickness, found changes in the cardio-vascular system. Electrocardiographic factors indicated primarily their dystrophic character. M. A. Kazakevich (1957) indicates similar changes concerning the heart disclosed by electrocardiographic examination of the chronic effect of radioactive light particles.

A. L. Morozov, E. A. Drogichina *et al.* have demonstrated a decrease in vascular tone, disturbances of vascular permeability and a change in the functions of the central nervous system and peripheral blood in people subjected to occupational ionizing radiation.

The analysis of the literature demonstrates the significant sensitivity of the heart to ionizing radiation as shown by clinical and electrocardio-

* Quoted by M. N. Pobedinskii: *Radiation Complications in X- and Radiotherapy.* (Luchevye oslozheniya pri rentgeno- i radioterapii.) Medgiz (1954).

graphic examination. A. V. Lebedinskii (1956) indicates that the cause of functional changes which arise in the cardio-vascular system after radiation injury consists in a disturbance of the neuro-endocrine mechanisms.

The results in the literature mentioned above concern the effect, both experimental and clinical, of external radiation on the cardio-vascular system. Reports of the effect on cardiac activity as demonstrated by electrocardiography of radioactive substances administered internally have been found in works by K. P. Markuze (1956) and E. I. Vasil'yeva (1957). K. P. Markuze, in an experiment on rabbits and rats undergoing prolonged intraperitoneal and subcutaneous injection of ^{32}P, in a dose of from 0.01 to 1–4 μc per 1 kg weight, detected deviations in the electrocardiograms with sharply pronounced changes in the animals' general condition. E. I. Vasil'yeva obtained similar results indicating pronounced changes in the electrocardiogram after intravenous, intramuscular and oral administration of ^{32}P.

No single point of view is expressed in the literature concerning the appearance of the initial changes in the electrocardiogram on exposure to radiation. A. V. Kozlova (1954–1957) considers that such changes are one of the early signs of radiation injury. N. A. Kurshakov (1954) asserts that only in the III dystrophic stage do clear changes appear in the electrocardiograms, indicating myocardial dystrophy. Most writers (Yu. I. Arkusskii, A. V. Lebedinskii, M. N. Livanov, Yu. M. Zaretskaya, F. A. Fanardzhyan *et al.*) consider that the impairment of the cardiovascular system is initially connected with changes of reflex activity on the part of the central nervous system. Other writers (M. I. Karlin, N. A. Shevchenko, V. Ch. Zairat'yants, etc.) point out the great sensitivity of the vessels and muscular tissue to penetrating radiation even in small doses.

It was thus thought important to stage an experiment in which the chronic effect of small doses of ^{60}Co on cardiac activity could be studied by electrocardiography. The precise physiological method of electrocardiography is able to disclose variations in the bioelectrical processes intimately bound up with the condition of the cardiac muscle.*

METHODS

Systematic electrocardiographic investigation was carried out on healthy young rabbits and lasted almost 2 years (22 months). The animals were divided into two groups: experimental and control and comprised 35 rabbits. The experimental group consisted of 18 rabbits and was in turn subdivided: the first subgroup (8 rabbits) received 1.25 μc/kg

---

* Assistant physician I. N. Golovshchikova took part in the present work.

[60]Co and the second 12.5 μc/kg [60]Co. Radioactive cobalt was administered orally each day from March 1955 to February 1957 (apart from rest days and holidays).

After equilibrium had been established this quantity of ^{60}Co created a mean body dose of γ-radiation equivalent to 0.24–1.16 r per day, and in the abdominal cavity 0.57–3.30 r per day (G. A. Abrunina).

At the same time the control group was subjected to electrocardiographic examination (18 animals). These animals were subdivided into three groups: the first (physiological control) consisted of 9 rabbits, the second, of 5 rabbits receiving 1.9 γ stable cobalt per 1 kg weight and the third, of 4 rabbits receiving 19 γ stable cobalt per 1 kg weight.

The electrocardiographic survey was carried out once every 5–6 weeks on an electrocardiograph ECP-4 with an energy of 1 mV = 2 cm. The electrocardiograms were taken at the same time each day from three standard limb leads and four thoracic leads with the animal on its back and after an interval of 5–7 min essential to calm the animal.

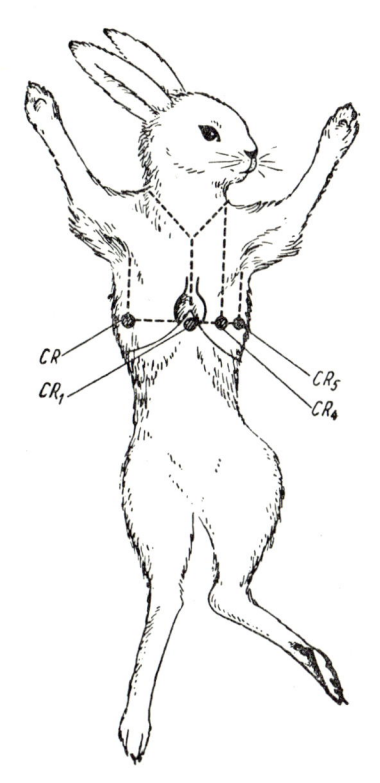

FIG. 1. Situation of points on the chest of rabbits from which the thoracic leads of the electrocardiogram were taken (described in the text).

Comparison has shown that there is no difference in the number of heart contractions whether the animal is on its front or its back. This has also been indicated by Massmann and Opitz (1954). Fine steel needles inserted under the skin (always in the same place) were used as electrodes. As it has been established that the bioelectric processes which take place in the heart are detected earlier and defined longer in the thoracic leads

(Wilson, Groedel, Yu. I. Arkusskii, K. P. Ivanov, N. A. Ginodman et al.) it was decided that the method of thoracic leads as used clinically should be applied with appropriate modifications.

The following points on the chest were used for the thoracic electrode (Fig. 1). The point CR on the right anterior midaxillary line and the point CR_5 on the left anterior midaxillary line are placed at the intersection with the horizontal line running parallel to the sterno-abdominal angle. The point CR_1 is found at the end of the sternum at the apex of the sterno-abdominal angle; the point CR_4, at the intersection of the line running midway between the points CR_1 and CR_5 to the left of the costal arch.

In all, more than 374 electrocardiograms were taken from the 7 leads (3 standard and 4 thoracic). Each rabbit was measured on average 8–10 times during the observation period.

THE ELECTROCARDIOGRAM OF THE CONTROL RABBITS

In total 156 electrocardiograms were taken. Comparison of the electrocardiograms of the physiological controls and those receiving 1.9 γ and 19 γ stable cobalt per kg weight showed that the electrocardiographic features characterizing the processes of automatism, excitation, conduction and contraction* were basically alike in all 3 subgroups (Table 1). The rhythm was sinus and was within 240–300 contractions per minute (in 6 rabbits sometimes up to 320–330 per min.). The average number was about 290 contractions per minute (cf. Table 1). The P wave was positive and only in a few cases was it low in the I and III leads. A small Q wave (up to 1 mm) was found in 4 rabbits in the standard I and thoracic CR_{4-5} leads.

The figures of wave and interval duration (cf. Table 1) were fairly constant in all the subgroups. Sometimes they changed somewhat within limits of ± 0.01–0.02 sec depending on frequency of heart beat. A low (up to 2 mm) R wave is noticed in 2 rabbits in the standard I, and in 4 rabbits in the thoracic CR_5 leads. A well pronounced S wave in the standard I lead was found in 8 rabbits, i.e. in almost half the control rabbits (Table 2).

Very little voltage variation, particularly of the R wave complex in the thoracic leads, was noticed in any of the rabbits. In a small number of rabbits (4) the S wave was well pronounced in the CR_4 lead. It can be assumed that the interrelation of the R and S waves in the standard and thoracic leads characterizes the direction of the electric axis in the rabbit heart. The electric axis in the majority (9 rabbits) was either longitudinal (in 4) or inclined to the right (in 5) (Table 3).

L. P. Peresad'ko (1953), observing the beneficial effect of ^{60}Co on the heart in rabbits, notes a preponderance of dextral or vertical type

---

* According to the data of the ventricular electric systole.

TABLE 1

Average figures of number of heart beats, conductivity and magnitude of the electric systole in control and experimental rabbits

Rabbit group	No. of rabbit	Range of variation of cardiac rhythm (per min)	Mean number of beats (per min)	Conductivity (seconds) P	PQ	QRS	Size of ventricular electric systole (seconds)
	Control groups						
Physiological control	12	240–300	285	0.04	0.06–0.07	0.03–0.04	0.14–0.15
	19	300	300	0.03–0.04	0.06	0.03	0.14
	23	260–320	300	0.03	0.06	0.03	0.14
	27	300	300	0.04	0.06–0.07	0.03	0.15
	32	250–300	270	0.03–0.04	0.07	0.03	0.15–0.14
	33	240–320	280	0.03–0.04	0.06–0.07	0.04–0.03	0.15–0.14
	34	240–280	260	0.04–0.03	0.07	0.03–0.04	0.15–0.14
	37	260–320	300	0.03	0.06	0.03	0.14
	39	300	300	0.03	0.05–0.08	0.03	0.14
Rabbits receiving 1.9 γ/kg stable cobalt	24	260–310	300	0.03	0.06	0.03	0.14–0.15
	25	230–240	240	0.04–0.03	0.07	0.03–0.04	0.15
	26	300–330	310	0.03	0.06	0.03	0.13
	28	240–330	300	0.03	0.06	0.03	0.13–0.15
	40a	270–300	290	0.04–0.03	0.06	0.03	0.13
Rabbits receiving 19 γ/kg stable cobalt	29	300	300	0.03	0.06	0.03	0.14
	30	300–320	310	0.03–0.04	0.06	0.03	0.13–0.14
	36	240–280	270	0.03	0.07	0.03	0.15
	35a	280–300	290	0.04	0.06–0.07	0.03	0.14
	Experimental group						
Rabbits receiving 1.25 μc/ ^{60}Co	11	240–260	250	0.03–0.04	0.07	0.03	0.14–0.16
	13	240–300	270	0.03	0.07	0.03	0.13–0.15
	14	250–300	280	0.03–0.04	0.06–0.07	0.03	0.14
	15	240–280	260	0.04	0.06–0.07	0.03	0.15
	18	260–300	290	0.03–0.04	0.06	0.03	0.14–0.15
	20	—	300	0.03	0.07	0.03	0.13–0.14
	21	260–300	285	0.03	0.06	0.03	0.15
	22	270–300	300	0.03	0.06	0.03	0.13–0.15
Rabbits receiving 12.5 μc/kg ^{60}Co	1	250–300	270	0.03	0.06	0.03	0.14–0.15
	2	260–270	250	0.04	0.06–0.07	0.04	0.15
	3	260–300	280	0.04	0.07	0.03	0.15
	5	240–300	285	0.03–0.04	0.06–0.07	0.03	0.13–0.15
	6	200–270	250	0.03–0.04	0.07	0.03	0.15
	10	240–300	270	0.04	0.07	0.03	0.15
	4a	260–400	300	0.04	0.07	0.03	0.14
	12a	200–300	240	0.04	0.06–0.07	0.03	0.15
	14a	–	300	0.03	0.06–0.07	0.03	0.14

TABLE 2

Changes in the size (millimetres) and form of the Q, R, S and T waves and the position of the S–T interval in control and experimental rabbits

Rabbit group	Rabbit sub-group	Changed P	Changed QRS	Observed Q_1CR_{4-5}	Observed R_1	Observed S_1	Slight interval inclination or decline in standard and thoracic leads	Slight T wave decrease or transition to biphase F in standard and thoracic leads	Return of T wave to initial state	Normal T wave	Remarks
Control (18 rabbits)	Physiological control	—	—	1	—	2	1	2 (decrease)	1 (No. 12)	6	
	1.9 γ/kg stable cobalt	—	—	2	1	3	—	1 (decrease)		5	
	19 γ/kg stable cobalt	—	—	1	1	3	1	—		4	
	Total	—	—	4	2	8	2	3	1	15	
Experimental (17 rabbits)	1.25 µc/kg ^{60}Co	1	1	4	4	1	3	7	3 (Nos. 11, 18, 22)	1 (No. 21)	In rabbit No. 4 the P wave was unchanged, in Nos. 11 and 22 ventricular electric alternation
	12.5 µc/kg ^{60}Co	2	1	4[1]	5	1	5	9	1 (No. 13)	1	$Q_{CR_{4-5}}$ observed
	Total	3	2	8	9	2	8	16	4	1	

TABLE 3

Deviation of the cardiac electric axis of rabbits of the control and experimental groups (summarized data)

Electric axis	Number of animals				Number of animals			total rabbits
	physio- logical control	stable cabalt		total rabbits	radioactive cobalt		
		1.9 γ/kg	1.9 γ/kg		1.25 μc/kg	1.25 μc/kg	
Normal	3	—	—	3	3 (in one transition to vertical)	4 (transition to the left in one)	7
Transitional	2	1	1	4	1 (with left transition)	1	2
Vertical	2	1	1	4	1	—	1
Right	1	2	2	5	—	1	1
Left	1	1	—	2	3 (with increase to the left in 2)	3 (transition to the left in one)	6
Total	9	5	4	18	8	9	17

electrocardiograms in healthy rabbits. Massmann and Opitz also often found a dextrogram in healthy rabbits.

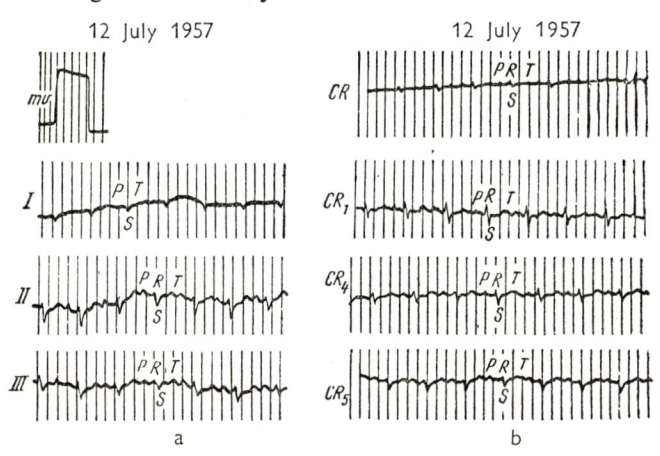

FIG. 2. Rabbit No. 12—physiological control. Observation period 15 months. a—the electrocardiogram in the standard and b—the thoracic leads. The $S-T$ interval in II III and CR_{4-5} slightly obliquely inclined; the T wave in I, II and III and CR_{1-4-5} positive.

The $S-T$ interval was isoelectric, sometimes in the thoracic leads slightly inclined obliquely downwards and in one case inclined downwards in the II and III leads (Fig. 2).

The *T* wave was always positive but in the standard I or *CR* leads, a low or levelled down *T* wave was frequently observed, sometimes even slightly biphasic. A biphasic *T* was never found in the two leads simultaneously.

Only in two rabbits of the physiological control (in No. 19 in III lead and in No. 23 in CR_4 lead) was a small decline of the *T* wave observed in one of the leads during the experimental period. The electric ventricular systole was within the limits 0.13–0.15 sec.

Impairment of excitation (extrasystolism) and conduction (blockage) was not observed in the control rabbits.

In the main, our results concerning the electrocardiogram of healthy rabbits were similar to those described in the literature (excepting rhythm which, in our rabbits, was of slightly higher frequency) (Massmann and Opitz, 1954).

As is seen from the results presented the electrocardiograms of rabbits of the physiological control did not materially differ from those of the rabbits receiving stable cobalt. According to the literature (L. P. Peresad'ko, 1953; R. Ya. Bernshtein, V. M. Lemesh and S. B. Grozhevskaya 1956; *et al.*) stable cobalt in small doses has a beneficial effect on the cardio-vascular system and hemopoiesis, being a microelement essential to normal activity.

THE ELECTROCARDIOGRAM OF THE EXPERIMENTAL RABBITS

Electrocardiographic examination was begun, both in the control and experimental groups, 6 months after the commencement of administration. By this time signs of radiation injury had already appeared, the earliest being observed in the group receiving 12.5 µc/kg ^{60}Co and concerning the blood system and protein metabolism.

Analysis of the electrocardiograms was carried out by comparing the results of each rabbit throughout the experimental period with the results obtained in the control group. More than 218 electrocardiograms were done in the experimental group.

Comparison of the electrocardiograms shows that in both experimental subgroups the rhythm was sinus within limits of from 240 to 300 contractions per minute, the average being about 277 per minute, which hardly differs from the results of the control group. In two rabbits (Nos. 11 and 22) which received the smaller ^{60}Co dose electric ventricular alternation of a temporary character with the appearance of a negative *T* wave and a convex *S–T* interval was registered (Fig. 3). The *P* wave was always positive, sometimes smoothed out in I lead and only in 3 cases towards the end of the observation period did it become high (twice as high by comparison with the initial value) and somewhat enlarged (up to 0.05 sec) in rabbit No. 11, receiving the small ^{60}Co dose, and in rabbits Nos. 3a and 4a receiving the large dose, which indicated a change in intra-atrial conductivity.

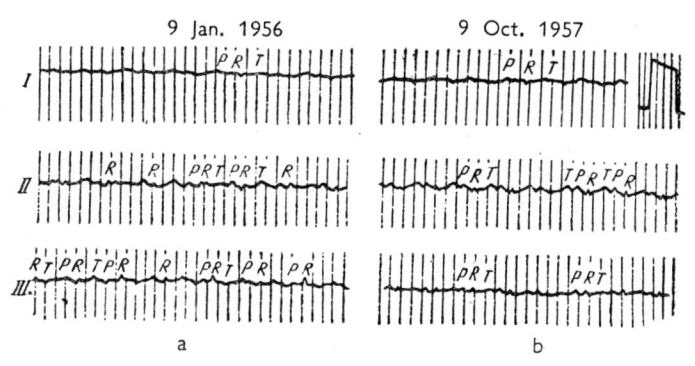

FIG. 3. Standard leads of the electrocardiogram. Rabbit No. 22 (1.25 μc/kg ^{60}Co). a—8 months after commencement of ^{60}Co administration. Ventricular electric alternation can be seen in the II and III leads; different size and form of the R wave and negative T_{III} wave. b—at the 18th month; no ventricular electric alternation.

A small, up to 1 mm, Q wave in standard I and II and CR_{4-5} leads was observed in 8 rabbits (4 rabbits of each subgroup), i.e. in almost half the experimental rabbits. Presumably this can be explained by the fact that in a large number of rabbits the cardiac electric axis was inclined to the left (L. I. Fogel'son).

The results concerning wave and interval duration were no different from those obtained with the control group varying also with rhythm frequency ±0.01–0.02 sec (cf. Table 1). On average the values were the same: for the P wave 0.03–0.04 sec, for the P–Q interval 0.06–0.07 sec, and for the QRS complex 0.03–0.04 sec.

As already mentioned, intraventricular conductivity was temporarily changed in 2 rabbits (Nos. 11 and 22) receiving the smaller ^{60}Co dose. Nine rabbits (i.e. more than half the experimental rabbits) displayed a small R wave in the standard I and CR_5 leads (4 rabbits receiving the smaller dose and 5 the larger). In rabbit No. 11 a sharp decline of the R wave in standard I and CR_{4-5} thoracic leads and the appearance of pronounced Q waves in these leads were noticed (Figs. 4 and 5).

The S wave in the standard I lead was observed only in 2 rabbits (one receiving the smaller and one the larger dose). In the majority of rabbits the ratio of the R and S waves was on the side of an enlargement of $R_1 (R_1 > S_1)$. A well pronounced S wave in the CR_4 thoracic lead was found more rarely than in the control and in the CR_5 lead, almost not at all.

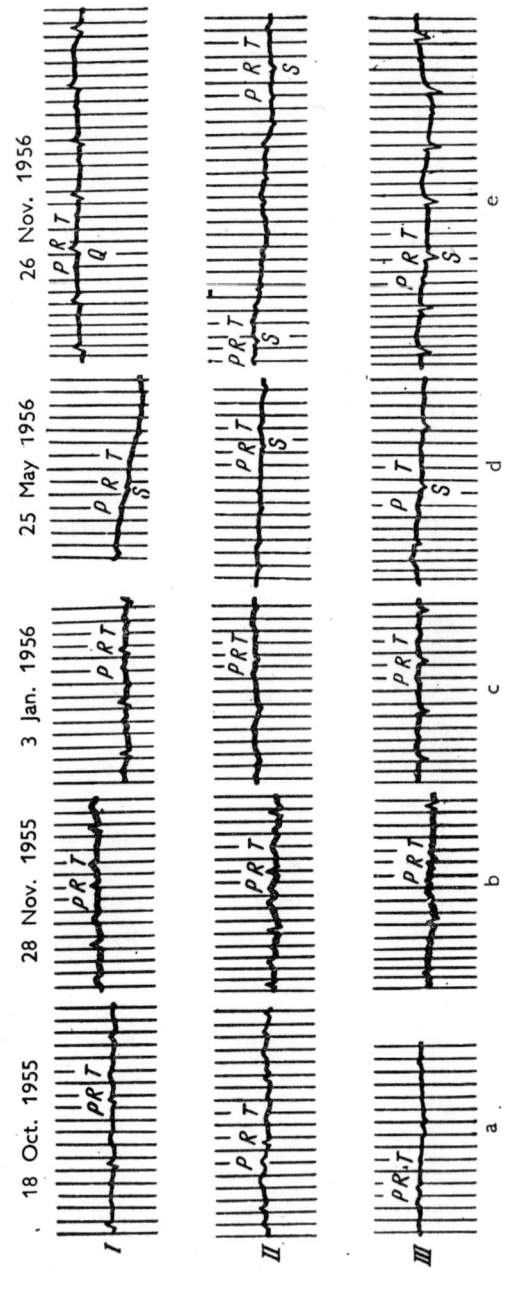

FIG. 4. Standard leads of the electrocardiogram. Rabbit No. 11(1.25 μc/kg ^{60}Co). a—6 months after commencement of administration of ^{60}Co the Q_I wave is small, T_I positive, electric axis has tendency to turn left; b—after 7 months a voltage increase of all waves is noticed, especially of the T wave; c—after 8 months the turning of the electric axis to the left has increased, the voltage declined; T_I has become slightly ±, T_{II} has smoothed out; d—after 13 months the R_I wave has declined; e—after 18 months a pronounced turn of the cardiac electric axis to the left. The T_I wave is biphasic(±), T_{II} low.

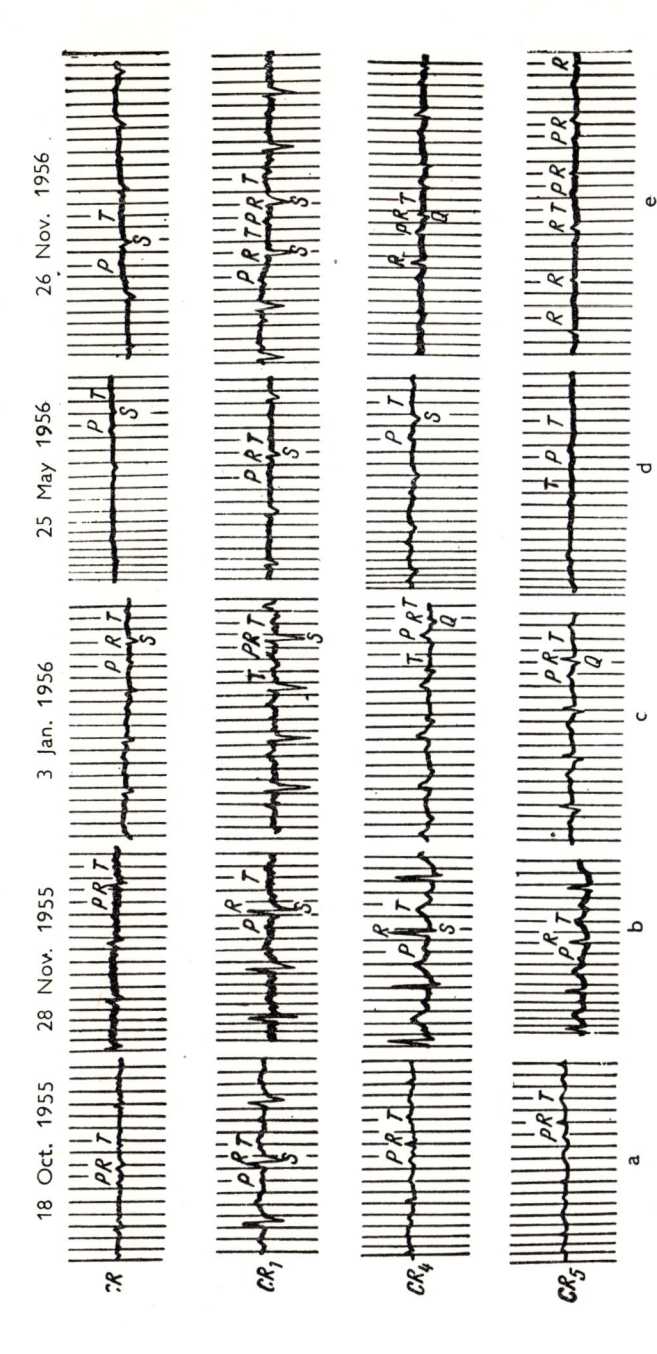

ELECTROCARDIOGRAPHIC INVESTIGATIONS OF RABBITS

FIG. 5. Electrocardiogram from thoracic leads. The same rabbit(No. 11). a—after 6 months T_{CR} low with other leads positive; b—after 7 months pronounced voltage increase is noticed (especially of T wave); c—after 8 months R_{CR_1} has declined; sharp decline of $R_{CR_{4-5}}$, P_{CR_4} and $Q_{CR_{4-5}}$ have become pronounced, $T_{CR_{1-4-5}}$ almost smoothed out; d—after 13 months voltage remained low; e—after 18 months ventricular electric alternation is noticed (in CR_{4-5} leads), R waves of different height, $T_{CR_{1-4-5}}$ smoothed out.

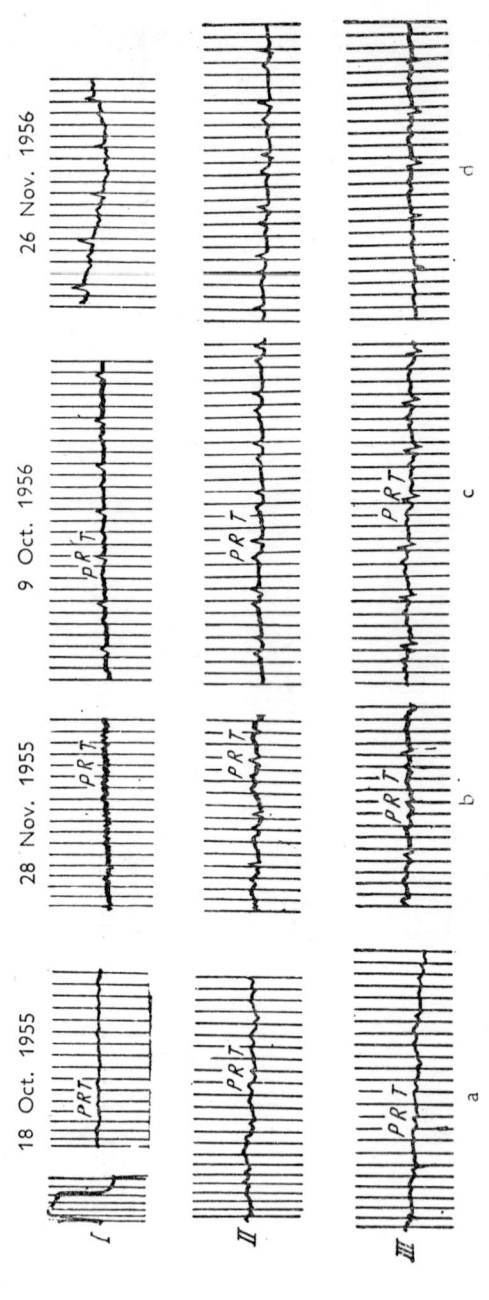

FIG. 6. Electrocardiogram from standard leads. Rabbit No. 15 (1.25 μc/kg). a—after 6 months no deviation in cardiac electric axis, T_I smoothed out, T_{II-III} positive; b—after 7 months slight voltage increase; c—after 18 months Q_{II} and sharp P_{II} appeared, T_{I-II} smoothed out, electric axis turned left; d—after 19 months leftward turn increased Q_{II} has appeared, T_I has become negative, T_{II} remained smoothed out and T_{III} positive.

In 7 rabbits the gradual turning of the electric axis was established, with a transition to a vertical and left deviation (Fig. 6, Table 3). This confirms the development of the sinistralgram in some of the rabbits undergoing prolonged irradiation.

The appearance of a leftward turn of the cardiac electric axis in irradiated rabbits has been reported by F. A. Fanardzhyan et al., and by Massmann and Opitz after ether and evipal narcosis.

M. N. Fateyeva, V. S. Klimov et al. have reported an increase in sinistralgrams in people who have long worked with radioactive substances in industrial conditions. Thus our results in this direction agree with those in the literature. A definite reason for this turning of the cardiac electric axis cannot be given on the basis of our material. Evidently the turning depends on the predominant change of the left ventricle because bigger changes in the electrocardiogram are observed in the left thoracic leads (Fig. 7).

In the experimental group of rabbits changes in wave height in the electrocardiogram bore a phasic character. At the 7th–9th months of ^{60}Co administration a pronounced enlargement (by more than twice of the voltage of all waves, especially of the P and T waves), was observed in most animals (18). The greatest increase was in the thoracic leads (cf. Fig. 7).

At the 18th–20th months, but in rabbit No. 11 at the 8th month, changes in the terminal part of the ventricular complex began to appear (third phase). In 7 rabbits of the first group and in 9 of the second group a tendency to voltage decline was noticed, predominantly of the T wave in the standard I and CR_{4-5} leads, more rarely in the standard II lead and still more rarely in the CR and CR_1 leads. In some cases (5 rabbits) the T wave became weakly biphase in the standard I and II and the left thoracic CR_{4-5} leads.

In the experimental group, as well as the change and transition to a biphase T wave, some change of direction of the S–T interval was observed. The latter became an upward convexity (mainly in the standard I or thoracic CR leads), obliquely inclined or slightly lowered (but not by more than 1 mm) below the isoelectric level.

Thus, in the rabbits of the experimental groups, changes in the terminal part of the ventricular complex were quite clearly detected. The ventricular electric systole, although remaining within the same limits as in the control animals, nevertheless approached the upper limit of the normal twice as often, and in one case exceeded it by 0.01 sec (rabbit No. 11).

No clear connection between changes in the terminal part of the ventricular complex and ^{60}Co dose was detected (Figs. 8 and 9).

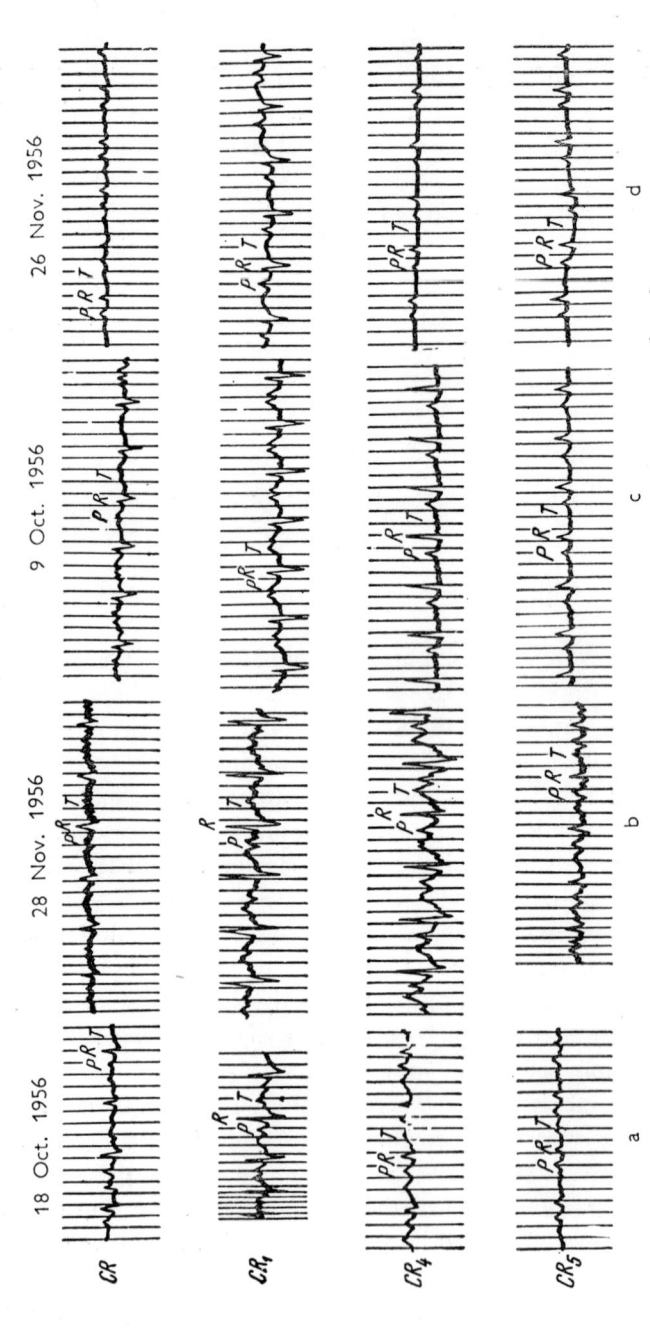

FIG. 7. Electrocardiogram from thoracic leads. The same rabbit (No. 15). a—after 6 months the T wave is positive in all leads; b—after 7 months pronounced voltage increase of P and $QRST$ complexes; c—after 18 months a sharp decline noticed—flattening of $T_{CR_{4-5}}$ waves; d—after 19 months the R_{CR_4} waves has also declined.

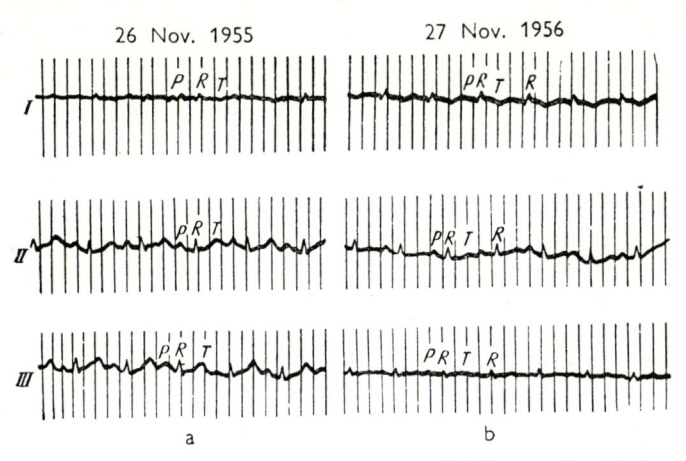

FIG. 8. Electrocardiogram from standard leads. Rabbit No. 4a (12.5 μc/kg ^{60}Co) a—after 8 months T_I low, slightly biphase ($\pm$). T_{II-III} positive, well pronounced; b—after 20 months T_I negative, T_{II-III} sharply declined, almost smoothed out.

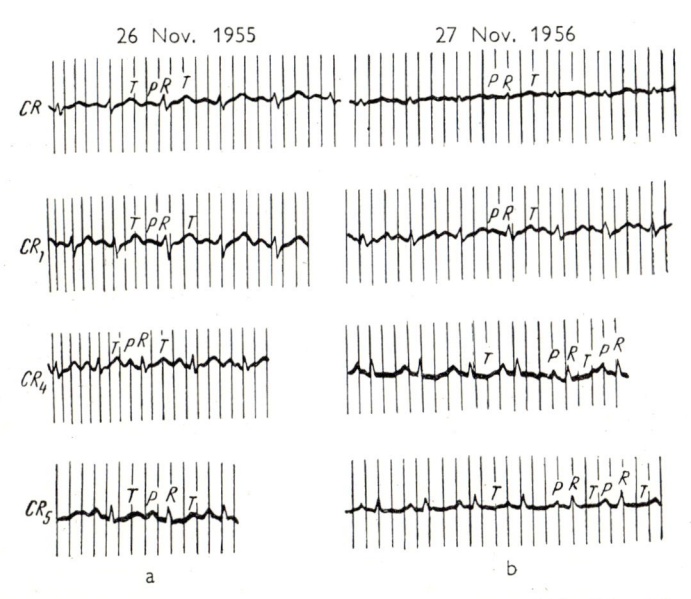

FIG. 9. Electrocardiogram from thoracic leads. The same rabbit (No. 4a). a—after 8 months T wave positive; b—after 20 months T_{CR-CR_1} have declined while $T_{CR_{4-5}}$ have become slightly biphase ($\pm$).

The return to its initial state of the T wave of the ventricular complex at the 20th month in 3 rabbits (Nos. 11, 18 and 22), receiving the smaller dose, and in one rabbit (No. 13) receiving the larger dose, deserves attention. This fact indicates that the T wave change (at least in some cases) is not produced by irreversible changes of the myocardium.

DISCUSSION

In analysing the electrocardiographic changes in the experimental group of rabbits it should be noticed that these changes were phasic: the most substantial were the deviations in the terminal part of the ventricular complex, chiefly in the T wave, observed more often in the leads taking the potentials of the left section of the heart. With the development of radiation injury at the 18th–20th months a gradual decline began, and later (at the 20th month) inversion of the T wave occurred. In some rabbits (especially those receiving the smaller dose) these changes were not recorded.

I. A. Pigalev (1956), in an experiment on dogs with subacute radiation sickness, has also observed the phasic character of electrocardiographic changes. Deviations in the electrocardiogram appeared after $1\frac{1}{2}$–2 months, then the results became normal again, to be followed towards the end of the animals' life by renewed deterioration—low biphase T waves and other changes appeared. M. N. Livanov and co-workers have observed an increase in the bioelectric activity of the cortex in the initial period of radiation sickness, while N. A. Kurshakov et al. have reported phasic changes during the development of radiation injury in the work of the gastro-intestinal tract, liver, kidneys and other organs and systems.

Among the large number of hypotheses advanced in explanation of the nature of the T wave of the electrocardiogram it was long ago suggested that it is connected with the metabolic processes of the myocardium. A. F. Samoilov (1910, 1922) was of the opinion that the T wave cannot be considered the result of the passage of excitatory waves. He believes that the T wave is connected with local moments.

Kan (1909) assigned material importance in the occurrence of the T wave to catabolic processes arising at the time of the ventricular systole. G. F. Lang emphasized the basic importance of metabolic factors in the formation of the T wave of the electrocardiogram. E. I. Borisova and V. S. Rusinov (1940–1941), M. E. Udel'nov and Yakovleva (1941), et al. consider the T wave to be the manifestation of the summation of trace potentials connected with restorative biochemical processes in the muscle, whereas the R wave (ventricular) reflects the diffusion of the excitatory wave—the encompassing of the myocardium by the excitation.

In clinical electrocardiography there are many examples confirming the significance of metabolic factors in the formation of the T wave. Known electrocardiographic changes include those occurring with Basedow's disease, myxedema, nutritional dystrophy, anemias, jaundice, diabetes, chronic occupational intoxications, and so on.

In the electrocardiographic picture obtained with the experimental group of rabbits it can be clearly seen that while the T wave was subject to pronounced changes the QRS complex was not materially affected (only in rabbit No. 11 was a significant decline observed). These results, indicating changes in the genesis of the T wave of the electrocardiogram, provide a basis for suggesting that the metabolic (bioelectric) processes in the cardiac muscle of rabbits are impaired by prolonged administration of ^{60}Co.

Pathoanatomical examination of the rabbits of the experimental groups, carried out by A. S. Kaplanskii, disclosed no clear indications of damage to the myocardium.

CONCLUSIONS

1. Both in the control and experimental rabbit groups the lability of the sinus rhythm was observed. The range of variation was 240–300 contractions per minute.
2. In more than half the rabbits (10) a normal or sinistral disposition of the cardiac electric axis predominated. During the observation period a leftward shift of the electric axis was observed in one third of the rabbits, connected possibly with large changes in the left ventricle.
3. The duration of waves and intervals was substantially the same in the experimental as in the control group. The electric ventricular systole in the experimental animals approached the upper limit of the norm twice as often as in the controls.
4. In some rabbits (3) a transitory change of intra-atrial, and in others (2), of intraventricular conductivity was observed. Also, electric ventricular alternation was seen in two rabbits. This indicates that in the experimental group, predominantly in those receiving the smaller dose, the function of conduction is somewhat temporarily modified.
5. In all the experimental rabbits throughout the observation period a change in voltage height of the electrocardiogram of a phasic character was noticed.
6. Progressive electrocardiographic examination showed the precise effect of prolonged administration of small doses of ^{60}Co in amounts of 1.25 and 12.5 $\mu c/kg$ on the terminal part of the ventricular complex of the waves (basically the T wave) of the electrocardiogram.

7. The use of the four thoracic leads enabled the magnitude of changes of the bioelectric processes in the different sections of the heart to be determined more accurately and earlier.
8. No material difference in electrocardiographic results in dependence on dose was established.
9. The normalization of the terminal part of the ventricular complex in some of the rabbits suffering radiation injury enables us to suppose that biochemical and not organic modifications of the myocardium lie at the root of the changes in the ventricular complex.
10. Special supplementary investigations are necessary for a more precise explanation of the genesis of changes in the terminal part of the ventricular complex during the administration of radioactive substances.

REFERENCES

ARKUSSKII YU. I., *Problems of Roentgenology and Radiology.* (Voprosy rentgenologii i radiologii.) A collection of papers by the State Research Institute of Roentgenology and Radiology, Medgiz (1955).

ARKUSSKII YU. I. and VOLKOVA K. G., *Vest. rentgenol. i radiol.* **20**, 38–56 (1938).

ARKUSSKII YU. I. and MINTS M. I., *Vest. rentgenol. i radiol.* **17**, 5–6, 334–432 (1937).

BERENSHTEIN R. YA. LEMESH V. M., GROZHEVSKAYA S. B., SHKOL'NIK M. N. and KOCHINA M. M., *The Effect of Cobalt on the Animal Body.* (Materialy o vliyanii kobal'ta na organizm zhivotnykh.) Proceedings of the 8th All-Union Conference of Physiologists, Biochemists and Pharmacologists, 71–72, Moscow (1955).

FANARDZHYAN V. A. et al., *Vest. rentgenol. i radiol.* **4**, 55–57 (1954).

FATEYEVA M. N., *Vest. Akad. med. nauk U.S.S.R.* **3**, 70–76 (1956).

FATEYEVA M. N., KLIMOV V. S., GORBARENKO N. I. et al., *Vest. rentgenol. i radiol.* **2**, 16–23 (1955).

FOGEL'SON L. I., *Clinical Electrocardiography.* (Klinicheskaya elektrokardiografiya.) Medgiz (1957).

FULTON G. P. and SUDAK F. N., *Amer. J. Physiol.* **179**, 135–138 (1954).

GORIZONTOV P. D. and MOROZ B. B., *Journal of the Academy of Medical Sciences of the U.S.S.R.* (Vestnik Akademii meditsinskikh nauk SSSR.) **3**, 63–70 (1956).

KASAKEVICH M. A., *Clinical Aspects of the Chronic Action of Radioactive Light Particles on the Body.* (K klinike khronicheskogo vozdeistviya na organizm radioaktivnykh svetosostavov.) Proceedings of the All-Union Conference on Medical Radiology, 36, Medgiz (1957).

KARLIN M. I. and MOGIL'NITSKII B. N., *Vest. rentgenol. i radiol.* **12**, 1–3, 103 (1933).

KOZLOVA A. V., *Vest. rentgenol. i radiol.* **4** (1954).

KOZLOVA A. V., MALENKOVA V. M., KARIBSKAYA YE. V. and SELETSKAYA T. S., *The Clinical Picture of Chronic Radiation Sickness.* (Klinika khronicheskoi luchevoi bolezni.) Proceedings of the All-Union Conference on Medical Radiology, 14, Medgiz (1957).

KURSHAKOV N. A., *The Biological Effects of Radiation and the Clinical Picture of Radiation Sickness.* (Biologicheskoye deistviye izluchenii i klinika luchevoi bolezni.) Medgiz (1954).

LEBEDINSKII A. V., *Med. radiol.* **1**, No. 2, 3–9 (1956).

LIVANOV M. N., *Med. radiol.* **1**, No. 1, 19–27 (1956).

MARKUZE K. P., *The Study of the Cardio-vascular and Respiratory Systems with Administration of Radioactive Phosphorus.* (Opyt izucheniya funktsii serdechno-sosudistoi i dykhatel'noi sistemy zhivotnykh pri vvedenii radioaktivnogo fosfora.) Sectional Proceedings of the Conference on Medical Radiology, Moscow (1956).

MIDTSEV F. I., *The Effect of Radioactive Substances on Isolated Heart and Vessels.* (Vliyaniye radioaktivnykh veshchestv na izolirovannoye serdtse i sosudy.) Novosibirsk (1939).

MOROZOV A. L., DROGICHINA E. A., KASAKEVICH M. A., IVANOV N. I. and BELOVA S. F. *The Condition of Healthy People subjected to Ionizing Radiation in Industrial-laboratory Conditions.* (K voprosu o sostoyanii zdorovykh lits, podvergavshikhsya vosdeistviyu ioniziruyushchei radiatsii v proizvodstvenno-laboratornykh usloviyakh.) Proceedings of the All-Union Conference on Medical Radiology, 20, Medgiz (1957).

MUSSMANN W. and OPITZ M., *Zschr. f. ges. exp. Med.* **124**, No. 1, 35, 43 (1954).

PERESAD'KO L. P., *The Effect of Cobalt on the Cardio-vascular System.* (Deistviye kobal'ta na serdechno-sosudistuyu sistemu.) Kharkov (1953).

POBEDINSKII M. N., *Vrach. delo* **3**, 233–236 (1955).

POBEDINSKII M. N., *Radiation Complications in X- and Radiotherapy.* (Luchevye oslozhneniya pri rentgeno-radioterapii.) (Abstracts from the literature), Medgiz (1954).

SELETSKAYA T. S., *The Cardio-vascular System in Radiotherapy.* (Izmeneniye serdechno-sosudistoi sistemy pri radiyevoi terapii.) Proceedings of the 30th. Anniversary Session of the Central Scientific Institute of Roentgenology and Radiology, Moscow (1954).

SEMIGLAZOVA YE. D., *Vest. rentgenol. i radiol.* **1**, 71–74 (1958).

VASIL'YEVA E. I., *Vest. rentgenol. i radiol.* **6**, 8–13 (1957).

WHITFELD A. and KUNKLER P., *Brit. Heart J.* **19**, No. 1, 53–58 (1957).

ZAKUTINSKII D. I., *The Effect of Radioactive Substances on the Body.* (Osobennosti deistviya radioaktivnykh veshchestv na organizm.) Sectional Proceedings of the All-Union Conference on Medical Radiology, 75, Moscow (1956).

ZAIRATYANTS V. G., *The Heart and Skeletal Musculature in Radiation Sickness.* (Serdtse i skeletnaya muskulatura pri luchevoi bolezni.) Sectional Proceedings on Medical Radiology, 39, Moscow (1956).

THE ELECTROCARDIOGRAM OF RABBITS DURING FUNCTIONAL TESTS (ASCHNER'S TEST, AMMONIA INHALATION AND ADRENALIN INJECTION) IN CONDITIONS OF CHRONIC ADMINISTRATION OF SMALL DOSES OF ^{60}Co

I. N. GOLOVSHCHIKOVA

IN THE paper by A. O. Saitanov the results are presented of a systematic electrocardiographic examination of two groups of rabbits under conditions of chronic internal administration of ^{60}Co in doses of 1.25 and 12.5 μc/kg weight per day.

The character of the electrocardiograms obtained in the course of the experiment indicate the phasic nature of the development of the chronic form of radiation sickness in rabbits. Three phases were noted. The first was detected at the 7th month and lasted until the 10th. It was expressed in a voltage increase of all the waves of the electrocardiogram by 2–3 times in comparison with the controls (especially in the thoracic leads), which would seem to indicate changes of the bioelectric processes in the cardiac muscle. Later, a period of electrocardiogram normalization was observed, lasting up to the 16th–18th months (the compensatory phase), and finally, 18–20 months after administration began a period of pronounced electrocardiographic changes occurred, primarily in the terminal part of the *QRST* complex.

It has now been established that the nervous system is very sensitive to radiation. As a result of more detailed study of radiation sickness more attention is being paid to the changes which occur in the autonomic nervous system, the functioning of which is modified by irradiation.

However, the state of the autonomic nervous system in its regulation of the cardio-vascular apparatus has not yet been sufficiently studied in radiation sickness. In particular, the condition and effect of the vagus nerve on the heart, under radiation conditions, is still obscure. The acute experiments of V. F. Cherkasov and Yu. M. Zaretskaya show a strengthening of the depressor reflex from the vagus nerve in acute radiation sickness. The experiments were carried out on animals subjected to external irradiation in large doses.

It is of some interest to study the vagus nerve in chronic radiation sickness occasioned by the internal administration of small radiation doses. Such was the task of the present work, since no treatment of this problem has been found in the literature. It is known that any stimulant in the body will bring about definite changes, the magnitude of which will depend on the strength of the stimulant, the duration of its activity, and on the functional condition of the body. If the changes produced are small then the body may compensate for them by the mobilization of all its resources. In such circumstances simple observation and the study of one or two processes is not nearly sufficient because concealed deficiencies will not be detected. Thus supplementary functional stresses must be applied, which will disrupt the temporary balance and so enable the detection of concealed changes in the body. With this aim (in the period of electrocardiogram normalization), three functional tests were used to disclose the condition of the regulatory mechanisms of the cardiovascular system: Aschner's test, the olfactory-cardiac reflex with ammonia inhalation and the reaction to intravenous injection of adrenalin. The first two tests were carried out 12 months after the beginning of the experiment and the third at 18 months. In all cases effects were studied by the electrocardiographic method.

The electrocardiogram was registered on an electrocardiograph type ECP-4M. Time record, 0.05 sec, speed of the drum, 7 cm/sec, energy, 1 mV = 2 cm. The efferent electrodes were steel needles inserted under the skin of the right upper and left lower limbs. Electrocardiograms were taken only in the II standard limb lead. While the electrocardiogram was being taken the rabbit was always in the same strictly fixed position—supine (for the adrenalin test—prone). The test was made 5–7 min after the animal had been placed in position.*

ASCHNER'S TEST

In total 8 rabbits from the group receiving 12.5 μc/kg ^{60}Co, and 12 control rabbits were examined. First, the initial electrocardiogram was taken (normal), then while finger pressure was applied to the eyeballs for 10–12 sec (always by the same person) and finally, after the original cardiac rhythm had been restored.

The results obtained (Table 1) indicate significant slowing down of the heart beat in both groups of rabbits (on average by half).

No marked difference was found between the experimental and control rabbits. Maximum retardation in the control group was on average 52 per cent of the initial rate, and in the experimental group, 48 per cent.

* A junior scientific colleague, A. O. Saitanov, took part in the present work.

TABLE 1
Cardiac activity with Aschner's test

	Control rabbits				Experimental rabbits		
No. of rabbit	number of contractions (per min)		maximum retardation as percentage of initial rhythm	No. of rabbit	number of contractions (per min)		maximum retardation as percentage of initial rhythm
	initial rhythm	maximum retardation			initial rhythm	maximum retardation	
32	270	120	44	4a	300	75	25
12	300	110	37	1	260	170	65
30	330	200	60	5	300	170	56
36	300	170	56	6	240	92	38
25	240	120	41.6	2	290	200	69
24	290	150	52	3	300	160	53
23	300	100	33	10	220	120	54
19	300	200	66	14a	270	66	24
36	270	240	88	—	—	—	—
29	300	200	66	—	—	—	—
2a	270	100	37	—	—	—	—
40a	260	120	46	—	—	—	—
			Average 52				Average 48

THE AMMONIA TEST

Insofar as the stimulant in the above test is difficult to measure without special devices it was decided to use a chemical stimulant in investigation of the magnitude and character of the vagus nerve's reaction to radiation,

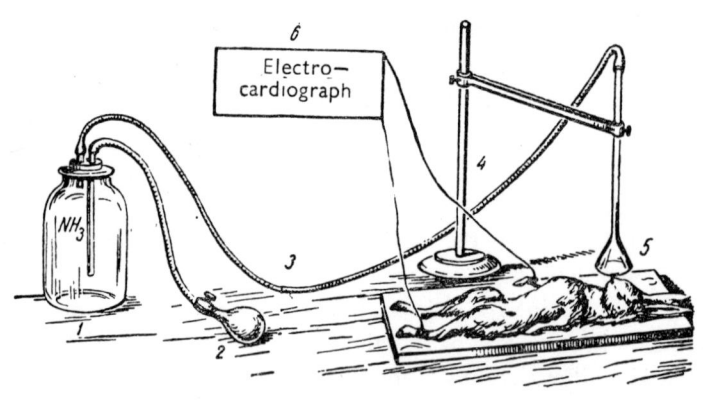

FIG. 1. Glass jar with attachments for conveying ammonia to the rabbit's nose 1—glass jar; 2—rubber squeezer; 3—rubber tube along which the ammonia reaches the rabbit; 4—stand with funnel for conveying the ammonia to the rabbit's nose (5); 6—electrocardiograph.

TABLE 2
Cardiac activity with the ammonia test (NH$_3$)

No. of rabbit	Initial contraction rate (per min)	Latent period (sec)	Maximum retardation as percentage of initial rate	Duration of the reaction (sec)
		Experimental rabbits		
1	260	immediate	25	12.5 (up to 200)
5	300	immediate	13	17.5 (up to 200)
6	240	immediate	21	15 (up to 170)
2	290	immediate	24	26.4 (up to 240)
3	300	immediate	19	18.4 (up to 200)
4a	300	1.2	15	14. (up to 240)
10	220	immediate	15	18 (up to 210)
14a	270	immediate	15	17 (up to 170)
		Control rabbits		
36	270	2.75	27	13.5
2a	270	0.50	20	More than 19 (up to 200)
32	270	0.60	22	More than 17 (up to 215)
12	300	1.00	25	More than 12 (up to 270)
36a	300	0.35	31	11
34	330	1.50	36	8
25	240	immediate	21	More than 18 (up to 220)
27	300	0.85	16	More than 19 (up to 240)
24	290	0.45	21	16
19	300	1.00	—	More than 15 (up to 260)
23	300	1.65	16	More than 15 (up to 200)
29	300	2.10	15	More than 13 (up to 220)
30	330	1.55	11	—

since it is easier to measure and the reflex obtained is more significant. Thus the olfactory-cardiac reflex which is clearly expressed in rabbits, was used. Ammonia vapour (NH$_3$) was used as the stimulant.

The test was carried out in the following manner. In an olfactometer of 1 litre capacity, 0.1 ml. ammonia water was placed. Ammonia vapour in a quantity of 150 ml. was presented to the rabbit's nose for 5 sec with a rubber squeezer of 50 ml. capacity (Fig. 1).

Five minutes after placing the animal in position, the initial electrocardiogram was taken. With the introduction of ammonia the record was continued until the initial rhythm had been restored.* In all, 8 rabbits receiving 12.5 µc/kg ^{60}Co (Fig. 2a, b) and 13 control rabbits (Table 2) were investigated. The latent period was absent in 7 of the 8 experimental rabbits and only in one case was it 1.2 sec. Among the controls it was absent only in one of 13 rabbits, its magnitude varying from 0.35 to 2.75 sec.

Inhalation of ammonia vapour in the dose and by the method described above produced significant retardation of the initial heart beat in both groups. The maximum retardation, expressed as a percentage of the initial rhythm, was in the control group from 11 to 36 per cent (average, 21 per cent) and in the experimental group, from 13 to 25 per cent (average, 16 per cent).

The results obtained indicate a certain increase of sensitivity to ammonia of the experimental animals by comparison with the controls. The increase of the depressor reaction obtained with the experimental group may be the result of increased excitability of the nn. vagi centres, greater receptivity of the heart to impulses from this nerve, an increase of sensitivity of the receptors of the respiratory tract and lungs; or different combinations of these causes. However, a precise explanation of this problem requires special investigation.

THE ADRENALIN TEST

Adrenalin is one of the sympathomimetic substances which participate in the regulation of the cardio-vascular system. It has been indicated in a number of works that adrenalin introduced into the blood stream acts not only directly on the nerve endings in the blood vessels but also on the central nervous system, its vasomotor and respiratory centres, and so on.

P. P. Belavenets' experiments on dogs have shown that injection of small doses of adrenalin (up to 0.05 mg/kg weight) retard cardiac rhythm by 3–4 times. With moderate doses (up to 1 mg/kg) this retardation is less acute and of shorter duration, being followed by an acceleration with subsequent return to normal. With large doses the retardation period is absent altogether and the acceleration period is increased. The writer believes that small doses of adrenalin stimulate the vagus nerve centres and, on the other hand, large doses, inhibit them.

---

* For technical reasons the termination of the reaction was not recorded in all cases.

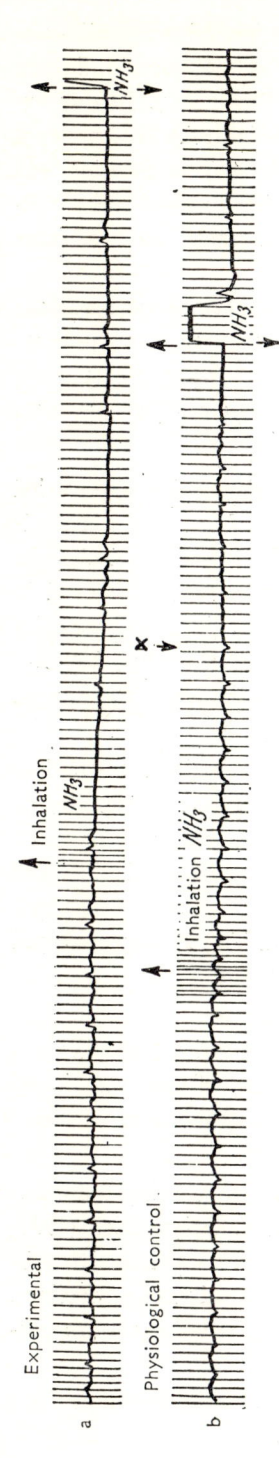

FIG. 2. Electrocardiogram. a—the ammonia test with rabbit No. 1, receiving 12.5 μc/kg ^{60}Co. A pronounced retardation of cardiac contractions is observed on the electrocardiogram immediately after inhalation; b—rabbit No. 34, physiological control. Slight retardation(x) appears only at the 3rd sec after inhalation.

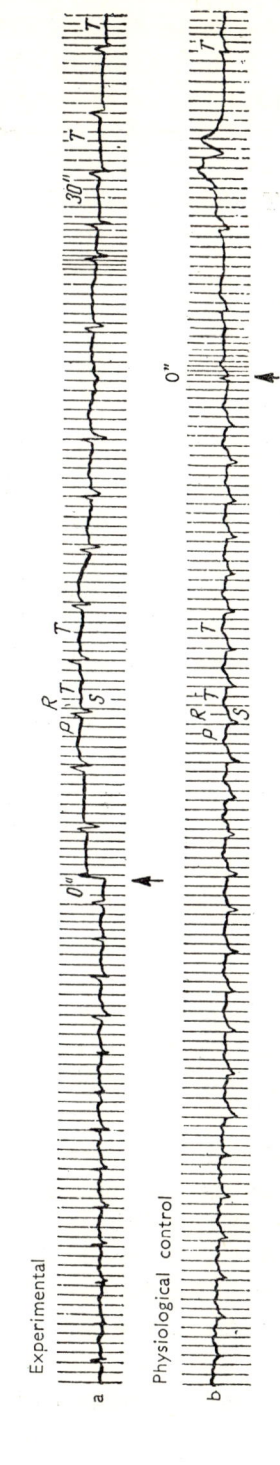

FIG. 3. Electrocardiogram. a—the adrenalin test with rabbit No. 1, receiving 12.5 μc/kg ^{60}Co. Retardation of rhythm appears on the electrocardiogram immediately after adrenalin injection(0"). The S–T interval fell to the lower limit of the isoelectric level while the T wave became flattened, slightly biphase(±); b—rabbit No. 1—physiological control. Retardation of rhythm occurred at 15th sec S–T interval isoelectric, T wave positive.

According to the literature, the previous condition of the cardio-vascular system and the species specific characteristics of the animal influence the character of the reaction to adrenalin (V. I. Skvortsov). In our experiments adrenalin was given in a dose of 4 γ/kg weight. An 0.01 per cent solution prepared *ex tempore* from an ampoule 0.1 per cent solution was used for injection in the marginal auricular vein. Injection time was a constant 5 sec. The method of taking the electrocardiogram was the same as in the previous experiments.*

The effect of adrenalin was studied in 5 experimental rabbits receiving 12.5 μc/kg ^{60}Co and in 11 controls. Intravenous injection of adrenalin in the above dose produced in both groups significant retardation of cardiac rhythm (by 2–4 times), which was maintained for 1–3 min with subsequent return to the initial level (Table 3).

The duration of the latent period in the experimental group varied from 6 to 10 sec (average, 8 sec), and in the controls from 2 to 7 seconds (average $3\frac{1}{2}$–4 seconds). In all 5 experimental rabbits pronounced changes in the terminal part of the $QRST$ complex were observed, expressed in a significant decline, almost flattening, of the T wave (in 3 rabbits) with transition to biphase ($\pm$) (in 2 rabbits). In 2 rabbits a fall of the S–T interval more than 1–1.5 mm below the isoelectric level was noted (Fig. 3a).

In the control group the S–T interval in 9 cases remained on the isoelectric level and the T wave either remained unchanged (4 rabbits) or even increased somewhat (5 cases). Only in 2 rabbits was some upwards displacement of the S–T interval and a biphase T wave observed. It should be noticed, however, that in one of these 2 cases the T wave was flattened out even on the initial electrocardiogram (Fig. 3b). The P wave declined in 2 experimental rabbits and also flattened out and became negative in 2 of the controls.

The adrenalin dose that we used had no effect on atrioventricular and intraventricular conduction, nor on the magnitude of the ventricular electric systole in either rabbit group. In one case in the control group a short (30 sec) sinoauricular blockage was noticed.

We have found no information in the literature concerning the effect of adrenalin on the heart in radiation sickness. T. V. Grigorovich (1937) indicates that after preliminary exposure of the heart to radioactive substances in frogs the threshold of sensitivity to adrenalin declines. V. A. Samtsov (1956) also shows that reaction to adrenalin is more pronounced in irradiated animals.

* Cf. the article by A. O. Saitanov in this collection.

TABLE 3

Cardiac activity with injection of adrenalin

No. of rabbit	Number of contractions (per min)	Latent period (sec)	Maximum retardation of contractions (per min)	Duration of the reaction (min)	S–T interval	T wave	Remarks
					Control rabbits		
8a	270	3.0	70	2	Unchanged	Enlarged at 40th sec but back to initial size at 1 min 45 sec	
6a	290	4.0	70	3	Declined somewhat but returned to initial level after 15 sec	Low, became biphase at start of reaction, returned to initial at 15th sec	P wave negative for first 2 sec of reaction
13a	240	7.0	160	1½	Unchanged	Somewhat enlarged at 25th sec	
12	300	3.0	120	2½	Unchanged	Enlarged at 15th sec, reverted at 45th	At 3rd sec P wave fell (almost flattened) and reappeared at 25th sec
2a	300	—	200	3	Unchanged	Unchanged	
15a	320	—	100	3	Unchanged	Somewhat enlarged	Sinoauricular blockage from 45th sec 1 min 15 sec P wave somewhat enlarged
12a	300	2.0	100	3	Unchanged	Somewhat enlarged throughout reaction	
6/No.	300	3.0	170	1½	Fell a little at 8 sec but had returned to initial level at 15 sec	At 3rd sec flattened, at 8th became biphase and at 15th—reverted to initial magnitude	

TABLE 3 (*continued*)

No. of rabbit	Number of contractions (per min)	Latent period (sec)	Maximum retardation of contractions (per min)	Duration of the reaction (min)	S–T interval	T wave	Remarks
9	280	4.5	100	More than 3	Unchanged	Unchanged	
40a	290	3.5	145	2½	Unchanged	Unchanged	From the group receiving stable cobalt in a dose of 1.24 1 kg weight
35a	280	3.0	170	More than 1	Unchanged Experimental rabbits	Unchanged	
4a	300	9.0	135	1½	From 1 min to 1 min 15 sec a little depressed with arch downwards	Became biphase from 1 min	*P* wave declined
3	300	8.0	110	3	Unchanged	Declined at 4th sec, reverted at 30th	
10	270	6.0	135	3	Unchanged	Declined at 5th sec, reverted at 30th	*P* wave declined (with retarded rhythm)
5	300	10.0	190	1	Unchanged	Declined at 4th sec, reverted at 30th	
1	300	8.0	170	1½	Lowered from 30th to 45th sec	Declined, became biphase at 30th sec and reverted to initial level at 45th	

The terminal part of the ventricular complex columns (S–T interval and T wave) are grouped under "Terminal part of the ventricular complex".

DISCUSSION

The results we obtained should be evaluated in two directions:
(1) the effect of adrenalin on the central nervous system (more precisely on the nn. vagi centres), expressed in a retardation of cardiac contractions;
(2) its direct effect on the myocardium, comprising metabolic changes in the cardiac muscle and, connected with this, corresponding changes of the T wave of the ventricular complex (M. V. Raiskina).

The effect on the central nervous system in our experiment was to lower the threshold of sensitivity to adrenalin by almost twice in all the experimental animals by comparison with the controls. This lowering may depend on metabolic changes, content of electrolytes, nutrients and particular specific products formed in the pace maker—hormones (Haberlan) or metabolites (P. P. Aver'yanov, L. I. Fogel'son and N. M. Fedorov). The sensitivity threshold depends on the rapidity of the blood flow and the condition and reaction of the sinus to constant exposure to radiation. However, this proposition requires future confirmation.

In analysing our results on the effect of adrenalin on the myocardium by electrocardiography, metabolic changes in the cardiac muscle of the experimental animals by comparison with the controls may be suggested. Apparently adrenalin, by producing changes in metabolic processes, discloses concealed deviations or impairments in the metabolism of the cardiac muscle produced by irradiation.

CONCLUSIONS

1. No significant difference was found in reaction to Aschner's test between experimental and control rabbits in the development of radiation sickness.
2. The ammonia test (olfactory-cardiac reflex) showed increased sensitivity to ammonia and enlargement of the depressor effect in experimental animals compared with the controls.
3. The adrenalin test produced in the experimental animals deformation of the terminal part of the ventricular complex $QRST$ after normal initial electrocardiographic results.
4. The ammonia and adrenalin tests can be recommended for a more accurate determination of the body's condition in chronic radiation sickness in rabbits. The adrenalin test may prove extremely valuable for detecting the state of the myocardium in animals with chronic radiation sickness. For a more precise and complete examination of changes in the autonomic nervous system in chronic radiation sickness, produced by small doses of radioisotopes, still more functional tests on a large amount of experimental material are needed.

REFERENCES

BELAVENETS P. P., *The Effect of Adrenalin on the Animal Body.* (K voprosu o deistvii adrenalina na zhivotnyi organizm.) Dissertation (1903).

CHERKASOV V. F., *Med. radiol.* **1,** No. 2, 57–64 (1956).

GRIGOROVICH T. V., *The Sensitivity Threshold of Frog's Heart to Adrenalin after Previous Exposure to Radium Emanation.* (Izmeneniye poroga chuvstvitel'nosti serdtsa lyagushki k adrenalinu pri predvaritel'nom vozdeistvii emanatsii radiya.) Sixth Caucasian Congress of Physiologists, Biochemists and Pharmacologists, 17–19 Rostov-on-Don (1937).

ZARETSKAYA Yu. M., *Med. radiol.* **1,** No. 3, 20–29 (1956).

RAISKINA M. Ye., *Farmakologiya i toksikologiya* **14,** No. 1, 31–33 (1951).

SKVORTSOV V. I., *A Course of Pharmacology.* (Kurs farmakologii.) Medgiz, pp. 247 (1948).

MORPHOLOGICAL CHANGES IN RABBITS DURING CHRONIC INTERNAL ADMINISTRATION OF ^{60}Co

A. S. KAPLANSKII[*]

IN THE literature there are a number of works devoted to the effect of external radiation from the gamma rays of ^{60}Co. However, we have been unable to find any references to the effect of ^{60}Co administered internally, when it acts both as a β- and a γ-radiator. Nevertheless, the wide use of ^{60}Co in industry, medicine and scientific research makes possible the chronic intake of small doses by people having contact with it.

The purpose of the present work is the detection of the morphological changes produced in the organs of experimental animals by chronic internal administration of small doses of ^{60}Co.

Investigations were made on rabbits weighing approximately 3 kg.

The division of the animals into groups was the same as that described in preceding articles. Since no morphological changes were observed in the animals which received stable cobalt these were combined with the physiological controls into one control group consisting of 10 rabbits and were killed 22–24 months after the beginning of the experiment.

All organs were submitted to histological examination. Pieces were fixed in 10 per cent neutral formalin. Sections were stained with hematoxylin-eosin, picrofuchsin and Sudan III, by Perles's method for iron.

RESULTS

The first group comprised 8 rabbits receiving 1.25 μc/kg, of which two died and the rest were killed (Table 1).

Changes in the killed rabbits will be examined first. No abnormalities were noticed in the bone marrow. In the spleen extensive foci of myeloid hemopoiesis attracted attention; these were made up predominantly of myelocytes and juvenile and stabnuclear neutrophils. The number of segmentonuclear neutrophils in the spleen pulp was also increased. In a number of animals, the spleen pulp contained cells of plasma type. It

---

[*] Scientific director Professor P. P. Dvizhkov.

TABLE 1
Length of life of first group animals and condition at death

No. of rabbit	Life-span (months)	Type of death	Condition at death
11	23	Killed	Satisfactory; thinning, loss of fur
13	22	Killed	Satisfactory; uterine myoma
14	24	Killed	Good
15	21	Killed	Satisfactory; thinning, loss of fur, abrasions on paws
18	24	Killed	Good
22	24	Killed	Good
20	22	Died	Abscessing pneumonia, pleurisy
21	21	Died	Pneumonia

must, however, be pointed out that in the control animals also, single myelocytes and even small groups of myelocytes were found in the spleen, so that in the normal rabbit spleen insignificant myelopoiesis may occur, acquiring greater magnitude in pathological conditions. These observations agree with the results of the cytological investigations carried out by N. L. Beloborodova, which indicated an increased number of neutrophilic myelocytes, and juvenile, stab and segmented neutrophils in spleen preparations.

A slight decline of the number of lymphoid elements of the spleen, primarily in the pulp, could be seen in 2 rabbits (Nos. 11 and 18). No marked changes in the lymph nodes were observed by comparison with the controls.

In 3 rabbits (Nos. 11, 13 and 18) weakly expressed focal interstitial infiltration of the myocardium by histiocytes, leukocytes and lymphocytes was found (with predominance of one or other of these cellular forms in particular cases). In the lungs of a number of rabbits (Nos. 11, 13, 14 and 15) a thickening of the interalveolar septa primarily because of a proliferation of histiocytes could be observed. In rabbit No. 13 formation of bone tissue was noticed in the lumen of one alveole.

There were no marked abnormalities in the gastro-intestinal tract with the exception of a certain diminution of the number of lymphoid follicles. Miliary and submiliary necrobiotic foci with infiltration by leukocytes were found in the liver of 3 rabbits (Nos. 11, 13 and 14). In 2 of these rabbits (Nos. 11 and 13) large fat droplets were observed extensively in hepatic cells. Different degrees of lymphoid infiltration around the blood vessels and common bile ducts were found in all the animals and in 3 (Nos. 14, 18 and 22), small clusters of lymphoid cells in the hepatic lobules.

Moderately pronounced focal interstitial nephrosclerosis could be seen only in 2 rabbits (Nos. 11 and 22), but in a number of cases around the tubules and in the interstitial tissue, structureless, weakly fuchsinophilic masses appeared. In 4 rabbits (Nos. 13, 14, 18 and 22) focal infiltration of renal tissue, chiefly of the medullary layer, by lymphocytes mixed with a small number of plasma type cells was observed. In rabbit No. 11 infiltration by immature cells of the myeloid series was found. In individual animals in the lumena of enlarged tubuli recti and contorti, granular and hyaline casts, and an amorphous mass giving a positive reaction for iron were found (in rabbits Nos. 11 and 13). Depositions of iron-containing masses in the basement membranes of some of the convoluted tubules were detected in rabbit No. 15.

In the urinary bladder there were lesions of the epithelium, becoming succulent, high and lightly vacuolated (rabbits Nos. 14, 18 and 22). Infiltration by leukocytes and cells of plasma type was sometimes found in the submucosa of the urinary bladder.

In rabbit No. 13 a tumour $5 \times 4 \times 3$ cm was found in the uterus, which on histological examination proved to be a myoma. No lesions were found in the gonads, thyroid or suprarenals. The central nervous system was not submitted to special examination; normal hematoxylin-eosin staining disclosed no lesions.

As shown in Table 1, 2 rabbits died from pneumonia. Histological investigation of the lungs of rabbit No. 20 disclosed abscessing pleuropneumonia with symptoms of tissue microbiosis; the number of cellular elements was considerable, among which round cells and histiocytes predominated (for greater detail, cf. the description of lesions in subgroup B below). In the bone marrow of this rabbit a shift to the left was observed due to an increase in the numbers of promyelocytes, myelocytes and juvenile neutrophils and a decrease in the numbers of stab and segmented. In the cardiac muscle, liver and kidneys lesions similar to those observed in the killed rabbits were found.

The picture of pneumonia in rabbit No. 21 was dominated by sharply pronounced oedema and plethora of lung tissue, with a small number of cellular elements. The almost complete absence of segmento-nuclear neutrophils was especially striking; round cells, histiocytes and cells of plasma type predominated. In some alveoli filled with transudate, only single cast-off cells of the alveolar epithelium were observed. The epithelium of some bronchi showed pronounced necrobiotic lesions and desquamation. In the thickened membrane of the bronchial epithelium, deposits of a structureless mass, giving a positive reaction for iron, were seen. Similar depositions of iron-containing masses were found within the vascular tunic in almost all organs; in the tunic itself; in cells of the mucous membrane and the tracheal cartilage; in the membrane and some of the cells of the gastric mucosa; in certain sections of the muscular lining of the stomach and intestine; in some sclerosed glomeruli, in the thickened Bowman's capsule and the enlarged tubuli contorti of the kidneys. In this rabbit's spleen significant diminution of lymphoid elements was observed; the pulp contained many immature cells of the myeloid series, cells of plasma type, dividing cells and deposits of hemosiderin. The bone marrow displayed a leftwards shift (cf. the description of rabbit No. 20).

Diffuse focal interstitial sclerosis with atrophy of the glomeruli and convoluted tubules, and infiltration by immature cells of the myeloid series and cells of plasma type were found in the kidneys. The picture of the liver was similar to that of the killed animals of this group.

TABLE 2

Length of life of second group animals and condition at death

No. of rabbit	Life-span (months)	Type of death	Condition at death
4a	21	Killed	Satisfactory; encapsulated liver parasite
5	22	Killed	Satisfactory; thinning, loss of fur
6	21	Killed	Satisfactory; tumour in cervical-axillary area
9	8	Died	Pneumonia
7	11	Died	Pneumonia
8	11	Died	Pneumonia; dead fetuses in uterine cavity; endometritis
4	12	Killed	Very serious; emaciation
2	17	Died	Pneumonia
1	19	Died	Abscessing pneumonia, pleurisy, pericarditis
3	20	Died	Pneumonia
14a	21	Killed	Abscessing pneumonia; dead fetuses in uterine cavity
10	23	Died	Abscessing pneumonia, pericarditis, pneumonia, pleurisy, peritonitis
12a	23	Died	

The second rabbit group, receiving 12.5 $\mu c/kg$ ^{60}Co, comprised 13 animals, of which 8 died and 5 were killed* (Table 2).

For the purposes of describing the changes in the second rabbit group the animals were further divided into 2 subgroups (A and B).

---

* Rabbits Nos. 14a and 4 were in a moribund state when killed and so it is preferable to consider them with those which died.

Subgroup A—those rabbits which were killed in a satisfactory condition (Nos. 4a, 5 and 6), and subgroup B—those rabbits which died or were moribund when killed (Nos. 9, 7, 8, 4, 2, 1, 3, 14a, 10 and 12a).

Subgroup A

So far as the hemopoietic organs are concerned no marked abnormalities were found in rabbit No. 4a. In the bone marrow of rabbit No. 5 a shift to the left, due to an increase in the numbers of promyelocytes, myelocytes, juvenile and stabnuclear neutrophils and a decrease in the number of segmentonuclear neutrophils, were observed. The number of immature cells of the red series was also increased (Fig. 1). In the spleen of rabbits Nos. 5 and 6 a significant number of immature cells of the myeloid series, segmentonuclear neutrophils, was found. These cells were distributed in clusters. The lymphoid tissue of the spleen and lymph nodes was well pronounced. No lesions were found in the heart in any of the three rabbits. In the lungs of rabbit No. 6 small focal thickening of the inter-alveolar septa was noticed due to proliferation of histiocytic elements. The epithelium of the tracheal mucosa of this rabbit had grown profusely, forming papillae, polystichous, vacuolated.

No lesions were observed in the gastro-intestinal tract, submaxillary and pancreatic glands. In the hepatic lobules of rabbits Nos. 5 and 6 small clusters of lymphoid cells were seen with a small admixture of segmented neutrophils; along the layers of connective tissue and around the vessels and common bile ducts, moderately pronounced lymphoid cell infiltration was observed. In rabbit No. 4a in sections of the liver, lying near an encapsulated parasite, pronounced leukocytic infiltration was seen.

In the kidneys of rabbit No. 5, pronounced focal interstitial sclerosis with atrophy of the tubules and glomeruli in the sclerosed areas, and compensatory hypertrophy and enlargement of the tubules in the surviving areas of the renal parenchyma, were observed. In two other rabbits (No. 4a and 6) similar changes were observed but the effect was not so marked. The epithelium of the tubuli recti in all cases became light and succulent with hyperchromic and pycnotic nuclei in places.

Similar lesions were detected in the epithelium of the mucous membrane of the urinary bladder. The submucosa of the urinary bladder of rabbit No. 6 was infiltrated with leukocytes and plasma type cells. As has already been mentioned, in rabbit No. 6 (Table 2) an extensive (20×15×10 cm) tumour in the cervical-axillary area was found, histologically like a myxosarcoma. No metastases of the tumour were detected.

Lesions of the uterus, gonads, thyroid and suprarenal glands are discussed below with the corresponding description of such effects in subgroup B.

Subgroup B

As far as the white and red series of the bone marrow are concerned in this subgroup the changes observed were similar to those in rabbit No. 5 of subgroup A. Also, in a number of animals the bone marrow contained a large number of cells of plasma type and cells with decaying nuclei (Nos. 9, 2 and 1). The megakaryocytes often had pycnotic, hyperchromic nuclei but no diminution of their number was observed.

In the spleen of animals which died at earlier intervals (Nos. 9, 7, 8, 4, 2 and 1) a decrease of the number of lymphoid elements was observed. In three rabbits (Nos. 7, 8 and 1) the spleen pulp contained a large number of cells of plasma type and in two rabbits (Nos. 7 and 14a) there were also immature cells of the myeloid series. In the spleen of rabbit No. 7 numerous miliary and submiliary necrobiotic foci were observed. In animals Nos. 2 and 3 pronounced hemosiderosis of the spleen indicated intensive hemolysis of the erythrocytes.

In the lymph nodes symptoms of plethora, oedema, enlargement of the sinuses and pronounced reticulo-endothelial proliferation were usually observed. In the lymph nodes of some rabbits a significant number of cells of plasma type were found (Fig. 2); in rabbit No. 1 they comprised the main mass of cells. In these animals many cells with decaying nuclei were found.

In the fatty cellular tissue surrounding the lymph nodes fine foci of leukocytic hemopoiesis were often found; a focus of myeloid hemopoiesis was detected in the sinus of a lymph node of rabbit No. 7.

In the cardiac muscle of most rabbits (Nos. 4, 3, 10, 7, 8, 1) moderately pronounced interstitial infiltration by leukocytic and histiocytic elements was observed. In 2 animals (Nos. 1 and 10) pericarditis could be seen (Table 2) with fibrinous deposits, necrobiotic lesions, accumulation of mounds of bacteria (tissue microbiosis) and moderate round cell infiltration. In rabbit No. 14a pustules were discovered in the cardiac muscle, composed of clusters of leukocytes with necrosis beginning in their centres.

Individual muscle fibres and groups of fibres in the myocardium of rabbit No. 2 gave a sharply positive reaction for iron when stained by Perles's method (Fig. 3).

In the rabbits (Nos. 2 and 3) in whose spleen increased erythrocyte hemolysis was observed (see above), deposits of iron-containing masses were found in the intestine, accompanied, in the arteries and muscular membrane of the vessels of all the internal organs, by desquamation of the endothelium and crumbling, homogenization and oedema of the vascular wall.

Pneumonia occurred in the lungs of all the rabbits of this subgroup, except No. 4, and was accompanied in 3 rabbits (Nos. 1, 10 and 14a) by the formation of numerous abscesses and symptoms of tissue microbiosis. In two animals, pneumonia was accompanied by pleurisy having a character similar to that of the pericarditis described above (Fig. 4). In the majority of animals (excluding Nos. 10 and 14a) the pneumonia exhibited certain specific traits: plethora and oedema of the pulmonary tissue predominated; the number of cellular elements in the interalveolar septa and alveolar lumena was small, among which the decrease in the number of segmentonuclear neutrophils was especially noticeable; the epithelium of some of the bronchi bore necrobiotic lesions and whole layers had peeled off, so that the lumena of some bronchi were filled exclusively with such cells. The exodus of formed elements of the blood through the crumbled, distended and homogenized vascular walls could be seen. There were no pronounced hemorrhages.

In rabbits Nos. 2 and 3 deposits of iron-containing masses in the tracheal and bronchial membranes and in the tissue of the interalveolar septa were found.

Prominent lesions were seen in different sections of the gastro-intestinal tract, with the exception of the esophagus. All the layers of the stomach wall were oedematous, especially the submucosa. In the gastric mucosa variously expressed atrophy of the adenose epithelium was observed, with which, at first, the number of major cells declined, and then the parietal acid cells. With sharply pronounced atrophy of the adenoblasts the stroma denuded of villi was easily discerned (Fig. 5). In a number of cases, developing sclerotic lesions of the gastric mucosa were noticed. The number of cells in the stroma and in the submucosa was small, round cells and cells of plasma type predominating. The muscular layer was oedematous and loose and the contours of individual muscle fibres were indeterminate.

Atrophy of the adenoblasts of the mucosa and sclerotic lesions were also observed in the small intestine (Fig. 6). The signs of oedema of the intestinal wall were similar to those in the stomach but were much less pronounced. In two rabbits (Nos. 2 and 9) karyorrhexis in many cells of the adenose epithelium was observed. In contrast to the stomach, in the small intestine significant infiltration of the mucosa had often taken place by lymphocytes and cells of plasma type, sometimes with an admixture of segmentonuclear neutrophils. In all animals of the second group complete atrophy of the lymphoid follicles of the intestine was observed. In individual animals a significant desquamatous–necrobiotic process had occurred, embracing the surface of the intestinal mucosa. Atrophy, sclerosis and infiltration of the mucosa was also seen in the large intestine, but was comparatively slight.

In rabbits Nos. 2 and 3, some of the adenoblasts of the mucosa, and also certain sections of the muscular lining of the stomach and intestine were positive for iron, when stained by Perles's method.

As has already been mentioned above (Table 2) peritonitis occurred in rabbit No. 12a; the serous membranes of the stomach and intestine were significantly enlarged due to fibrinous deposits and profusely infiltrated by leukocytes; necrobiotic lesions of the serous membrane were noticed in places. Leukocytic infiltration was also observed in the connective tissue layers of the pancreas.

In the liver of 4 rabbits (Nos. 7, 4, 10 and 12a) miliary and submiliary necrobiotic foci with leukocytic infiltration were detected. Around the vessels, common bile ducts and along the connective tissue layers in all rabbits, lymphoid-histiocytic infiltration was noticed (in rabbit No. 3, small clusters of lymphocytes were also found in the hepatic lobules). In a number of animals disproportionate size and staining of nuclei of hepatic cells was observed, and also some breakdown of hepatic structure. Large fat droplets in hepatic cells were found in 3 rabbits (Nos. 4, 10 and 14). No lesions of the submaxillary and pancreatic glands were observed.

In the kidneys of 6 rabbits (Nos. 9, 7, 8, 2, 3 and 14a), sharply pronounced, and in 4 rabbits (Nos. 4, 1, 10 and 12a), moderately pronounced, focal interstitial sclerosis with compression of the glomeruli and atrophy of the tubules was observed.

Infiltration of the interstitial tissue of the kidneys by cells of plasma type and lymphocytes was observed in most animals, and in 4 rabbits (Nos. 7, 8, 10 and 14a) infiltration by immature cells of the myeloid series (myelocytes, juvenile and stabnuclear neutrophils) was also present (Fig. 7). In some tubules granular and hyaline casts were detected. In 5 animals (Nos. 2, 8, 9, 1 and 5) the epithelium of the convoluted and straight tubules contained an insignificant number of fine fat droplets. The deposition of iron-containing structureless masses occurred in some sclerosed glomeruli and enlarged Bowman capsules, and also in the basement membrane of the convoluted tubules of rabbits Nos. 2 and 3 (Fig. 8). In rabbit No. 12a focal necrotic nephrosis of the convoluted tubules was observed.

Lesions of the urinary bladder were similar to those of the rabbits of subgroup A.

No marked lesions were detected in the central nervous system with hematoxylin-eosin (rabbits of subgroups A and B).

Examination of the uterus of two rabbits of subgroup B (Nos. 8 and 14a) disclosed dead macerated fetuses, the size of which was not proportional to (it was significantly less than) the supposed length of pregnancy.

The uterine mucosa of rabbit No. 8 was plethoric and infiltrated by leukocytes, among which were many immature cells of the myeloid series; some sections of the mucous membrane were necrotic. No inflammatory lesions of the uterine mucosa were observed in rabbit No. 14a. There were no marked abnormalities of the uterus in the other animals.

Serious lesions were detected in the testes. In 5 of 6 rabbits the seminiferous tubules were obliterated, stripped of spermatogenic epithelium, rather collapsed. Single cells of the spermatogenic epithelium had pycnotic nuclei or were breaking down, and only in the basal section could intact Sertoli cells be seen. As far as the interstitial tissue is concerned no lesions were detected, apart from slight sclerosis; its cellular elements were preserved (Fig. 9). Less pronounced lesions were observed in the ovaries where only some decrease in the number of primordial and developing ovarian follicles could be seen.

In most cases there were no marked abnormalities in the thyroid and suprarenals.

DISCUSSION

In comparing the changes which occurred in the rabbits of the first and second groups it is seen that the pathological processes which in the first group are incipient, moderately pronounced or well pronounced in individual animals, in the second group are increased in frequency and strength. Thus, whereas in the first group, 2 out of 8 animals died, in the second group the corresponding figures were 10 out of 13. At the same time, the wide range of individual sensitivity to internal radiation among the animals was also revealed, a fact which has more than once been indicated in the literature. This situation was well shown in our experiment by differences in time of death of the animals of the second experimental group; the first animal died after 8 months and the last two, 23 months after the beginning of the experiment. Three rabbits of this group were more resistant to radiation (the rabbits which were killed in a satisfactory condition) and the character of the changes observed in them approximated to the killed animals of the first group.*

The occurrence in the spleen in the killed animals of the first and second experimental groups of foci of myeloid hemopoiesis with completed differentiation of cellular elements and normal quantitative ratios (N. L. Beloborodova) is a relatively early nonspecific reaction of the spleen to irradiation.† Although hemopoiesis in the spleen was normal, a significant

---

* Rabbit No. 4a displayed an especially high degree of resistance, a fact also observed in N. L. Beloborodova's investigations.

† A similar spleen reaction has been observed in rabbits suffering from suppurative-inflammatory processes, but not exposed to radiation of any sort.

number of cells of plasma type were observed. Later, this qualitative disturbance of the hemopoietic process (in the second group, i.e. the rabbits which died) became dominant in the spleen, evidence of which was the sharp increase in the number of cells of plasma type in the pulp and the disappearance therein of foci of myeloid hemopoiesis. A greater degree of hemopoietic impairment in rabbits of the second group compared with those of the first group was also detected in other organs. Whereas in the killed rabbits of the first group no marked changes were observed in the bone marrow and lymph nodes, in the second group, (the rabbits which died) examination of the bone marrow revealed a pronounced shift to the left, on the part of the white series, an increase in the number of immature elements of the red series and also of cells of plasma type.

Nuclear hyperchromatism and pycnosis of megakaryocytes without diminution of their number has earlier been mentioned by V. K. Veidman and G. V. Yasvoin after intravenous injection of radon.

In the lymph nodes proliferation of the reticulo-endothelium and formation of a significant number of plasma type cells were noticed. In a number of cases in the adipose cellular tissue surrounding the lymph nodes fine foci of leukocytic hemopoiesis were observed.

In the kidneys of the killed animals (Group 2) instead of the primarily lymphoid infiltration with a small number of cells of plasma type which occurred in the first group, the plasma type cells predominated and foci of myeloid hemopoiesis were observed.

S. Worren and C. E. Dunlap indicate that the spleen is considered less sensitive to radiation than the lymph nodes. This belief contradicts the results of A. A. Pinus, which were obtained with various animals after a single intratracheal injection of radon, and our own observations which established a diminution of lymphoid tissue in the spleen without such diminution in the lymph nodes. The decline in the body's resistance, so characteristic of acute and chronic radiation damage, is linked with a decrease in the amount of lymphoid tissue in the body and still more, with the qualitative deficiency of the existing lymphocytes (Ackerman and Bellios). In our experiments, the presence in the rabbits of the second group of pneumonia, pleurisy, pericarditis and tissue microbiosis with, at the same time, a decrease in the quantity of lymphoid tissue, confirms this opinion.

The inflammatory lesions of the pulmonary tissue which were observed in most of the rabbits which died of pneumonia and the lesions of the lung vessel walls, were characterized by a series of moderately pronounced specific symptoms (see above) which have been noted by many writers at the climax of acute radiation sickness (specific pneumonias)

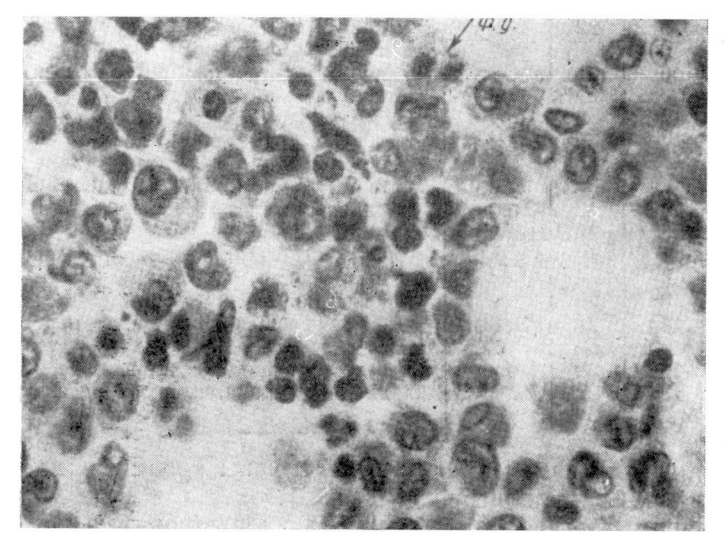

Fig. 1. Bone marrow with predominance of myelocytic type cells. Hematoxylin-eosin stain. Oc. 6, ob. 90. Фд—mitosis.

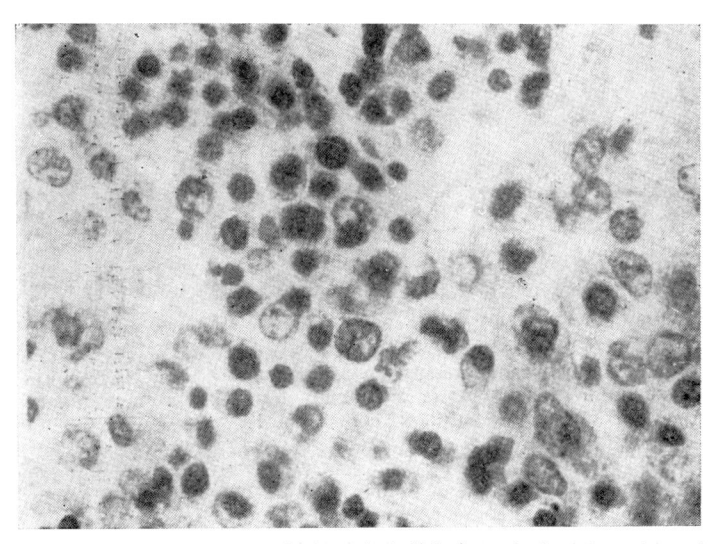

Fig. 2. Proliferation of reticulo-endothelial tissue in lymph node and accumulation of plasma type cells. Hematoxylin-eosin stain. Oc. 6, ob. 90.

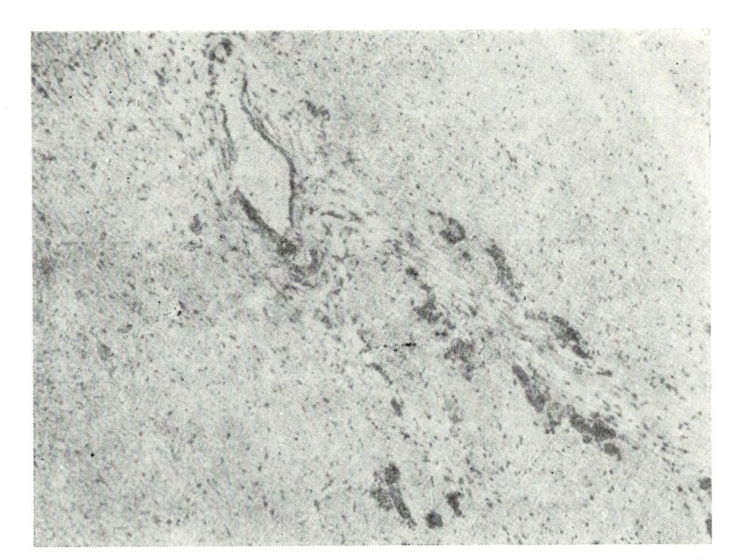

Fig. 3. Deposits of iron-containing masses in the muscle fibres and vascular wall of the heart. Hematoxylin-eosin stain. Oc. 6, ob. 10.

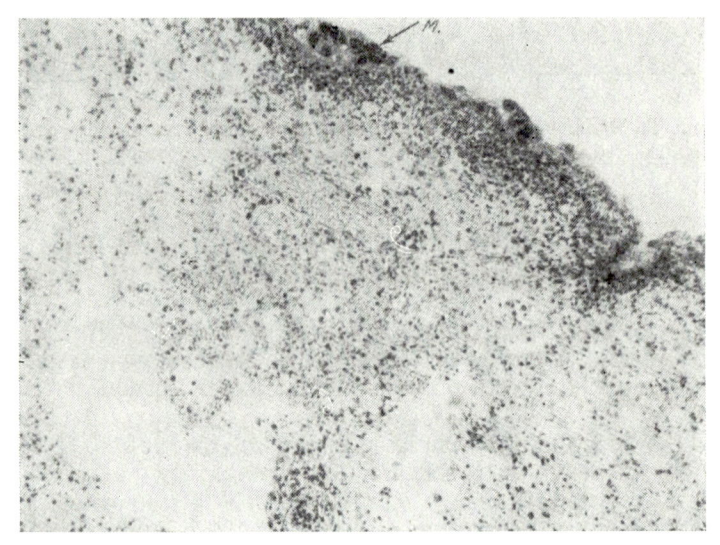

Fig. 4. Lung (pneumonia). Necrobiotic lesions of the pleura. Hematoxylin-eosin stain. Oc. 6, ob. 10. m — tissue microbiosis.

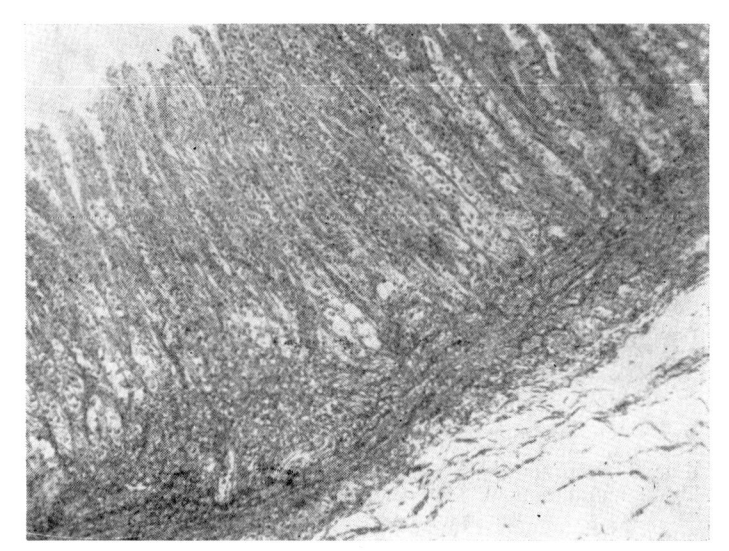

FIG. 5. Atrophy of adenose cells of the mucous membrane of the stomach. Sclerotic lesions of the stroma. Van Gieson's stain. Oc. 6, ob. 10.

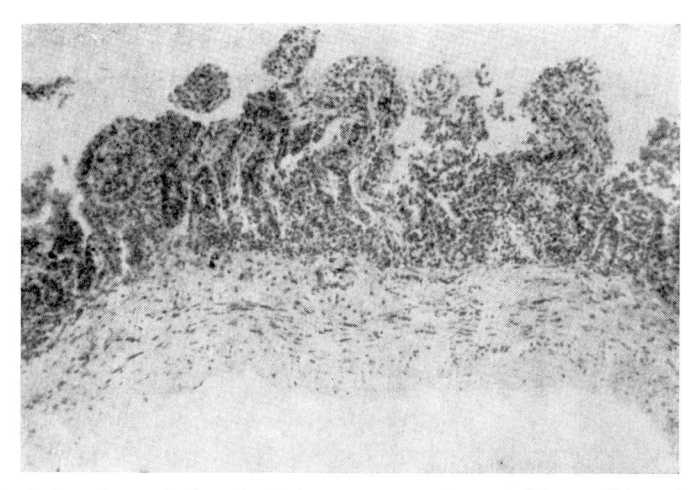

FIG. 6. Atrophy and sclerosis of the mucous membrane of the small intestine. Infiltration by round cells and cells of plasma type. Hematoxylin-eosin stain. Oc. 6, ob. 10.

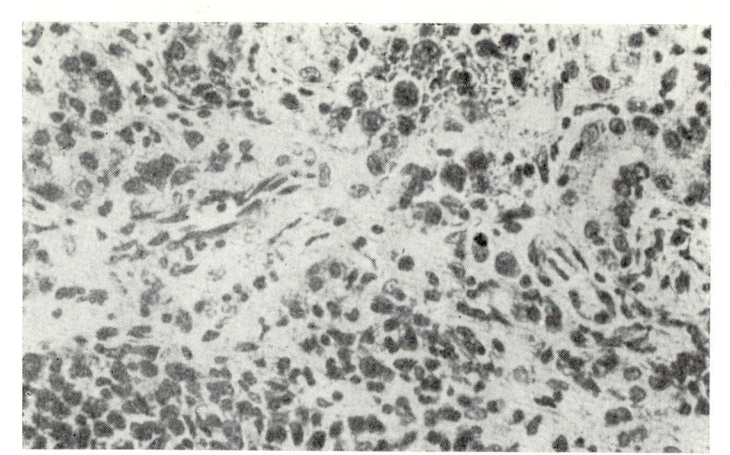

FIG. 7. Kidney. Infiltrates of plasma type cells and cells of the myeloid series. Hematoxylin-eosin stain. Oc. 6, ob. 40.

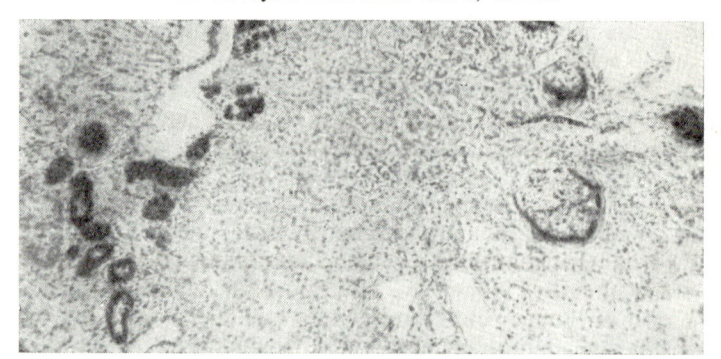

FIG. 8. Deposits of iron-containing masses in renal glomeruli and tubules. Perles's stain. Oc. 6, ob. 10.

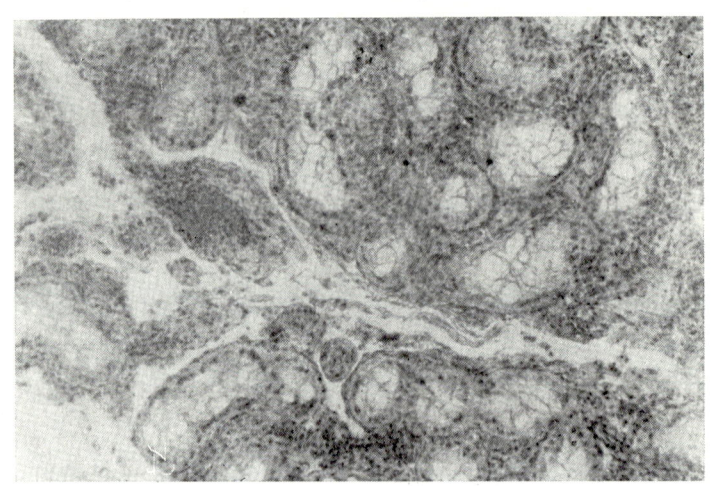

FIG. 9. Atrophy of spermatogenic epithelium and obliteration of seminiferous tubules of the testes. Hematoxylin-eosin stain. Oc. 6, ob. 10.

(A. E. Ivanov, N. A. Krayevskii, B. N. Mogil'nitskii and M. S. Brumshtein, Engelstad).

The picture of damage to the gastro-intestinal tract in the rabbits which died (Group 2) agrees in its main features with the observations in chronic radiation sickness made by other writers (G. A. Tapunova).

The proliferation of lymphoid-histiocytic elements of the liver, observed in the animals of the first and second groups, is apparently a function of the reaction of all the reticular tissue, as described above. The dystrophic lesions of hepatic cells and foci of necrobiosis observed in both groups, but more pronounced in the second group, must evidently relate primarily to the direct damaging action of ^{60}Co absorbed in the liver.

The dystrophic lesions of the liver had a predominantly metabolic character; adipose dystrophy of the liver in our experiments occurred only in 2 rabbits of the first group and 3 rabbits of the second group. Whereas, among the killed animals (Group 1), focal interstitial nephrosclerosis was found in only 2 rabbits, in the second group it was well pronounced in 7 rabbits and in 6, moderately pronounced diffuse interstitial nephrosclerosis was observed, "developing like direct cell-less sclerosis" (N. A. Krayevskii).

As can be seen from the literature (N. A. Krayevskii, A. P. Novikova, E. V. Erleksova, L. N. Burykina, Yu. I. Moskalev and V. N. Strel'tsova, V. N. Strel'tsova, V. N. Strel'tsova and Yu. I. Moskalev) and from our own results, nephrosclerosis is a constant symptom of chronic forms of radiation sickness, produced by intake of radioactive substances.

The lesions observed in the epithelium of the straight tubules of the kidneys and the urinary bladder were most clearly seen in rabbits of the second group and are obviously connected with the prolonged direct effect of ^{60}Co excreted by the kidneys. As has already been mentioned above, in two pregnant rabbits of the second group, early intrauterine fetal death was observed. Whether the cause of death was a disturbance of uterine-placental circulation (L. A. Kulikovskaya), or the toxic effect of ^{60}Co circulating in the blood, remains obscure. The serious dystrophic and atrophic lesions discovered in the gonads in a number of cases led to the complete breakdown of the seminiferous tubules of the testes and a decrease in the number of primordial and maturing follicles of the ovaries. These changes are similar to those described by other writers with general and local external, and internal radiation (N. N. Litvinov; A. V. Mel'nichenko; B. A. Fedorov; Bloom; L. Gempel'man, G. Lisco and D. Gofman).

The hemosiderosis of internal organs noticed in 3 rabbits is apparently connected with the hemolysis of qualitatively deficient erythrocytes produced by the bone marrow. This possibility is indicated by the serious lesions of the liver and gastric mucosa.

Pulmonary lesions in some of the killed rabbits (thickening of the interalveolar septa due to proliferation of histiocytes) can hardly be considered specific because similar thickenings were observed in some of the control rabbits. Interstitial infiltration of the myocardium occurring mainly in the second group rabbits which died, is evidently connected with a change in the reactive properties of the whole body.

To conclude this discussion we would once again like to remark that in 2 of 21 experimental rabbits tumours developed: myxosarcoma and myoma. These observations are of considerable interest in the light of the known capacity of radioactive substances to produce growths.

CONCLUSIONS

1. Chronic administration to rabbits of ^{60}Co (in doses of 1.25 and 12.5 μc/kg weight of animal) produces significant pathological lesions in the organs and in a series of cases leads to death of the animal.
2. Chronic administration to rabbits of ^{60}Co sharply lowers the body's resistance.
3. In most rabbits as a rule the following were noticed: (a) pronounced lesions of the hemopoietic organs; (b) proliferation of cells of the reticulo-endothelial system in various organs; (c) so-called specific pneumonias; (d) atrophic and sclerotic lesions of the mucous membrane of the gastro-intestinal tract; (e) dystrophic, and sometimes even necrobiotic, lesions of the liver; (f) diffuse interstitial focal sclerosis of the kidneys; (g) lesions of the urinary bladder epithelium; (h) dystrophic and atrophic lesions of the gonads.
4. In some cases the following were observed: hemosiderosis of internal organs, intrauterine fetal death and development of tumours.
5. The degree of evidence of these pathological changes in the organs depended on ^{60}Co concentration and the individual sensitivity of the animal.

REFERENCES

ACKERMAN and BELLIOS, Quoted by Ya. L. Rapoport, *Arkh. patolog.* **2,** 13 (1957).
BLOOM W., *Radiology* **49,** 3, 344 (1957).
BURYKINA L. N., *Toxicology of Radioactive Substances.* (Materialy po toksikologii radioaktivnykh veshchestv.) Vol. I, 102–115 (1957). English translation published by Pergamon Press (1962).
ENGELSTAD R. B., *Acta radiologica*, Stockholm (1934).
ERLEKSOVA YE. V., *Proceedings of a Conference on the Remote Effects of Radiation Injury.* (Referaty dokladov na konferentsii po otdalennym posledstviyam porazhenii, vyzvannykh vozdeistviyem ioniziruyushchei radiatsii.) 33–35, Medgiz (1956).

FEDOROV B. A., *Proceedings of a Students' Conference on Medical Radiology.* (Tezisy dokladov konferentsii molodykh uchenykh po voprosam meditsinskoi radiologii.) 12, Leningrad (1955).
GEMPEL'MAN L., LISKO G. and GOFMAN D., *The Acute Radiation Syndrome.* (Ostryi luchevoi sindrom.) Leningrad (1954).
GUSEV N. G., *A Reference Book on Radioactive Radiation and Protection.* (Spravochnik po radioaktivnykh izlucheniyam i zashchite.) Medgiz, (1956).
IVANOV A. E., *Arkhiv patologii* 1, 31-36 (1957).
KRAYEVSKII N. A., *Outlines of the Pathological Anatomy of Radiation Sickness.* (Ocherki patologicheskoi anatomii luchevoi bolezni.) Medgiz, Moscow (1957). English translation in preparation by Pergamon Press.
KRAYEVSKII N. A., *Radiation Medicine. A Handbook for Doctors and Students.* (Radiatsionnaya meditsina. Rukovodstvo dlya vrachei i studentov.) 257-275, Medgiz, Moscow (1955).
KULIKOVSKAYA L. A., *Proceedings of a Conference on the Effect of Ionizing Radiation on Pregnancy, Development of the Fetus and Newborn.* (Tezisy dokladov konferentsii po voprocam vliyaniya ioniziruyushchego izlucheniya na techeniye beremennosti, razvitiye ploda i novorozhdennogo.) 12-13, Leningrad (1957).
LITVINOV N. N., *Outlines of the Pathological Anatomy of Radiation Sickness.* (Ocherki patologicheskoi anatomii luchevoi bolezni.) by N. A. Krayevskii, 92-111, Medgiz, Moscow (1957).
MEL'NICHENKO A. V., *The Use of Radioactive Isotopes in Medicine.* (Opyt primeneniya radioaktivnykh izotopov v meditsine.) Ed. R. E. Kavetskii and I. G. Shevchenko, 169-174, Kiev (1955).
MOGIL'NITSKII B. N. and BRUMSHTEIN M. S., *Arkh. patolog.* 8, 3, 48-58 (1943).
MOGIL'NITSKII B. N. and BRUMSHTEIN M. S., *Vest. rentgenol. i radiol.* 1, 49-56 (1952).
MOSKALEV Yu. I., and STRELTSOVA B. N., *Med. radiol.* 1, 6, 14-20 (1956).
NOVIKOVA A. P., *Proceedings of a Conference on the Remote Effects of Radiation Injury.* (Referaty dokladov na konferentsii po otdalennym posledstviyam porazhenii vyzvannykh vozdeistviyem iziziruyushchei radiatsii.) 22-25, Medgiz (1956).
PINUS A. A., *Med. radiol.* 1, 55-63 (1957).
STREL'TSOVA V. N. and MOSKALEV Yu. I., *Med. radiol.* 3, 23-34 (1957).
TAGUNOVA G. A., *Outlines of the Pathological Anatomy of Radiation Sickness.* (Ocherki patologicheskoi anatomii luchevoi bolezni.) by N. A. Krayevskii, 74, Medgiz, Moscow (1957). English translation in preparation by Pergamon Press.
VEIDMAN V. K. and YASVOIN G. V., *Vest. rentgenol. i radiol.* 13, No. 4, 250-261 (1934).
WORREN S. and DUNLAP C. E., *Arch. Pathol.* 34, 562 (1942).

THE EFFECT OF CYCLOHEXANDIAMINOTETRA-ACETIC ACID (CDTA) ON EXCRETION OF RADIOACTIVE STRONTIUM ADN COBALT

A. A. Rubanovskaya

The search for means of stimulating the excretion of radioactive isotopes localized in different parts of the body is of great theoretical and practical interest. It is especially important in the case of radioisotopes which localize in bone, because many of them (Pu, ^{89}Sr and ^{90}Sr, ^{91}Y) have a long effective half-life and constitute a significant potential danger.

More than one attempt has been made to find such agents which stimulate excretion. The attempts of a number of writers, using different biochemical and physiological processes, have been unsuccessful. Action on mineral and protein metabolism, endocrine system (hyperthyroidism, injection of parathormone) and other methods have not produced satisfactory results in the treatment of radiation injuries.

Some preparations have however proved extremely promising e.g. chelating agents or complex forming compounds.

The mechanism of action of complex forming compounds lies in the fact that the metallic ion loses its capacity for chemical reactions and is quickly removed through the kidneys.

These preparations must fulfil the following requirements: (1) dissolve in water; (2) not be retained for long and not dissociate in the body; (3) not be toxic, because in order to retard dissociation of the complex in the body the preparation is injected in excess; (4) the dissociation constants of the compounds and the isotopes must have fairly low pH and low ion concentration in the body.

A number of the preparations which have been tried have been ineffective because they failed to meet the above requirements (bile acids, dithizone, ascorbic, nicotinic, isothiopropionic acids, carboxyethylsulphide, etc.) (Scott, Crowley and Foreman, 1949; Catsch, 1956).

Sodium citrate, BAL, unithiole, poly- and metaphosphates, EDTA and some others, have proved effective for particular radioisotopes. Sodium citrate increases excretion of plutonium and thorium but has little effect on excretion of radiostrontium; BAL sharply increases excretion of polonium in the urine and redistributes the isotope away from the sensitive hemopoietic organs and tissues to the less sensitive muscular tissue (Hurch, 1945, 1949). The attempts to use BAL for stimulating excretion of other isotopes—radium (Weikel and Lorenz, 1948), yttrium (Kawin and Copp, 1953), strontium (Cohn and Gong, 1953), thorium (Neuman and Harbers, 1953) and others—have been unsuccessful.

Thus BAL has only a limited use. Polyphosphates, hexametaphosphate, metaphosphates, nitriltriacetate and uramyldiacetate also influence the speed of excretion from the body of a number of metals (D. I. Semenov, 1957).

Yatren, euphilline and dimethylaminoantipyrine intensify excretion of radiostrontium in the later stages of intoxication (G. E. Fradkin, 1954).

EDTA is the most effective preparation. EDTA forms exceptionally strong compounds with the cations of a number of metals, especially with the rare earth and transuranic elements. These compounds are rapidly excreted from the body.

However, even this preparation is ineffective with radioactive barium, strontium and radium. This absence of a therapeutic effect can be explained by the fact that the EDTA binds with calcium in the body and the bond with calcium is more stable by about a factor of 2 than with strontium and radium.

At later periods after radioisotope poisoning EDTA also has only a slight effect.

According to Schubert (1947), 1955) zirconium citrate intensifies excretion of plutonium and yttrium from the body and lessens deposition of these isotopes in the skeleton. With strontium poisoning the effect is much less pronounced.

The mechanism of action of zirconium salts, according to Schubert, is as follows. Within the limits of physiological magnitudes of pH zirconium salts hydrolyse with formation of highly dispersive colloidal aggregates, passing easily through the kidneys. The aggregates adsorb or include the radioactive isotope, thus facilitating its excretion. The effect of zirconium is greater at short times after injection of the radioisotope. The efficacy of Zr in chronic intoxication has been studied in a few experiments. It was shown that at later periods after Pu poisoning, when excretion of Pu from the bones has reached a low level, injection of Zr also increases excretion of Pu in the urine by approximately 10 times. However, this treatment can have no practical importance because the amount of the isotope excreted is negligible compared with skeletal content. Many years of zirconium treatment would be required for the complete removal of the plutonium deposited in the bones.

Following along these lines of the mode of action of zirconium salts, various colloidal substances were tested (colloidal stains: congo red, trypan blue, albumin, peristone, etc.), but they all proved virtually ineffective.

Thus, despite the many investigations in this direction, the arsenal of means for stimulating excretion of radioactive isotopes especially of the bone group is at present very limited. Therefore the search for new stimulants is all the more urgent.

Tests have been carried out on a preparation synthesized in the All-Union Scientific Chemico-Pharmaceutical Institute—cyclohexandiamino-tetra-acetic acid and its calcium disodium salt ($CaNa_2$ CDTA). The effect of this preparation on deposition and excretion from the body was studied on two elements having a different pattern of localization, radiostrontium and radiocobalt. Strontium was used as a represetnative of the bone group, accumulating in the skeleton; ^{60}Co is diffusely dispersed, with predominant deposition in the parenchymatous organs.

The experiments were carried out on rats. Each series in each set of experiments comprised 10 rats (5 controls receiving the isotope and 5 experimental, the isotope plus the therapeutic preparation). The doses were chosen on the basis of a preliminary investigation on the tolerance of white mice (Table 1).

TABLE 1

Tolerance of the preparation (doses in milligrams) with intraperitoneal injection

No. of experiment	Number of animals	Injections	After ½ hr	After 1 hr	After 1½ hr	After 2 hr	After 3 hr	Total dose	Number of mice surviving a month
1	20	10	10	10		10	10	50	20
2	20	10	10	10	10	10		50	20

No symptoms of intoxication were observed in mice 2–3 hr after intraperitoneal injection of $CaNa_2$ CDTA in a dose of 200 mg per 100 g weight. The animals were kept under observation for a month. This preparation was later used in doses of 40–120 mg per rat.

FIRST SERIES. ^{89}Sr EXPERIMENTS

Radioactive strontium was injected intraperitoneally at a level of 5 μc per animal. Immediately afterwards the 5 rats in each experiment were given an intraperitoneal injection of a neutralized solution of cyclohexandiaminotetra-acetic acid (40 mg per rat) and a simultaneous subcutaneous injection of an equivalent amount of calcium gluconate.

Injection of the preparation without calcium produces convulsions and death within a few minutes or hours depending on the dose. This effect is brought about by developing hypocalcaemia resulting from the fixation of blood calcium by the preparation. A second injection of the preparation was given an hour after the first.

The rats were kept in interchangeable cells. After 2 days they were killed and the ^{89}Sr content of the bones, soft tissues and excreta were determined. The tests were made on 32 rats. The amount of ^{89}Sr excreted during the 2 days comprised from 28.4 to 40.5 per cent of the injected dose of ^{89}Sr. No differences were detected in the excretion of ^{89}Sr between the control and experimental rats. Correspondingly, deposition of ^{89}Sr in the bones was approximately the same in both groups (Table 2).

TABLE 2

Effect of CDTA on deposition in the skeleton and excretion of ^{89}Sr in rats

No. of experiment	Number of animals	in complete femur control	in complete femur experimental	in g weight of femur control	in g weight of femur experimental	in excreta control	in excreta experimental
1	6	3.62±0.23	3.70±0.25	—	—	40.5±1.57	30.2±1.26
2	10	3.36±0.14	3.33±0.18	5.57±0.23	5.21±0.42	28.4±1.73	30.0±2.1
3	10	3.15±0.13	2.95±0.17	5.50±0.22	5.15±0.4	34.6±2.58	37.1±2.07
4	6	1.46±0.10	1.34±0.07	1.63±0.08	1.42±0.11	—	—

The radioactivity of the soft tissues and organs of control and experimental rats was negligible scarcely exceeding background. In an attempt to create a more prolonged circulation of the preparation in the blood a droplet method of injection was used in one experiment. A single dose of the preparation (80 mg) in 2 ml. of solution was injected intraperitoneally into three old rats for 1–1½ hr. Injections were repeated for 3 days (Table 2, experiment 4). Under these conditions, CDTA had again no detectable effect on deposition of ^{89}Sr in the bones. As can be seen from Table 2, the radioactivity of the femur of the experimental rats did not differ from that of the controls.

Thus, injection of CDTA immediately after ^{89}Sr intoxication, i.e. under the most favourable conditions for interaction with the isotope, does not increase excretion nor lower deposition of ^{89}Sr in bone.

SECOND SERIES. ^{60}Co EXPERIMENTS

^{60}Co was injected intraperitoneally in a dose of 5–8 μc per rat (3.5 μc per 100 g weight).

The calcium disodium salt of cyclohexandiaminotetra-acetic acid was injected in different doses: a single 40 mg injection or a double injection of 20 mg or 30 mg.

The preparation was injected at various times after ^{60}Co administration; immediately, after 30 min, 1 hr, 3 hr and 48 hr.

Immediately after injection of the preparation the rats were placed in interchangeable cells from which excreta were collected daily.

Table 3 gives the results of the ^{60}Co activity in one day's urine and feces of both the controls and the experimental rats which received CaNa$_2$ CDTA immediately after ^{60}Co injection.

It can be seen that during the first day after intraperitoneal injection of ^{60}Co the control rats excreted from 50.5 to 66.3 per cent of the injected dose. Under these conditions excretion occurs chiefly in the urine (from 40.5 to 57.1 per cent) while only from 5.2 to 10.0 per cent of the dose is excreted in the feces. Resorption by the organs and excretion of most of the ^{60}Co terminates within a short period after administration. Maximum excretion of ^{60}Co is reached $3\frac{1}{2}$ hr after intraperitoneal injection. During the following 8–20 hr the intensity of excretion changes little. Excreta collected at $3\frac{1}{2}$, 11 and 24 hr exhibit almost identical radioactivity.

It can be seen from Table 3 that injection of the preparation immediately after ^{60}Co injection produces a significant rise in activity of excretion. Rats which had received the preparation excreted on average from 77.5 to 88.1 per cent of the injected dose.

Compared with the controls, excretion in these rats was increased by 26–53 per cent. This increased excretion of ^{60}Co occurred in the urine. ^{60}Co content of the feces of experimental rats differed little from that of the controls. This fact that the preparation increases ^{60}Co excretion only in the urine and within a short time after injection indicates that compound formation occurs in the blood. The compound formed is highly soluble and rapidly filters through the kidneys.

Comparison of the doses used shows that the 40 mg dose gives greatest fixation and excretion of injected ^{60}Co. Subsequent increase of the total dose to 60 mg (2 injections of 30 mg an hour apart) does not modify the effect. Division of the total dose of 40 mg into two injections of 20 mg also has virtually no effect on the amount of ^{60}Co excreted.

Increase in ^{60}Co excretion from the body causes a decline in deposition in the tissues and organs. Less radioactivity was found in the tissues and organs of rats which had received the preparation immediately after

EFFECT OF CDTA ON EXCRETION 169

TABLE 3

Excretion of ^{60}Co in urine and feces of rats following immediate injection of CaNa$_2$ CDTA

No. of experiment	Number of animals	Dose CaNa$_2$ CDTA per rat	in the urine control	in the urine experimental	in the feces control	in the feces experimental	total control	total experimental	Excretion as percentage of control
1	10	40 mg once	40.5±1.70	71.6±1.94	10.0±2.90	5.9±1.41	50.5±2.18	77.5±2.30	153.4
2	10	20 mg twice	52.4±4.12	77.1±4.89	5.2±0.70	11.0±1.10	57.6±4.47	88.1±4.00	152.9
3	10	20 mg twice	—	—	—	—	63.4±0.31	80.0±2.64 in 11 hr	126.1
4	10	30 mg twice	—	—	—	—	54.8±0.52	79.8±2.12 in 3½ hr	145.6
5	10	30 mg twice	—	75.5±3.00	—	8.8±0.48	—	84.3±2.57	—
6	10	30 mg twice	57.1±0.58	71.3±0.70	9.2±0.57	16.0±2.40	66.3±0.93	87.3±3.10	131.6

TABLE 4

^{60}Co *content of organs and tissues of rats following immediate injection of CaNa$_2$ CDTA (as percentage of amount injected in whole organ)*

No. of experiment	Dose of CaNa$_2$ CDTA per rat	Blood	Liver	Kidneys	Lungs	Spleen	Small intestine	Muscle	
1	0	1.16±0.170	6.60±0.630	0.72±0.050	0.08±0.006	0.12±0.015	—	—	
	40 mg once	0.12±0.010	0.26±0.020	0.37±0.020	0	0	—	—	
2	0	2.0±0.110	7.89±0.250	1.22±0.060	0.15±0.010	0.16±0.013	1.77±0.065	2.96±0.300	Killed after 11 hr
	20 mg twice	0.16±0.020	0.45±0.005	0.52±0.030	0.025±0.002	0.01±0.001	0.20±0.020	1.27±0.170	
3	0	2.29±0.130	11.30±0.820	1.76±0.098	0.17±0.012	0.22±0.028	3.30±0.170	2.70±0.230	Killed after 3½ hr
	20 mg twice	0.13±0.007	0.95±0.059	0.62±0.047	0.22±0.002	0.04±0.006	1.55±0.290	1.80±0.510	
4	0	3.02±0.220	10.80±1.400	2.26±0.060	0.18±0.018	0.24±0.017	5.11±0.340	3.80±0.440	
	30 mg twice	0.43±0.014	1.95±0.240	0.79±0.030	0.04±0.002	0.04±0.002	0.68±0.013	0.78±0.120	
5	0	—	5.81±0.770	0.78±0.080	0.08±0.004	0.09±0.010	—	0.71±0.060	
6	30 mg twice	0.18±0.030	0.48±0.037	0.50±0.044	0.015±0.000	0.009±0.0003	0.18±0.020	0.71±0.130	
7	30 mg twice	0.25±0.028	0.36±0.038	0.36±0.010	0.012±0.002	0.009±0.0003	0.17±0.010	0.29±0.017	
	0	—	2.45±0.190	0.31±0.014	0.038±0.001	0.044±0.003	—	—	Killed after 5 days
	20 mg twice	—	0.10±0.010	0.075±0.010	0.018±0.000	0.011±0.002	—	—	

injection of ^{60}Co than in those of the control animals. Most experimental rat tissues examined contained several times less ^{60}Co than the tissues of the controls. ^{60}Co content of the liver—the organ of greatest accumulation of this isotope—fell particularly fast. Radioactivity in the liver of experimental rats was in some tests 25 times less than in the control animals.

As Tables 4 and 5 show, the ^{60}Co content in the liver of experimental rats is only 4 to 18 per cent of liver content in the controls.

These experiments have shown that injection of the preparation immediately after ^{60}Co intoxication gives rise to increased excretion of the isotope from the body and forestalls its deposition in the organs and tissues.

TABLE 5

^{60}Co *content of rat liver following immediate injection of* CaNa$_2$ *CDTA*

No. of experiment	Control rats percentage of injected in whole organ	Experimental rats percentage of injected in whole organ	percentage of control
1	6.60	0.26	4.0
2	7.89	0.45	5.7
3	11.30	0.95	8.4
4	10.80	1.95	18.0
5	5.81	0.48	8.2
7	2.45	0.10	4.0

In a further series of experiments the effect of the preparation on excretion of ^{60}Co fixed in the tissues was tested. In these experiments the preparation was injected at various intervals after ^{60}Co injection: 48 hr, 3 hr, 1 hr and $\frac{1}{2}$ hr. Injection of the preparation was begun 48 hr after an injection of 18 μc ^{60}Co. The preparation was injected intraperitoneally in two doses of 30 mg (0.3 ml.) 2 days apart. The control rats received an equal volume of physiological saline.

When radioactivity of tissues and organs was measured no positive effect of the preparation could be detected.

The ^{60}Co found in the tissues of experimental and control rats under these conditions is alike. Since at 48 hr after injection the ^{60}Co contained in the body is more or less fixed in the tissues it can be concluded from these experiments that the preparation does not stimulate excretion of ^{60}Co from the tissues. It is clear that cobalt fixation by the tissue components is stronger than by the preparation. The preparation cannot

TABLE 6

^{60}Co content of tissues and organs of rats following injection of CaNa$_2$ CDTA 2 days, 3 hr, 1 hr and $\frac{1}{2}$ hr after ^{60}Co administration as percentage of amount received in whole organ

No. of experiment	Interval after ^{60}Co intoxication	Dose of CaNa$_2$CDTA per rat	Blood	Liver	Kidneys	Lungs	Spleen	Small intestine	Muscle
8	48 hr	0	0.42±0.030	5.51±0.30	0.67±0.018	0.07±0.002	0.09±0.008	0.62±0.045	1.60±0.140
		30 mg times	0.40±0.026	5.82±0.34	0.79±0.022	0.06±0.003	0.08±0.006	0.67±0.014	1.75±0.076
9	3 hr	0	2.27±0.110	7.30±0.44	1.03±0.060	0.12±0.004	0.11±0.007	1.62±0.100	1.60±0.150
		30 mg twice	1.98±0.080	5.85±0.11	1.57±0.200	0.11±0.006	0.10±0.006	1.85±0.160	1.70±0.080
10	3 hr	0	2.71±0.200	8.70±0.26	1.30±0.170	0.15±0.007	0.11±0.010	1.90±0.140	2.38±0.200
		30 mg twice	2.55±0.220	6.50±0.51	2.00±0.130	0.13±0.020	0.14±0.006	1.53±0.140	1.63±0.120
11	1 hr	0	2.93±0.050	7.26±0.50	1.22±0.090	0.17±0.020	0.14±0.014	2.38±0.360	2.37±0.130
		30 mg twice	2.70±0.200	5.60±0.37	2.67±0.260	0.18±0.017	0.18±0.010	2.28±0.070	1.75±0.140
12	$\frac{1}{2}$ hr	0	2.52±0.063	6.40±0.31	0.92±0.038	0.14±0.014	0.11±0.010	1.77±0.083	1.80±0.200
		30 mg twice	2.16±0.130	4.30±0.37	2.27±0.240	0.15±0.018	0.11±0.016	1.57±0.140	2.00±0.130
	$\frac{1}{2}$ hr	30 mg twice	2.20±0.28	4.00±0.12	2.40±0.190	0.16±0.010	0.075±0.006	1.76±0.210	1.90±0.240

dislodge the cobalt from the tissues. The binding of ^{60}Co with the preparation occurs only in the blood.

With shortening of the time interval between injections from 3 hr to ½ hr the preparation has a slight effect. Injection at these times produces a small decline of ^{60}Co in the liver but the amount of the isotope contained in the kidneys increases. In the other organs examined no radioactivity changes were noted.

The results of these experiments are presented in Table 6.

Thus, CaNa$_2$ CDTA is a means of accelerating excretion of ^{60}Co from the body and of preventing its deposition when it is administered very soon after intake of the isotope.

These results are similar to those obtained by other writers with EDTA. Although the dissociation constant of the compound of EDTA and cobalt is fairly low the use of EDTA gives only slight therapeutic effect. Some writers (Schubert) put forward the explanation that cobalt enters easily into reactions with various organic compounds, and in the body cobalt comes into contact with natural compound-formers (aminoacids, oxyacids and other products of metabolism) which have higher stability constants with ^{60}Co, than does CaNa$_2$ CDTA.

It can be assumed that the lack of effect of the preparation when injected 2 days after ^{60}Co intoxication is caused by this fixation with "compound-formers" in the body. The lack of effect with ^{89}Sr engenders the conclusion that the compound of CDTA with Ca is more stable than with Sr, as has been established for EDTA. A comparison of EDTA with CDTA was not part of the present work and should be the subject of special investigation. However, the most superficial comparison of our results with those of other writers concerning EDTA indicates that with ^{60}Co intoxication CDTA is no less effective than EDTA.

CONCLUSIONS

1. Cyclohexandiaminotetra-acetic acid does not react in the body with Sr even under the most favourable conditions. The preparation does not lower deposition of the isotope in the bones.
2. CaNa$_2$ CDTA intensifies excretion of ^{60}Co from the body and diminishes its deposition in the organs and tissues when injected immediately after injection of the isotope. The efficacy of CaNa$_2$ CDTA declines sharply with increase of the interval between ^{60}Co injection and administration of the preparation.

REFERENCES

CATSCH A., Experimentelle Grundlagen einer Therapie der Vergiftung mit radioaktiven Substanzen, *Strahlentherapie* **99**, 2 (1956).

COHN J. Cited by SCHUBERT J., *Annu. Rev. Nuclear Sci.* **5** (1955).

Cohn J., Gong K. and Fischler, *Nucleonics* **1** (1953).
Cohn S. and Gong K., *Proc. Soc. Exper. Biol. Med.* **83,** 3 (1953).
Foreman H. and Hamilton J., *AECD,* 3247 (1951).
Foreman H., Fugua Th. and Norwood, *Arch. Ind. Hyg. Occup. Med.* **10,** 3 (1954).
Hart H. and Laszlo D., *Science* **118,** 3053 (1953).
Hurch J., *J. Pharmac. Exper. Therap.* **103,** (1951).
Kawin B. and Copp, *Proc. Soc. Exper. Biol. Med.* **84,** 576 (1953).
Luganskii N. I. and Loboda Yu. A., *The Effect of Unithiole on Distribution, Accumulation and Excretion of Radioactive Arsenic in Rabbits.* (Vliyaniye unitiola na raspredeleniye, nakopleniye i vyvedeniye radioaktivnogo mysh'yaka u krolikov.) Proceedings of the All-Union Conference on the use of radioactive and stable isotopes in agriculture and science, Moscow (1957).
Neuman K. and Harbers E., *Arch. Exper. Pathol. Pharmac.* **217,** 64 (1953).
Scott K. G., Crowley J. and Foreman H., Cited by Schubert J., *Annu. Rev. Nuclear Sci.* **5** (1955).
Schubert J., *Science* **105,** 2728 (1947).
Schubert J., *Annu. Rev. Nuclear Sci.* **5** (1955).
Semenov D. I., *The Effect of Chemical Agents on Mineral Metabolism in the Body.* (Vliyaniye kompleksonov na mineral'nyi obmen v organizme.) Proceedings of the All-Union Conference on the use of radioactive and stable isotopes in agriculture and science, Moscow (1957).
Weikel J. and Lorenz, *Radiology* **51,** 865 (1948).

THE LONG-TERM EFFECTS OF INTRATRACHEAL INJECTION OF SOLUBLE AND INSOLUBLE COMPOUNDS OF CERTAIN RADIOISOTOPES (^{24}NaCl, Cr^{32}PO$_4$ AND COLLOIDAL ^{198}Au)*

T. A. KOCHETKOVA and G. A. ABRUNINA

A NUMBER of factors are important in the action of radioactive substances on the body: toxicity, solubility, distribution, duration of action, methods of administration and excretion, doses, state of reactivity of the body, species, sex and age, etc. (D. I. Zakutinskii, B. N. Taruzov, N. A. Krayevskii, E. B. Kurlyandskaya, G. S. Strelin, P. D. Gorizontov, I. A. Pigalev et al.).

With inhalation of radioactive aerosols the respiratory tracts receive the "first blow" of radiation. When the substance is absorbed rapidly its effect on the lungs is short-lived. If, however, it is only slightly soluble or completely insoluble then it is expelled slowly or remains almost wholly in the lungs subjecting them to prolonged selective irradiation.

The changes which arise in consequence of prolonged irradiation of the body, and the long-term effects of brief, single and multiple exposures constitute one of the problems of contemporary radiobiology so far largely neglected.

There is no information in the literature on the changes arising after intratracheal injection of experimental animals (white rats) with radioactive sodium (^{24}Na) and phosphorus (^{32}P). Meneely et al. have reported on the effect of gold (^{198}Au) but only over short observation periods (up to 15 days).

In L. N. Burykina's experiments with ruthenium dioxide (^{103}RuO$_2$) lesions of the epithelium of the bronchial mucosa developed 37, 44, and 60 days after an intratracheal injection of 0.7–1.4 mc, changing from cylindrical to stratified squamous; after 7, 9 and 18 months foci of squa-

---

* This work was carried out in the Radiobiological Laboratory (Director: Professor E. B. Kurlyandskaya) and in the Pathoanatomy Laboratory (Director: Professor P. P. Dvizhkov).

mous cell carcinoma arose in the lungs. In certain animals bone tissue developed in the connective tissue of the lungs and in vascular walls. Engelstadt has described bone tissue growth in the lungs of rabbits after X-irradiation of the thorax. The formation of tumours after subjection of animals to other radioactive substances has been described by A. P. Novikova, V. N. Strel'tsova, P. L. Khamaide, Z. M. Bukhtoyarova, V. K. Lemberg, *et al.*

Three series of experiments were carried out with intratracheal injection: (1) ^{24}Na in the form of a solution of sodium chloride as a rapidly acting substance; (2) ^{32}P in the form of a suspension of insoluble chromium phosphate, and (3) colloidal ^{198}Au to elucidate the nature of changes arising with more prolonged local irradiation of the lungs.

The radiation doses received by the lungs after intratracheal injection of these radioactive substances were calculated and the damage in the lungs observed. Corresponding to the different half-lives and retention in the lungs of ^{24}NaCl, Cr^{32}PO$_4$ and colloidal ^{198}Au the doses varied for each substance. Dosimetric methods are described in an earlier article (pp. 16–17).

Radioactive sodium chloride in an amount of 1 ml. of 2.5 per cent ^{24}NaCl was injected once or several times (up to 6 times) into the trachea of white rats under ether (158 animals in all).

Radioactive sodium has a short half-life (T$\frac{1}{2}$ = 14.8 hr). Since NaCl solution is rapidly and comprehensively absorbed it is not retained long in the lungs. The action of ^{24}Na in the lungs was studied in a special experiment, in which the animals (28 rats) each received intratracheally 1 ml. of 2.5 per cent ^{24}NaCl and were killed after $\frac{1}{4}$, $\frac{1}{2}$, 1, 3, 6, 22 and 69 hr. The whole lungs were charred in sulphuric acid and activity of the hydrolysate determined. Activity was measured with an end-window β counter and expressed in units $S = c/c_0$ (p. 16).

Figure 1 shows activity in the lungs and other tissues. It can be seen that at different time intervals the activity in the lungs is dominant only during the first 3 hr, after which it falls to the level of that of the other organs. Activity in the muscles is throughout 1$\frac{1}{2}$–2 times less than in the other organs and blood.

The radiation dose in the lungs during the first 3 hr after injection of the substance, (Fig. 1), is fairly high. At this time the dose in all other tissues is many times less, indicating selective irradiation of the lungs with intratracheal injection of ^{24}NaCl. The calculated dose of β-radiation received selectively by the lungs (the γ-radiation dose in the lungs is low because of their small volume) is about 220 rep after injection of 1 mc ^{24}NaCl. The general radiation dose under these conditions does not exceed 10 rep. After 3 hr, when activity in all tissues has become almost similar, activity throughout the body is uniform at a low dose. The radiation dose decreases with the effective half-life, which is 12½ hr according to our data. The overall radiation dose (up to the virtual complete decay of the isotope, i.e. approximately 2–3 days), may reach the same magnitudes as the initial dose in the lungs.

FIG. 1. Specific activity of the lungs and other tissues in S units (specific activity of the tissue after administration of 1 mc) per animal weight with intratracheal injection of white rats with ^{24}NaCl. — Lungs; —·— Parenchymatous organs; —··— Muscles.

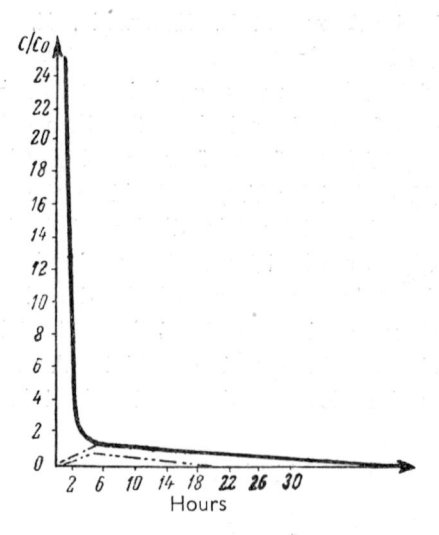

Table 1 gives the values of injected activity and the corresponding radiation doses in the lungs. The activity administered was limited by the low specific activity of the ^{24}NaCl obtained. The greatest single amount we were able to inject was 2.14 mc, which is equivalent to a selective lung

TABLE 1

Selective lung radiation doses with intratracheal injection of white rats with ^{24}NaCl

Animal group	Number of animals	Single dose (mc)	Dose (rep) single	Dose (rep) total
single I	34	0.17–0.22	35–45	
single II	29	0.765–1.17	150–250	
single III	12	2.14	460	
multiple IV (2–3 injections)	28	0.3–0.5	65–115	185–205
multiple V (4 injections)	22	0.7–1.9	160–420	1050
multiple VI (5–6 injections)	33	0.1–0.3	20–60	260–280

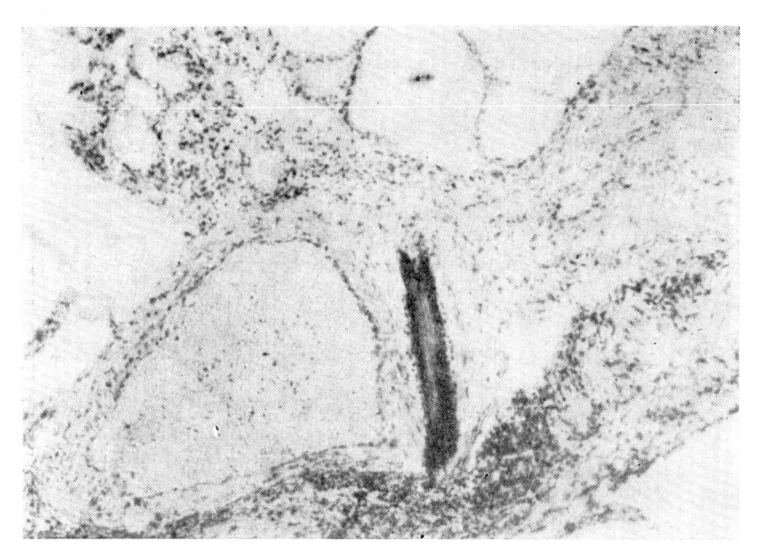

Fig. 2. Multiple injection of ^{24}NaCl (1.250 mc). Lung. Development of bone tissue in the muscle layer of the pulmonary artery. 5½ months after the last injection.

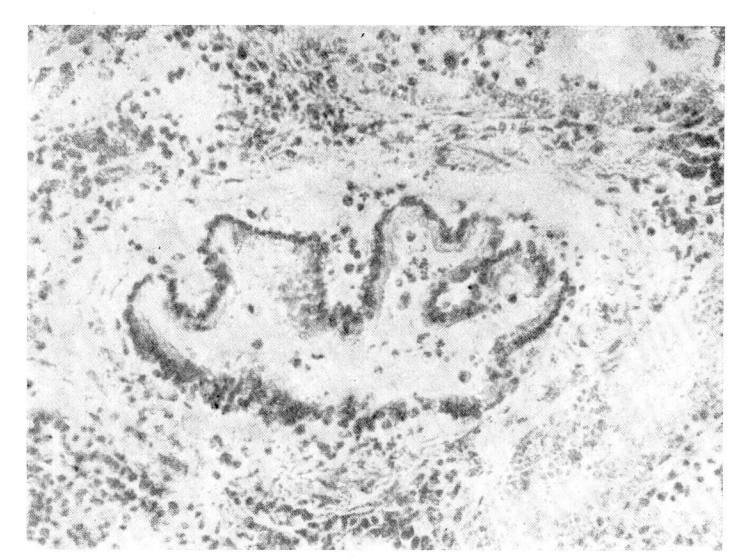

Fig. 3. Injection of 30 mg Cr^{32}PO$_4$ with activity 0.270 mc. Lung. Acute peribronchial oedema. Flaking-off of bronchial mucosa. 20 days.

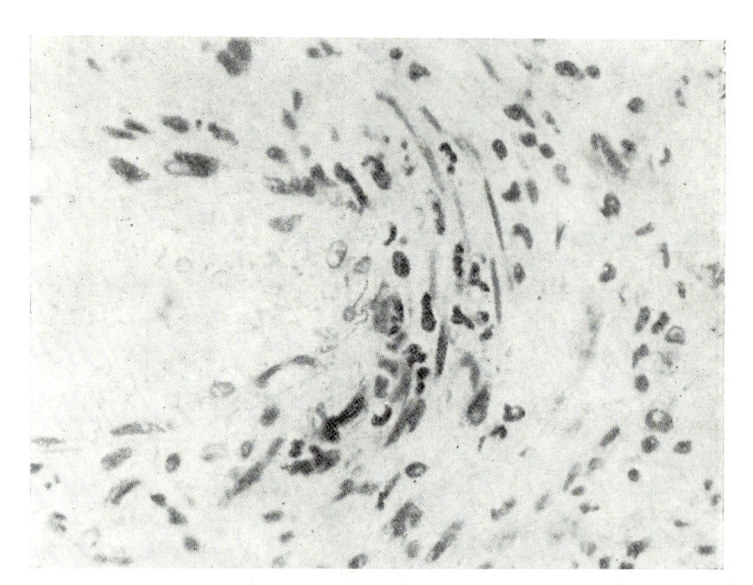

FIG. 4. Injection of 30 mg Cr^{32}PO$_4$ with activity 0.270 mc. Lung. Stratification of artery walls and infiltration by leukocytes. 8 days.

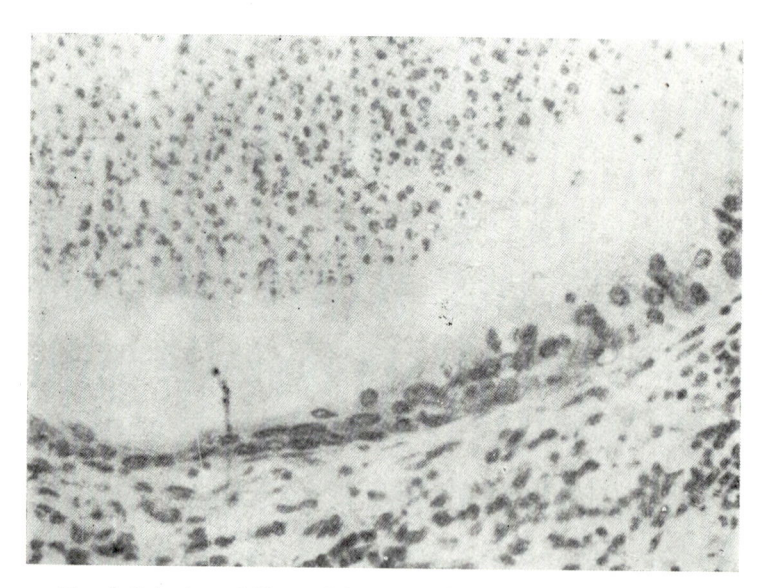

FIG. 5. Injection of 30 mg Cr^{32}PO$_4$ with activity of 0.270 mc. Lung. Suppurative bronchitis. Metaplasia of cylindrical epithelium of bronchial mucosa into stratified squamous 19 days.

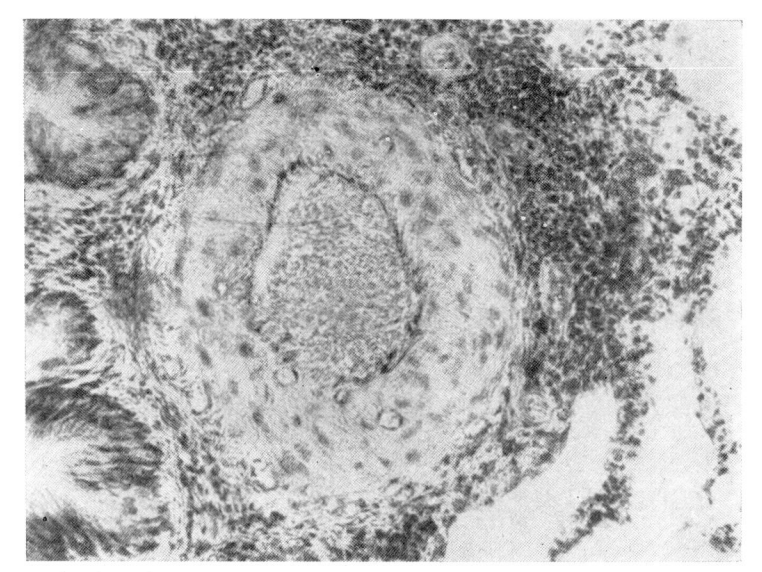

FIG. 6. Injection of 2 mg Cr^{32}PO$_4$ with activity 0.04 mc. Lung. Hypertrophy of muscle layer of blood vessel wall, hyperchromatism of nuclei. 150 days.

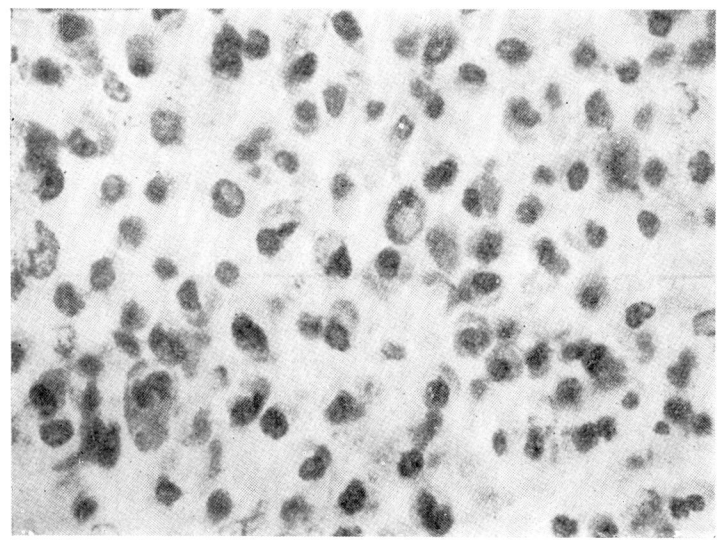

FIG. 7. Injection of 30 mg Cr^{32}PO$_4$ with activity 0.07 mc. Lung. Polymorphism of cell nuclei of an infiltrate around the bronchi and blood vessels.

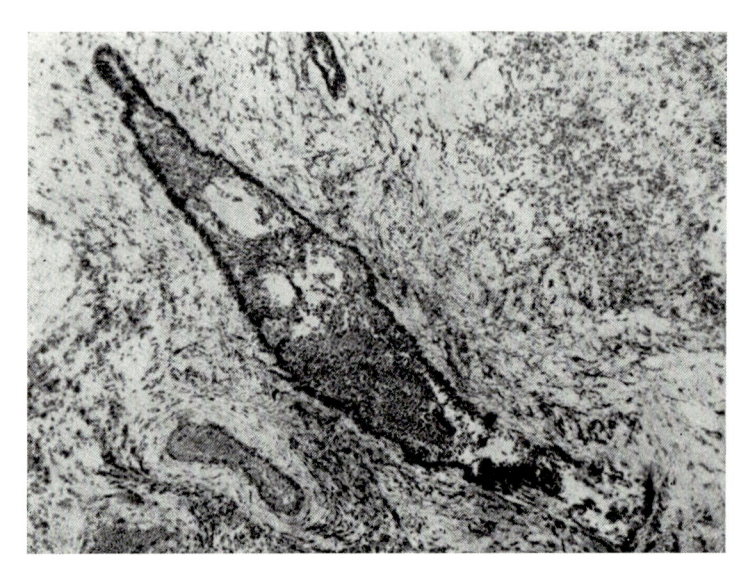

FIG. 8. Injection of 30 mg Cr^{32}PO$_4$ with activity 0.1 mc. Lung. Extensive perivascular and peribronchial scleroses. 58 days.

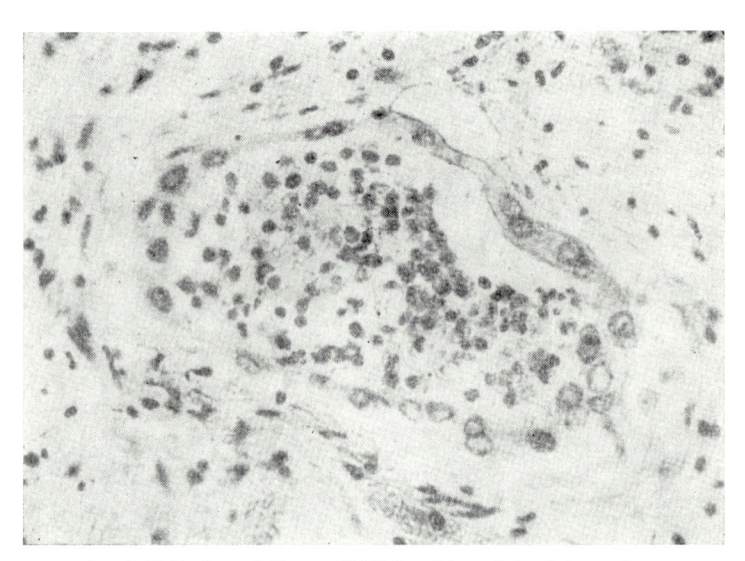

FIG. 9. Injection of 30 mg Cr^{32}PO$_4$ with activity 0.1 mc. Lung. Suppurative bronchitis. Metaplasia of the cylindrical epithelium of the bronchial mucosa into stratified squamous. 20 days.

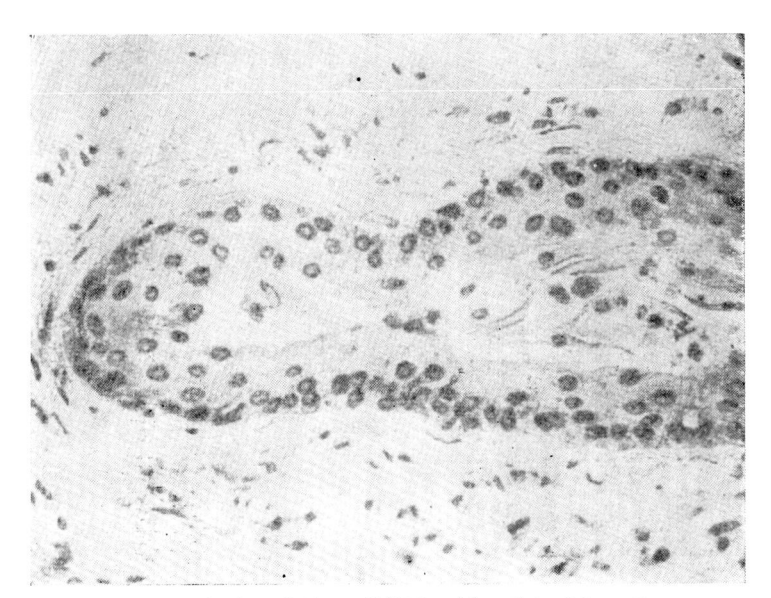

FIG. 10. Injection of 30 mg Cr^{32}PO$_4$ with activity 0.1 mc. Lung. Metaplasia of the epithelium of the bronchial mucosa. 58 days.

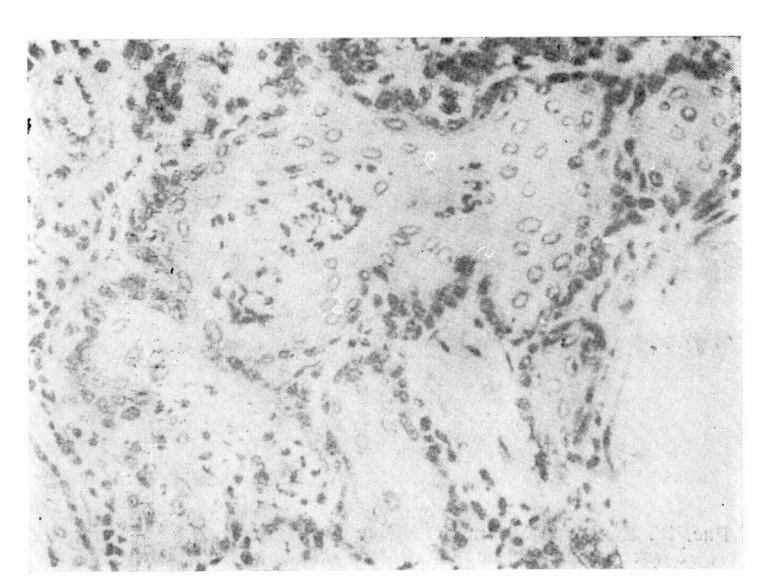

FIG. 11. Injection of 30 mg Cr^{32}PO$_4$ with activity 0.07 mc. Lung. Islets of stratified squamous epithelium with symptoms of keratinization. 58 days.

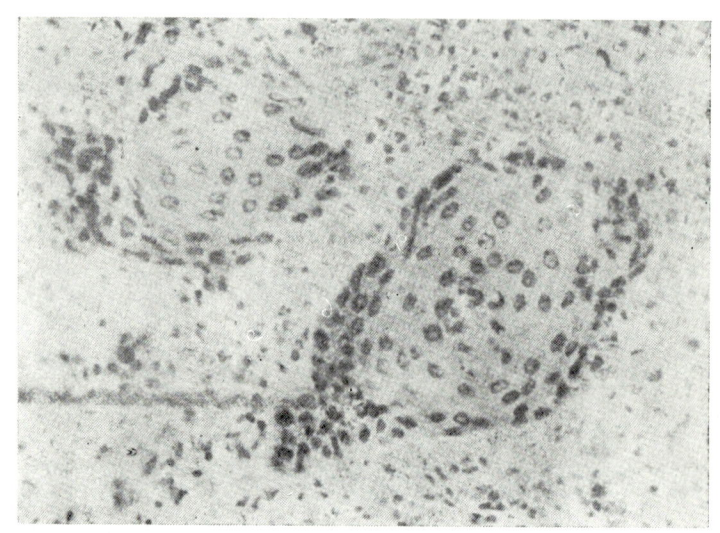

FIG. 12. Injection of 30 mg Cr^{32}PO$_4$ with activity 0.1 mc. Lung. Foci of stratified squamous epithelium with symptoms of keratinization (formation of pearls). 59 days

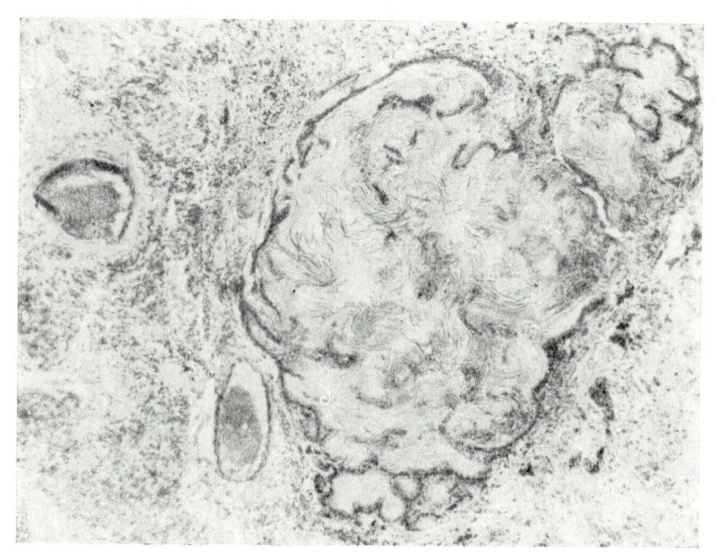

FIG. 13. Injection of 30 mg Cr^{32}PO$_4$ with activity 0.1 mc. Lung. Nodes of keratinous squamous cell carcinoma. 193 days.

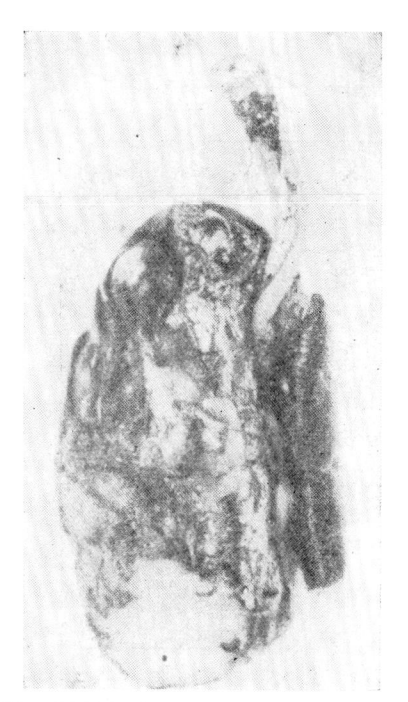

FIG. 14. Injection of 30 mg Cr^{32}PO$_4$ with activity 0.07 mc. Cancer of left lung with metastases in the right lung, pleura and regional lymph nodes. 395 days.

FIG. 15. Injection of 2 mg Cr^{32}PO$_4$ with activity 0.04 mc. Cancer of left lung with metastases along the pleura and in the regional lymph nodes. 510 days.

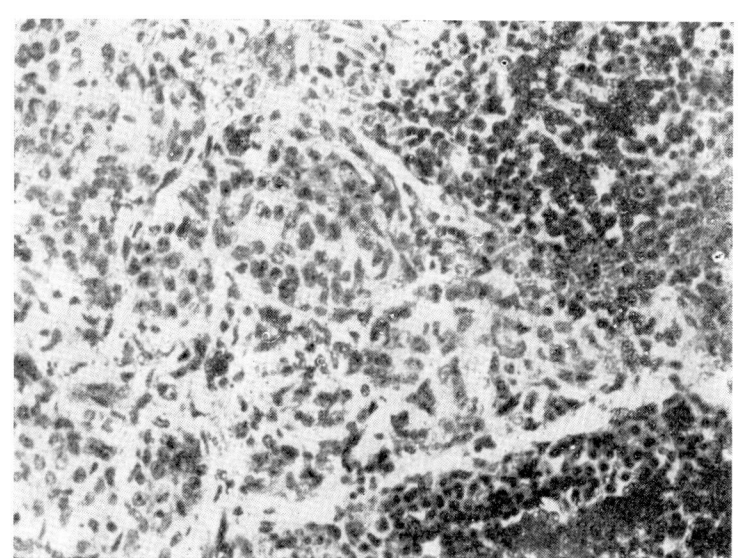

FIG. 16. Injection of 30 mg Cr^{32}PO$_4$ with activity 0.04 mc. Bifurcated lymph node. Metastases of squamous cell carcinoma. 210 days.

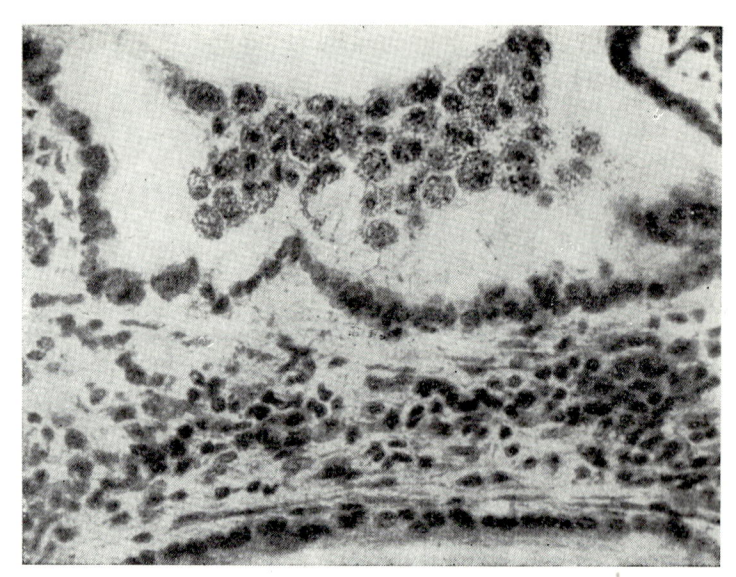

FIG. 17. Injection of 2 mg Cr^{32}PO$_4$ with activity 0.04 mc. Lung. Excretion of the substance by the epithelium of the bronchial mucosa. 75 days.

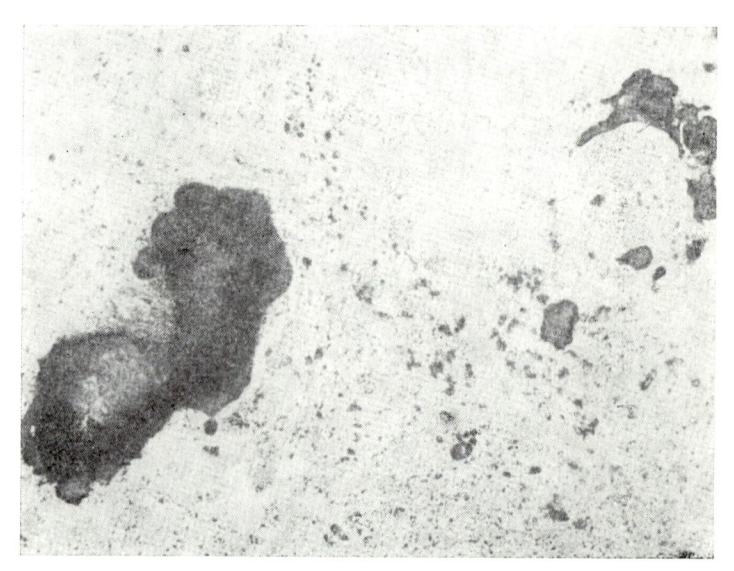

FIG. 18. Injection of 30 mg Cr^{32}PO$_4$ with activity 0.1 mc. Lung. Calcareous deposition, formation of bone tissue. 193 days.

radiation dose of about 450 rep. No marked clinical symptoms of radiation damage were observed with injection of this dose of ^{24}Na.

The rats died at various intervals after injection (from a month to $2\frac{1}{2}$ years). In more than half the animals (82 of 120) suppurative processes were observed in the lungs, middle ear cavity, skin, subcutaneous tissue, and purulent liquefaction of the fetus in uncompleted pregnancy. Such complications were rarely found in the control group injected intratracheally with 2.5 per cent sodium chloride (stable).

Histological examination of internal organs of 77 rats of this group disclosed the following lesions. In the lungs of rats which received a single dose of 0.170–0.220, 0.765, 1.17 and 2.14 mc and which died $2\frac{1}{2}$ months after injection, moderate enlargement of the alveolar septa due to proliferation of histiocytic elements, small round-cell infiltrates, catarrhal bronchitis, minor peribronchial and perivascular sclerosis and pulmonary emphysema were observed. After 5–6 months and 8–$10\frac{1}{2}$ months these same lesions were to be observed in the lungs, but more pronounced; in two rats with purulent-destructive bronchitis, symptoms of metaplasia of the epithelium of the bronchial mucosa from cylindrical to stratified squamous were observed.

In histological examination of the lungs of rats which had received several doses (up to 6) of radioactive sodium each of 0.1, 0.3 to 1.9 mc and which died early (21st–24th day) from chance causes (asphyxia, shock), symptoms of moderately expressed catarrhal bronchitis, diffuse peribronchial, perivascular oedema and small round-cell (mainly of lymphoid character) infiltrates around the bronchi and vessels were detected. In animals which died after 4–5 months, symptoms of focal interstitial pneumonia were also observed, and after 8–12 months and more, a chronic interstitial process and diffuse oedema. In one animal of this group, massive necrosis of the lung and purulent bronchitis was accompanied by metaplasia of the bronchial mucosal epithelium (from cylindrical to stratified squamous), as in the previous group; in another, bone tissue developed in the muscle layer of the pulmonary artery (Fig. 2). Formation of bone tissue was observed in several sites in animals receiving ^{24}NaCl. Thus, $2\frac{1}{2}$ months after a single injection of 0.170 mc, bone tissue was detected in the tracheal cartilage; 5 months after a single injection of 1.17 mc, in the blood vessels of the pia mater; and 6 months after 6 injections to a total quantity of 1.323 mc, in the spermatic artery walls. Calcareous deposition and formation of bone tissue was observed in 16 animals.

Apart from the changes described, lesions of vascular walls were found in the lungs of all the animals examined: dilation, fraying and enlargement of muscle fibre nuclei was also found. In and around suppurative foci a significant number of macrophages were detected, caused by bacteria. In all the experimental series moderate hyperplasia of the reticulo-endothelial elements was established in the spleen, in some cases the following were also observed: deletion of the pattern, slight sclerosis and different number of cells with a brown pigment giving a positive reaction for iron (by Perles's method). In the liver small fat droplets and nuclei, pycnotic and of different sizes, were observed; in the kidneys, degenerative lesions of the epithelium of the convoluted tubules; in the myocardium, uneven staining of fibres and interstitial oedema. Vacuolization occurred in the protoplasm of nerve cells of the brain and spinal cord and moderate oedema around blood vessels and cells. No marked pathological lesions were found in the bone marrow and other organs.

The effect of insoluble radioactive chromium phosphate injected intratracheally as a 1 ml. suspension in 5 per cent glucose was studied on 96 white rats. In most experiments the amount of chromium phosphate injected was 30 mg and only in a few cases, 2 mg. Chromium phosphate is highly insoluble. According to Jones and Wrobel, et al., $Cr^{32}PO_4$ when injected intravenously accumulates rapidly in the liver (up to 90 per cent) and virtually no excretion occurs in the course of a year. In an experiment *in vitro* (Neukomm and Lerch, et al.) it has been shown that not more than 1.5 per cent of $^{32}PO_4^{3-}$ ions are exchanged in 21 days with $^{31}PO_4^{3-}$ ions found in the physiological environment. By our data, after subcutaneous injection of mice with $Cr^{32}PO_4$ an average of 93 per cent of the injected dose was found at the site of injection for a month without detectable decline. Also no significant sustained diminution is observed when the substance is injected into the lungs, as will be seen below. The half-life of ^{32}P is 14.3 days, so that fairly prolonged selective irradiation of the lungs occurs with intratracheal injection of $Cr^{32}PO_4$. Without carrying out a special experiment the radiation dose was determined according to the activity detected in the lungs of experimental animals dying in the first 2–3 months after injection, when it was still possible to measure directly the activity of ^{32}P in the lungs. The activity in other organs was determined at earlier periods.

Table 2 shows the radioactivity of the lungs and other organs as a percentage of the activity administered to rats dying at various intervals after injection of the suspension.

It can be seen that during the first 20 days, the activity of all the organs is negligible compared with that of the lungs. For almost 3 months, no regular decline in lung activity can be discerned although large variations in activity are found (from 54 to 100 per cent of the injected dose).

The substance is distributed unevenly in the lungs, forming more or less diffuse brown-grey foci 0.5–5 mm in size which are easily seen with

TABLE 2

Activity of rat organs after intratracheal injection of a suspension of $Cr^{32}PO_4$

No. of rat	Amount of isotope (μc)	Length of life	\multicolumn{4}{c}{Activity of organs as a % age of amount administered}
			lungs	liver	kidneys	spleen
18	540	12 hours	59.0	0.06	0.004	0.002
17	270	1 day	95.0	0.16	0.020	0.003
15	270	8 days	73.0	0.04	0.010	0.010
13	270	10 days	64.0	0.13	0.010	0.010
12	270	14 days	58.5	0.57	0.050	0.050
11	270	19 days	70.0	2.50	0.010	0.020
13a	70	0 days	76.0	—	—	—
11a	70	50 days	76.0	—	—	—
15a	70	58 days	71.5	—	—	—
18a	70	80 days	78.5	—	—	—
31	100	19 days	54.0	—	—	—
27	100	25 days	95.0	—	—	—
26	100	35 days	100.0	—	—	—
32	100	38 days	85.0	—	—	—
30	100	59 days	67.0	—	—	—

the naked eye. Taking into account, on one hand, the impossibility of evaluating precisely the unevenness of distribution of the substance in each concrete case, and on the other, the fact that the penetration of ^{32}P β-particles (mean energy 0.7 MeV) in the tissues is 7–8 mm, thereby irradiating areas between accumulations of the substance, the lung radiation dose from $CrP^{32}O_4$ was calculated as for an even distribution.

Of course, at particular points the actual dose might vary by several times from this average figure. The generalized dose is negligible as compared with the lung dose, as can be seen from Table 2. The mean dose received from injection of $Cr^{32}PO_4$ in an amount of 1 μc/g lung weight (average lung weight of rats in these experiments was 3.3 g) was calculated as 885 rep throughout the isotope's life, in practice 3–5 months. The dose received during the first day after injection was 41.5 rep.

The doses received by our rats are presented in Table 3. For the animals which died up to 3 months after injection these doses were calculated from the activity found in the lungs. For rats dying at later periods the doses were calculated according to the mean values of activity found.

The organs of 80 rats were submitted to histological examination.

With injection of 30 mg of radioactive chromium phosphate with an activity of 0.270 mc, all the animals died within 36 days; the total dose was 19,000–46,000 rep. Many died during the first 3 days with symptoms of exhaustion; hemoconcentration was noted. It was also noted that in

TABLE 3

Lung activity and radiation dose after intratracheal injection of white rats with a suspension of $Cr^{32}PO_4$

Amount injected (mc)	Number of animals	Mean magnitude of lung activity as a % age of amount injected	Specific lung activity (μc)	Radiation dose on first day (rep/day)	Length of life (days)	Total dose throughout life (rep)
0.270	10	67.0	70±7	2900±270	3–32	19,000–46,000
0.100	42	81.5	20±2	830±80	19–65	10,300–18,000
0.070	34	77.0	16±2	670±30	15–395	8300–16,600
0.040	10	95.0	8.3±5.2	350±210	60–451	1300–13,000

some rats on the 8th–20th days there was flaking-off of the epithelium of the bronchial mucosa (Fig. 3), acute diffuse oedema, in part phagocytosed, and acute lesions of vascular walls, dilation, fraying of layers and penetration by leukocytes (Fig. 4). In one rat on the 19th day suppurative bronchitis was observed with, in places, metaplasia of the epithelium of the bronchial mucosa from cylindrical to stratified squamous (Fig. 5), moderate peribronchial sclerosis and foci of catarrhal pneumonia (the injected substance was found in the lungs of all animals regardless of the amount injected and the time of death).

With injection of an amount of isotope 2½–3 times smaller (0.07–0.1 mc) the radiation dose during the first day was 670–830 rep. The animals died from secondary infections or exhaustion at periods from 15 days to 3 months (individual rats survived up to 13–20 months); the radiation dose received at death was 8000–18,000 rep.

Histological examination of internal organs of animals of this group also disclosed lesions of blood-vessel walls as in the animals which received $^{24}NaCl$, but more pronounced (Fig. 6), widespread polymorphic cellular infiltrates (Fig. 7) and extensive perivascular and peribronchial scleroses (Fig. 8). In 8 animals metaplasia of the epithelium of the bronchial mucosa from cylindrical to stratified squamous with symptoms of anaplasia (Figs. 9 and 10) and formation of complexes of epithelial cells which characterize a precancerous condition were observed (Figs. 11 and 12). Similar lesions of the epithelium of the bronchial mucosa were noticed also at later periods after 11–13 months. In one animal at the 193rd day (Fig. 13) a true blastomatous growth was observed. In 9 animals which received 30 mg $Cr^{32}PO_4$ with an activity of 0.07–0.04 mc and died at 210–395 days, and in one animal which received 2 mg $Cr^{32}PO_4$ with an activity of 0.04 mc and died at 510 days, keratinous squamous cell carcinoma of a lung (left or right) was observed, with metastases along the pleura and regional lymph nodes (Figs. 14, 15 and 16). No such lesions of the epithelium of the bronchial mucosa were detected in the control experiments with stable chromium phosphate. In all the animals which died at different periods after injection of radioactive chromium phosphate as well as the lesions described, various forms of bronchitis were observed (desquamatous, suppurative, destructive), peribronchial and perivascular oedema, scleroses, emphysema, the injected substance, partly phagocytosed and a very little excreted by the bronchial mucosa epithelium (Fig. 17). Lesions of the trachea took the form of catarrhal, desquamatous and even suppurative trachitis. In all animals, lesions of the muscle layer of the arterial walls similar to those described above, were observed, and in 10 animals, calcium deposition and formation of bone tissue in the pulmonary arteries and in the lung tissue itself (Fig. 18). In the regional lymph nodes (paratracheal), cells with a brown pigment giving a positive reaction for iron when stained by Perles's method were found, and isolated cells with a pigment which failed to give a positive reaction for iron (chromium phosphate). In certain animals a lack of colloid in the thyroid gland, and a shedding of the epithelium of the follicles in the lumen were observed; in the spleen, a diminution of follicles, sclerosis of the tissue and cells with a brown pigment positive for iron were found. No marked pathological lesions were detected in the bone marrow, liver, kidneys, gastrointestinal tract, sex organs, brain and spinal cord.

Study of the effect of radioactive gold was made on rats injected intratracheally with 1 ml. colloidal solution with gold content at about 0.5–1 mg/ml. It is known that when colloidal gold is injected into the lungs the liquid phase of the preparation is rapidly absorbed while the gold particles settle on the alveolar walls. Some of them undergo phagocytosis and are carried into the regional lymph nodes; the main mass remains at the site of injection (Meneely *et al.*). This was verified on 18 rats which received colloidal gold intratracheally and were killed 20 min, 2 hr, 2, 4, 6 and 8 days later. The activity of the lungs of these rats, expressed as a percentage of the activity administered, is plotted logarithmically in Fig. 19. The last points, relating to the 15th and 35th days after injection, are taken from the main experiment in which rats which had received 0.320 mc ^{198}Au died at these times. No precise correlations were detected, apparently because of the significant variations in the amount of the substance reaching the lungs. To approximate, it may be said that liberation of the lungs from the isotope occurs with a period of half-excretion of 18 days. The effective half-life is 2.3 days.

The calculated dose of β-radiation received by the lungs on injection of 1 μc/g ^{198}Au is 65 rep up to the complete decay of the isotope and 17 rep during the first day. The γ-dose in the lungs is not more than 4 per cent of the β-dose. The gold distributes more evenly in each lung than chromium phosphate but usually more enters one lung than the other. As in the ^{32}P experiments, the dose was calculated on the assumption of an even distribution of the substance in both lungs. The actual dose in this case may also be 2–3 times higher than the mean. The general dose of γ-radiation does not exceed 0.6 per cent of the lung dose.

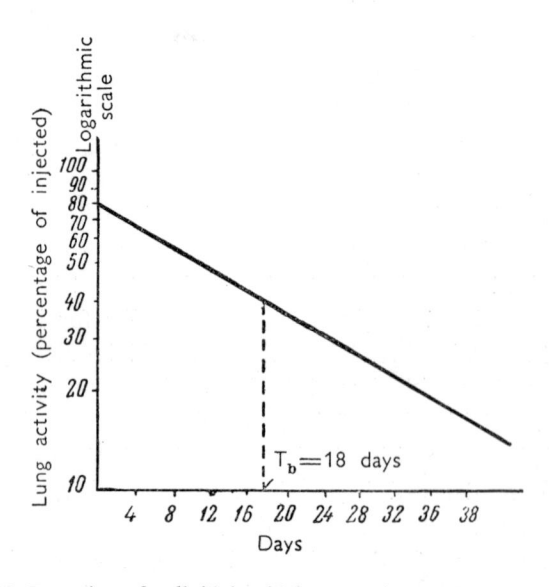

FIG. 19. Excretion of colloidal gold from rat lungs after intratracheal injection (semilogarithmic scale).

Twenty-five rats each receiving 0.320 mc ^{198}Au died in the course of $2\frac{1}{2}$–3 months. The radiation dose received on the first day comprised on average 3200–3400 rep, and in total (counting also excretion from the lungs), 12,000–13,000 rep.*

The radiation dose received on the first day after injection of 0.320 mc ^{198}Au was compared with that received with 0.270 mc Cr^{32}PO$_4$. The later times of death are explained by the fact that the radiation dose in the lungs from ^{198}Au was smaller.

Histological examination of the lungs of 5 rats at periods of from 19 to 36 days after injection disclosed symptoms of diffuse suppurative, in places destructive, bronchitis, fraying of bronchial and vascular walls, focal hemorrhages and oedema; in 4 rats 4–69 days after injection pro-

* In an earlier article a total radiation dose of 9000–9700 rep was suggested, based on preliminary data which gave the impression that colloidal gold behaves linearly. With accumulation of further data this figure has been made more precise.

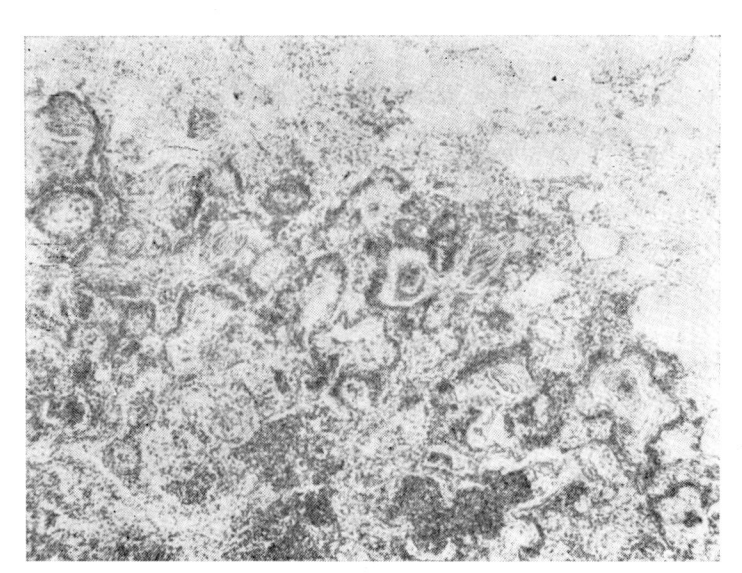

FIG. 20. Injection of 1 mg ^{198}Au with activity 0.320 mc. Lung. Foci of keratinous squamous cell carcinoma. 70 days.

nounced focal metaplasia of the epithelium of the bronchial mucosa to stratified squamous was observed. Two of these showed formation of complexes of epithelial cells having a blastomatous character with bone tissue in the lungs. In 4 animals examined at 36–70 days, foci of keratinous squamous cell carcinoma were found (Fig. 20). Similar foci were also detected in 3 of 30 animals which received ^{198}Au in amounts of 0.1–0.15 mc (after 9, 15 and 19 months).

Other symptoms disclosed by histological examination of the organs of this group included degenerative lesions of the liver and kidneys and a scarcity of lymphoid tissue in the spleen.

DISCUSSION

Radioactive isotopes injected intratracheally in soluble compounds do not create significant radiation doses selectively in the lungs. The changes observed in the lungs after injection of ^{24}NaCl did not indicate specific radiation damage to the lungs because such damage was no more pronounced than that found in other internal organs. The suppurative processes in the lungs, like the pustules in the subcutaneous tissue, abdominal cavity and elsewhere, which were found even in the control animals, can be ascribed to the effect of the hypertonic solution, and their somewhat greater frequency in the experimental animals to the lowering of their over-all immunobiological reactivity.

Even the largest amount of ^{24}NaCl (12.5 mc/kg) did not give rise to serious pathological lesions in the lungs. For technical reasons it was not possible to give large doses of ^{24}NaCl, but on the basis of data on the radiotoxicity of ^{24}Na, according to which an amount over 35 mc/kg is fatal, and 70 mc/kg absolutely fatal, it can be said with certainty that even with intratracheal injection of large quantities the general harmful effect woulfd lead to death of the animals before local damage in the lungs could develop.

A different picture is observed when insoluble preparations of ^{32}P and ^{198}Au are injected into the lungs.

These are retained for a long time in the lungs giving rise to a selectively high radiation dose there. With injection of large amounts of these preparations (0.270 mc Cr^{32}PO$_4$ and 0.320 mc ^{198}Au), creating not less than 2000–3000 rep on the first day and not less than 12,000–13,000 rep throughout the isotope's existence, the animals die during the first 1–2 months. Although in some animals, specific lesions have already developed in the lungs, their death is caused by the general harmful action of the isotope. This agrees with N. G. Darenskaya's results, which show that a dose of 10,000 r applied as a single external irradiation of the thorax is absolutely fatal.

In rats receiving 0.04–0.07 mc $Cr^{32}PO_4$ the dose in the first day reached 500–700 rep, and despite the fact that the total dose was sometimes 16,000–18,000 rep, they died at periods of from 8 to 20 months after injection, more from secondary infections or from exhaustion. In 11 of 80 such animals, keratinous squamous cell carcinoma of the lung with metastases in the pleura and regional lymph nodes were observed. In 8 animals of this group metaplasia of the bronchial mucosa with symptoms of anaplasia was detected. Similar lesions were noticed in 3 of 30 rats dying 9, 15 and 19 months after injection of 0.1–0.15 mc ^{198}Au.

The frequency of the observed lesions in general has little connection with the total dose received, but times of death and development of blastomatous tissue are delayed with diminution of the dose. Thus, the principle difference in the action of soluble and insoluble compounds of radioactive isotopes seems obvious. No less obvious is the carcinogenic capacity of insoluble preparations which create powerful foci of local irradiation in the lungs when injected intratracheally.

CONCLUSIONS

1. Intratracheal injection of white rats with radioactive insoluble chromium phosphate and colloidal gold gives rise to anaplasia of the epithelium of the bronchial mucosa; in some animals foci of keratinous squamous cell carcinoma appear after 2–6 months. In individual animals which received 30 mg chromium phosphate (0.1–0.07–0.04 mc) and died after 7, 11, 15 months, and in animals which received 2 mg (0.04 mc) and died at 12, 15, 17 months, keratinous squamous cell carcinoma of the lung, with metastases in the pleura and regional lymph nodes, was detected. No such lesions were observed in the lungs of rats injected with radioactive sodium, even after 24 months.

2. After administration of radioactive sodium chloride, chromium phosphate and colloidal gold, lesions of blood vessel walls, mainly in the lungs, are observed in the form of dystrophic lesions and impairment of permeability with subsequent development of perivascular peribronchial scleroses. In some animals calcareous deposition in the muscle layer of the arteries of the lungs, pia mater and testes, and formation of bone tissue there and in the pulmonary connective tissue were observed.

3. The experimental results obtained raise the problem of the possibility of the occurrence of large tissue radiation doses at foci of deposition of insoluble radioactive compounds. The necessity for stricter regulation of insoluble radioisotopes is indicated.

REFERENCES

BLOOM W., *Histopathology of Irradiation from External and Internal Sources*, New York. (1948).

BUKHTOYAROVA Z. M. and LEMBERG V. K., *The Long-term Effects of Plutonium Injury*. (Otdalennyye posledstviya porazheniya plutoniyem.) Paper read at a Conference on the long-term effects of radiation injuries, Moscow (1956).

BURYKINA L. N., *Toxicology of Radioactive Substances*. (Materialy po toksikologii radioaktivnykh veshchestv.) Vol. 1, Moscow (1957). English translation published by Pergamon Press (1962).

DOMSHLAK M. P., ABRUNINA G. A., DARENSKAYA N. I. and GRIGOR'YEV YU. G., *Vest. Rentgenol. Radiol.* **2** (1957).

ENGELSTADT, *Bull. et mem. de la societe medical des Hôpitaux de Paris* **63**, 4 ser., 7–8 (1947).

GORIZONTOV P. D., *Arkh. Patolog.* **4**, (1955).

HEVESY G., *Radioactive Indicators*, Interscience, New York (1948).

HODGE H. C., KOSS W. F., GINN J. T. et al., *J. Biol. Chem.* **148** (1943).

JONES H. B., WROBEL G. J. and LYON W. R., *J. Clin. Investig.* **23**, 5 (1944).

KHAMAIDE L. L., *Development of Tumours at the Site of Injection of Radioactive Substances*. (Razvitiye opukholei na meste vvedeniya radioaktivnykh veshchestv.) Paper read at a Conference on the long-term effects of radiation injuries, Moscow (1956).

KRAYEVSKII N. A., *Outlines of the Pathological Anatomy of Radiation Sickness*. (Ocherki patologicheskoi anatomii luchevoi bolezni.) Moscow (1957). English translation in preparation by Pergamon Press.

KURLYANDSKAYA E. B., RUBANOVSKAYA A. A., BELOBORODOVA N. L. et al., *The Toxicology of Radioactive Substances*. (Materialy po toksikologii radioaktivnykh veshchestv.) Vol. 1, Moscow (1957). English translation Published by Pergamon Press.

KURLYANDSKAYA E. B., RUBANOVSKAYA A. A., BELOBORODOVA N. L. et al., *The Chronic Effect of Radioactive cobalt*. (Materialy po khronicheskomu deistviyu radioaktivnogo kobal'ta.) Report on the All-Union Conference on the uses of radioactive and stable isotopes in technology, industry, agriculture, medicine and biology, Moscow (1957).

LEBEDINSKII A. V., *Med. Radiol.* **2**, 1 (1956).

MENEELY G. R., AUERBACH S. H., WOODCOCK C. C., KORY K. C., HAHN P. F., *Amer. J. Med. Sci.* **225**, 2 (1953).

NEUKOMM S., LERCH P., PEGUIRON L. and RICHARD M., *Acta Radiol.* **36**, 3 (1952).

NOVIKOVA A. P., *Morphological Changes in Animals at Long Periods after Administration of Certain Radioactive Substances*. (Morfologicheskiye izmeneniya u zhivotnykh v otdalennye sroki posle vvedeniya nekotorykh radioaktivnykh veshchestv.) Paper read at a Conference on the long-term effects of radiation injuries, Moscow (1956).

STRELIN G. S., *Med. Radiol.* **1**, 1 (1956).

STREL'TSOVA V. N. and MOSKALEV YU. I., *The Long-term Effects of a Single and Chronic Administration of Radioactive Isotopes (^{144}Ce, ^{108}Ru, $^{89-90}Sr$) and a Mixture of β-ray Emitters in the Gastro-intestinal Tract*. (Otdalennyye posledstviya odnokratnogo i khronicheskogo postupleniya radioaktivnykh izotopov (^{144}Ce, ^{108}Ru, $^{89-90}Sr$ i smesi β-izluchatelei cherez zheludochno-kishechnyi trakt.) Paper read at a Conference on the long-term effects of radiation injuries, Moscow (1956).

TARUSOV B. N., *Fundamentals of the Biological Effect of Radioactive Irradiation*. (Osnovy biologicheskogo deistviya radioaktivnykh izluchenii.) Moscow (1954).

ZAKUTINSKII D. I., *Med. Radiol.* **1**, 1 (1956).

ZAKUTINSKII D. I., *The Long-term Effects of Radiation Injuries*. (Otdalennyye posledstviya porazhenii, vyzvannykh ioniziruyushchei radiatsiyei.) Moscow (1956).

AUTHOR INDEX

ABRUNINA, G. A.   3, 4, 5, 12, 14, 30, 61, 91, 98, 123, 174, 185
ACKERMAN   160, 162
AMDURSKAYA, N. M.   106
AMSLER   109
ANDREONI, O.   75, 83, 84, 86, 89
ANDRIEVSKII, B. Y.   85, 88
ANGER, R.   89
ARKUSSKII, Y. I.   120, 121, 138
ARLASHCHENKO, N. I.   108, 109, 117
ARZHILAS, F. I.   119
AUERBACH, S. H.   185
AVER'YANOV, P. P.   149

BABAEVA, A. K.   85, 88
BALABUKHA, V. S.   74, 89, 90, 97, 102, 103, 106
BARANOVA, Y. F.   30, 43, 44, 47, 60
BARRON, E. S. G.   89
BAURNE, E.   96
BEDYURFTIG   121
BELAVENETS, P. P.   144, 150
BELLIOS   160, 162
BELOBORODOVA, N. L.   5, 8, 30, 43, 44, 47, 60, 61, 87, 117, 152, 159, 185
BELOVA, S. F.   139
BEREZOV, E. L.   51, 60
BERNSHTEIN, R. Y.   128
BLOOM, W.   161, 185
BLUM, H. F.   89
BOCHKAREV, V. V.   15, 29, 60
BOGDANOV, K. F.   85, 88
BORISOVA, E. I.   136
BRANDHENDLER, W.   85, 89
BRUMSHTEIN, M. S.   161, 163
BUKHTOYAROVA, V. K.   175, 185
BUNYATYAN, G. K.   102, 106
BURYKINA, L. N.   30, 43, 61, 73, 161, 162, 174, 185
BUSH, F.   18
BUSINI, P. A.   89
BUSTAD, L. K.   30, 43
BYKOV, K. M.   119

CALVIN, D. B.   85, 89
CATSCH, A.   164, 172
CHAIKOVSKAYA, M. Y.   72, 73
CHANUTIN, A.   89
CHERKASOV, V. F.   140, 150
COHN, J.   165, 172, 173
COLVIN, J. R.   89
COOP, D. H.   29
COPP   165, 173
COULTER, E. G.   86, 89
CRONKITE, E. P.   108, 117, 118
CROWLEY, J.   164, 173

DARENSKAYA, N. G.   183, 185
DAVEY, H. W.   89
DENSON, J. R.   102, 103, 106
DICKMAN, S.   89
DMITRIYEVA, Y. P.   109, 113, 118
DOBROVOLSKAYA-ZAVADSKAYA, W.   90, 96
DOMPE, M.   89
DOMSHLAK, M. P.   185
DROGICHINA, E. A.   121, 138
DUNLAP, C. E.   160, 163
DVIZHKOV, P. P.   151, 174

EBY, J. O.   97
EGOROV, A. P.   49, 51, 119
ELBERT, O.   85, 89
ELMAN, R.   85, 89
ELY, J. O.   103, 107
ENGELSTAD, R. B.   161, 162, 175, 185
ENTENMANN, C.   89, 103, 106
EPSHTEIN   103, 106
ERLEKSOVA, E. V.   161, 162

FANARDZHYAN F. A.   120, 122, 133, 138
FATEYEVA, M. N.   121, 133, 138
FEDOROV, B. A.   161, 162
FEDOROV, N. M.   149
FEDOROVA, T. A.   89, 97, 103, 106

FEDOTOV, V. P. 102, 103, 106
FISCHEL, E. 102, 106
FISCHER, M. A. 75, 83, 84, 86, 89
FISCHER, P. 90, 96
FISCHLER 173
FOGEL'SON, L. I. 129, 138, 149
FOREMAN, H. 164, 173
FRADKIN, G. E. 165
FRIEDEN, J. 75, 84, 89
FUGUA, T. 173
FULTON, G. P. 120, 138

GABE, M. 105, 106
GEMPEL'MAN, L. 118, 161, 162
GEORGE, L. K. 30, 43
GINN, J. T. 185
GJESSING 75, 83, 84, 89
GOFMAN, D. 161, 162
GOLDNER, M. G. 107
GOLOVSHCHIKOVA, I. N. 10, 87, 122, 140
GONG, K. 165, 173
GORBUNOVA, N. A. 85, 89
GORIZONTOV, P. D. 138, 174, 185
GORMAN, D. 118
GRAY, E. J. 102, 106
GRAY, J. L. 102, 106
GRAYEVSKAYA, B. M. 90, 96, 102, 106
GRIGOROVICH, T. V. 146, 150
GRIGOR'YEV, Y. G. 185
GRISHCHENKO, Y. D. 8, 9, 74, 87, 89, 98, 105
GROZHEVSKAYA, S. B. 128
GRYUSNER 121
GUILLET, G. 105, 106
GURVICH, A. E. 75, 89
GUSEV, N. G. 15, 29, 98, 106, 162

HAHN, P. F. 185
HAMBERLAN 149
HAMILTON, J. 173
HARBERS, E. 165, 173
HART, H. 173
HAUSSCHILDT, J. D. 89
HEMPELMANN, 108
HERBERT, E. J. 106
HEVESY, G. 185
HINE, G. J. 29
HODGE, H. C. 185
HOFFMAN, 108

HOHNE, G. 75, 89
HUBE, S. 97
HUBER, A. 109, 117
HURCH, J. 173

INGRAM, M. 90, 97
ITKIN, S. I. 108, 118
IVANOV, A. E. 161, 163
IVANOV, I. I. 74, 89, 90, 97, 103, 106, 139
IVANOVA, T. A. 61, 72, 73

JENSON, H. 106
JOHNSON, W. 85, 89
JONES, H. B. 178, 185
JOYET, G. 29

KAKUSHKINA, Y. A. 73
KAN 136
KAPLANSKII, A. S. 7, 10, 12, 47, 49, 58, 137, 151
KARIBSKAYA, Y. V. 48, 60, 121, 138
KARLIN, M. I. 120, 122, 138
KASSIRSKII, I, A. 47, 60
KAVETSKII, R. E. 102, 103, 106
KAWIN, B. 165, 173
KAY, R. E. 103, 105, 106
KAZAKEVICH, M. A. 121, 138, 139
KEILINA, R. Y. 96, 97, 102, 105, 106
KEIRIM-MARKUS, I. 29
KHAMAIDE, P. L. 175, 185
KISELEV, P. N. 74, 89, 108, 118
KLIMOV, V. S. 121, 133, 138
KOCHETKOVA, T. A. 5, 7, 174
KOCHNEVA, N. I. 90, 97
KOHN, H. J. 89
KORY, K. C. 185
KOSS, W. F. 185
KOZLOVA, A. V. 121, 122, 138
KRAYEVSKII, N. A. 73, 161, 163, 174, 185
KREBS, A. 88, 89
KRYUKOV, P. G. 14, 29
KULIKOVSKAYA, L. A. 161, 163
KUNKLER, P. 121, 139
KUNNEL, H. A. 89
KURLYANDSKAYA, E. B. 1, 4, 30, 43, 45 73, 106, 174, 185
KURSHAKOV, N. A. 122, 136, 138
KYANDARYAN, K. A. 120

AUTHOR INDEX

LACASSAGNE, A. 47, 60
LANDS, A. M. 85, 89
LANG, G. F. 136
LAPTEVA-POPOVA, M, S. 11, 44
LARTIQUE, O. J. 90, 97, 107
LASZLO, D. 173
LAZARUS, S. S. 107
LEBEDINSKII, A. V. 109, 118, 122, 138, 185
LEE, C. C. 14, 29
LELIÈVRE, P. 102, 107
LEMBERG, V. K. 175, 185
LEMESH, V. M. 128
LERCH, P. 178, 185
LEVY, B. 90, 97, 102, 107
LISCHER, C. E. 89
LISKO, G. 108, 118, 161, 162
LITVINOV, N. N. 161, 163
LIVANOV, M. N. 122, 136, 138
LOBODA, Y. A. 173
LOMOVSKAYA, E. G. 62, 73
LONDON, E, S. 90, 97
LORENZ 165, 173
LOURAN, M. 90, 97, 103, 106
LOWMAN 102
LUGANSKII, N. I. 173
L'VOVA, M. 29
LYON, W. R. 185

MACCHI, L. 96
MAGEE, M. Z. 89
MALENKOVA, K. M. 48, 60, 121
MALENKOVA, V. M. 138
MANOILOV, Y. S. 96, 106
MARINELLI 16, 29
MARKS, S. 43
MARKUZE, K. P. 122, 138, 139
MASON, W. B. 97
MASSMANN 127, 128, 133
MCCUTCHEON, M. 108, 118
MEL'NICHENKO, A. V. 161, 163
MENEELY, G. R. 174, 185
MESSIK, R. E. 85, 89
MIDTSEU, F. I. 119, 139
MINTS, M. M. 121, 138
MODESTOV, V. K. 119
MOGIL'NITSKII, B. N. 108, 120, 138, 161, 163
MOROZ, B. B. 138
MOROZOV, A. L. 121, 138

MOSKALEV, Y. I. 161, 163, 185
MUNTZ, J. A. 89
MUSSMANN, W. 139
MYASNIKOV, A. L. 119
MYTAREVA, L. V. 104, 107

NEUKOMM, S. 178, 185
NEUMAN, K. 165, 173
NIKITENKO, R. D. 106
NIKITENKO, V. V. 87, 89
NIMS 102
NORWOOD 173
NOVIKOVA, A. P. 72, 73, 161, 163, 175, 185

OGANEZOVA, A. A. 75, 84, 89
OIVIN, I. A. 113, 118
OIVIN, V. I. 113, 118
O'NEILL, T. 88, 89
OPITZ, M. 127, 128, 138, 139
ORD, M. G. 97
OSTERN, P. 97

PARR, W. 88, 89
PASCHUE, G. 89
PASSALACQUA, W. 75, 89
PASSARO, G. 75, 89
PEAT, W. J. 96
PEGUIRON, L. 185
PERESAD'KO, L. P. 128, 139
PETROVA, A. N. 91, 97, 104, 106, 107, 117
PETROVA, A. S. 118
PETROVICH, Y. A. 109, 113, 118
PETROVNIN, M. G. 14, 91
PIGALEV, I. A. 136, 174
PINUS, A. A. 160
PLODOVSKAYA, L. A. 73
POBEDINSKII, M. N. 121, 139
PRUSLIN, Y. 29
PUCAR, Z. 89

QUIMBY, S. H. 29

RAISKINA, M. Y. 150
RAVILAND, J. W. 97
RED'KINA, E. K. 8, 61
RICHARD, M. 185

AUTHOR INDEX

Rivosh, F. I. 97
Romanova-Bokhon, O. A. 109, 113, 118
Romantsev, Y. F. 89, 97, 103, 106
Ross, M. H. 90, 97, 103, 107
Rubanovskaya, A. A. 4, 9, 30, 43, 61, 73, 87, 108, 164, 185
Rugh, R. 97
Rusinov, V. S. 136
Russo, A. M. 89
Ruzdic, I. 89

Saitanov, A. O. 10, 87, 119, 140, 141, 146
Sakharov, P. P. 62, 73
Samoilov, A. F. 136
Samtsov, V. A. 146
Sanotskii, U. A. 119
Schubert, J. 165, 173
Scott, K. G. 164, 173
Seletskaya, T. E. 121, 138, 139
Semenov, D. I. 165, 173
Semiglazova, E. D. 121, 139
Semina, V. A. 89
Shevchenko, N. A. 122
Shielding 103
Shilinsh, G. 75, 83, 89
Skvortsov, V. I. 146, 150
Sokolov, V. I. 76
Somodyi, M. J. 97
Sorochkina, S. N. 85, 88
Starosel'tseva, L. K. 76
Stender, H. S. 75, 83, 84, 89
Stocken, L. 97
Stolyarova, L. B. 106
Strelin, G. S. 174, 185
Strel'tsova, V. N. 161, 163, 175, 185
Sudak, F. N. 138
Supplee, H. 75, 83, 89
Svigris, A. Y. 61, 72, 73

Tagunova, G. A. 161, 163
Taruzov, B. N. 174, 185
Tew, J. T. 106
Tkachenko, I. S. 85

Udel'nov, M. E. 136
Ulrich, F. 29
Ushakova, V. F. 43, 73

Valedinskii, A. 119
Vasil'yeva, E. I. 122, 139
Veidman, V. K. 160, 163
Veksler, Y. I. 108, 118
Vernadskii, V. I. 2
Viktorova, V. L. 8, 61
Vinogradova, N. I. 9, 87, 90, 98, 100, 102
Vlasenko, V. I. 76
Voinar, A. O. 48, 60, 88
Volin, M. A. 85, 88
Volk, B. W. 107
Volkin, E. 75, 83, 89
Volkova, K. T. 120, 138
Volynets, I. T. 85, 89
Vorob'yeva, E. I. 62, 73
Voskresenskii, S. P. 72, 73

Warker, D. E. 43
Weikel, J. 165, 173
Wesselkin, W. 109, 113, 118
Whipple, H. 97
White, A. 89
Whitfeld, A. 121, 139
Winkler, C. 75, 84, 87, 89
Wolterink, L. F. 14, 29
Woodcock, C. C. 185
Worren, S. 160, 163
Wrobel, G. J. 178, 185

Yakovleva 136
Yasvoin, G. V. 160, 163
Yegorov, A. P. 44, 60

Zairat'yants, V. G. 122, 139
Zakutinskii, D. I. 73, 139, 174, 185
Zaretskaya, Y. M. 122, 140, 150

SUBJECT INDEX

Anemia (*see* Blood and Hemopoietic System)
Aschner's test 10, 141–42

BAL, effect on excretion, radioactive isotopes 164–65
Bladder, urinary
   lesions 10
   morphological changes after chronic internal ^{60}Co administration 153, 155, 158, 161–62
Blood (*see also* Hemopoietic system)
   albumin–globulin ratio
      irradiated rabbits 8, 76–89
   capillaries, permeability after ^{60}Co 3, 9, 108–18
   ^{60}Co content after injections of CaNa$_2$, CDTA 171
   erythropoiesis
      changes induced ^{60}Co 5–7, 11, 45–48, 54–59
      in offspring of irradiated rats 63–64
   leukopoiesis, changes induced ^{60}Co 6, 11, 48, 52–59
   percentage of body weight 25
   specific activity after oral ^{60}Co intake 22, 32, 33, 36, 39
   thrombopoiesis absence of any change after ^{60}Co 52
Blood sugar, levels, irradiated rabbits 8, 9, 99–106
Bone marrow,
   after blood loss 56, 59
   changes induced ^{60}Co 6, 7, 36, 39, 46, 151, 156, 160
   in offspring of irradiated rats 64–67
Bones (*see also* Skeleton)
   in ^{60}Co excretion 4
Brain, specific activity after oral ^{60}Co intake 36, 39

Carbohydrate metabolism, changes induced ^{60}Co 3, 9, 11, 90–97
Carbohydrate–Phosphorus metabolism, after prolonged ^{60}Co administration 98–106
Carcinoma (*see* Tumours)
CDTA, effect on excretion rate, ^{60}Co, strontium 12, 164–73
Chromium phosphate, radioactive, effects of intratracheal injection 13, 178–84
Cobalt
   chemical and physical characteristics 2
   distribution routes in rats, rabbits 3, 14
   dose calculation 16–18
   equilibrium between administration and excretion 4
   excretion
      action of CDTA 164–73
      rate 3, 12, 14, 19–21
   maximum permissible concentrations 11, 12, 14
   metabolism in rats, rabbits 14
   vit. B$_{12}$ content 2

EDTA, effect on excretion, radioactive isotopes 164–65
Eye, capillary permeability changes induced ^{60}Co 3, 9, 108–118
Equilibrium level of body activity after oral ^{60}CoCl$_2$ 40–42

Gastro-intestinal tract
   ^{60}Co absorption 20, 21
   ^{60}Co content after injections of CaNa$_2$, CDTA 171
   lesions 10
   percentage of body weight 25
   reaction to chronic internal ^{60}Co administration 152–55, 157–58, 161–62
   specific activity after oral ^{60}Co administration 36, 38

[190]

SUBJECT INDEX

Glycogen
   liver content after ^{60}Co 90–97
   synthesis, irradiated rabbits 8, 9, 98–106
Gold, effect of intratracheal injection 13, 174, 181–84
Gonads, lesions following chronic internal ^{60}Co administration 10, 161

Heart
   electrocardiograph, changes induced ^{60}Co 3, 9, 10, 119–39, 140–50
   specific activity after oral ^{60}Co administration 36, 39
Hemopoietic system
   changes induced ^{60}Co 3, 5–7, 10, 11, 44–60, 159, 161
   in offspring of irradiated rats 61–73

Intestine (see Gastro-intestinal tract)

Kidneys
   activity after intratracheal injection Cr^{32}PO$_4$ 179
   ^{60}Co content after injections of CaNa$_2$, CDTA 171
   in offspring of irradiated rats 71–72
   morphological changes after chronic internal ^{60}Co administration 153–55, 158, 160–62
   percentage of body weight 25
   role in ^{60}Co excretion 4
   specific activity after oral, subcutaneous ^{60}Co 27–28–32, 36, 38–39

Liver
   activity after intratracheal injections Cr^{32}PO$_4$ 179
   carbohydrate metabolism after ^{60}Co 90–97, 98–106
   ^{60}Co content after injections of CaNa$_2$, CDTA 171
   enzyme systems, direct damage 8, 9
   in offspring of irradiated rats 70–71
   morphological changes after chronic ^{60}Co administration 10, 152–53, 158, 161–62

   percentage of body weight 25
   maximum permissible radiation doses 5
   role in ^{60}Co excretion 4
   specific activity after oral and subcutaneous ^{60}Co administration 27–28, 32, 36, 38, 39
Lungs
   ^{60}Co content after injections of CaNa$_2$, CDTA 171
   effects of intratracheal injections 12, 13
   effects of prolonged local irradiation, ^{24}Na, ^{32}P, ^{198}Au 175–84
   in offspring of irradiated rats 71–72
   percentage of body weight 25
   pneumonia, pleurisy, induced chronic internal ^{60}Co administration 10, 152–57, 160, 162
   specific activity after oral ^{60}Co intake 32, 36, 39
Lymph nodes, reaction to ^{60}Co 48–52, 58–59, 155–56, 160

Morgan's maximum permissible ^{60}Co dose for water 11, 12
Muscle(s)
   ^{60}Co content after injections of CaNa$_2$, CDTA 171
   skeletal, in ^{60}Co excretion 4
   specific activity after oral ^{60}Co intake 32, 36, 39

Nervous system
   autonomic in radiation sickness 140–50
   central, reaction to chronic internal ^{60}Co administration 153
   role in ^{60}Co excretion 4
Nitrogen, residual content, after chronic internal ^{60}Co administration 76–88

Pancreas
   morphological changes after chronic internal ^{60}Co administration 155, 158
   role in ^{60}Co excretion 4
Peritoneum, peritonitis, induced chronic internal ^{60}Co administration 154, 158

SUBJECT INDEX

Phosphorus, intratracheal injection long-term effects 3
Phosphorus-carbohydrate metabolism, after prolonged ^{60}Co administration 98–106
Pregnancy, parturition, irradiated animals 6, 10, 52–54, 155–59
Protein
 complement, blood serum, irradiated rabbits 8, 11
 content, aqueous humour of eye, after ^{60}Co 113–15
 metabolism changes induced ^{60}Co 3
 serous, after chronic internal ^{60}Co administration 74–89

Radiation, measurement techniques 15
Resistance, body, decline after ^{60}Co damage 160, 162
Reticulo-endothelial system, proliferation of cells after ^{60}Co 5, 6, 10, 160, 162
Ruthenium dioxide, effect on bronchial mucosa 174

Sensitivity, wide range in resistance of individual animals 159, 162
Skeleton, strontium deposition, action of various substances 164–67
Skin, capillary permeability, changes induced ^{60}Co 3, 9, 108–18
Sodium chloride, effects of intratracheal injection 3, 174–84
Sodium citrate, effect on excretion, radioactive isotopes 164
Spleen
 activity after intratracheal injection, Cr^{32}PO$_4$ 179
 ^{60}Co content after injection of CaNa$_2$, CDTA 171
 in offspring of irradiated rats 67–70
 morphological changes after chronic internal ^{60}Co administration 6, 151–52, 156, 159–60
 percentage of body weight 25

role in ^{60}Co excretion 4
specific activity after oral ^{60}Co intake 32, 36, 39
Stomach (see Gastro-intestinal tract)
Strontium, excretion, action of CDTA 12, 164–73
Suprarenals
 reaction to chronic internal ^{60}Co administration 159
 role in ^{60}Co excretion 4

Testes, lesions following chronic internal ^{60}Co administration 159
Thyroid, reaction to chronic internal ^{60}Co administration 159
Tumours,
 induced chronic internal ^{60}Co 153, 162
 induced intratracheal injections 12, 13

Urine, excretion of ^{60}Co during daily ^{60}Co administration 33
Uterus, lesions after chronic internal ^{60}Co administration 155, 159

Vagus nerve, reactions in radiation sickness 140–50
Vascular system, changes after chronic internal irradiation 108–18
Vitamin B$_{12}$ in cobalt 2

Weight, changes in radiation sickness, rabbits 5

X-irradiation
 effect on serous proteins 84, 88
 protective action of stable cobalt doses 88
 tumour patients electrocardiographic changes 119–22

Zirconium citrate, effect on excretion, radioisotopes 165